Health Plans and
Collective Bargaining

A Publication of the
Institute of Industrial Relations
University of California

Health Plans and

Collective Bargaining

JOSEPH W. GARBARINO

Berkeley and Los Angeles, 1960
UNIVERSITY OF CALIFORNIA PRESS

UNIVERSITY OF CALIFORNIA
BERKELEY AND LOS ANGELES
CALIFORNIA

CAMBRIDGE UNIVERSITY PRESS
LONDON, ENGLAND

Foreword

)

Two decades ago, only a small minority of the American people had access to coverage under a voluntary health insurance program. Today the majority are protected by some type of private health insurance. With the growth of voluntary insurance programs, agitation for a government-sponsored compulsory health insurance system, which had been so conspicuous a part of the American scene two decades earlier, has largely subsided. Whether it will reappear in vigorous form clearly depends on the success of the voluntary plans in meeting the health needs of the American people.

Playing a highly significant role in the growth of private health insurance since the late 1940's have been the negotiated plans. Development of these plans has not only extended private health insurance to many families not previously covered, but has also introduced a new element into the market for medical services. For the first time, consumers of medical care have been represented by professional negotiators, who have attempted, at least in some instances, to use their economic power to force concessions from suppliers of medical services.

Professor Garbarino's study is concerned with the impact of this development on the terms and conditions under which medical care is provided. Has the growth of collectively bargained health plans played a major role in driving up the cost of medical care? What has been its effect on the relative positions of the insurance companies, Blue Cross and Blue Shield Plans, and the so-called independent plans in the health insurance field? To what extent and in what ways have the hospital associations and the county medical societies been drawn into the process of collective bargaining? What has been the impact of the collectively bargained plans on the organization of medical services?

Although these problems are nationwide in character, they cannot be readily analyzed on a nationwide scale, since the most significant developments are occurring in a limited number of metropolitan areas, in which consumers of medical services have some degree of choice between private doctors and a large-scale medical service organization. The San Francisco Bay Area, which forms the locale for much of Professor Garbarino's analysis, is one such metropolitan region.

Joseph W. Garbarino is Associate Professor of Business Administration and a member of the research staff of the Institute of Industrial Relations.

Arthur M. Ross, Director
Institute of Industrial Relations
University of California

Acknowledgments

Completion of this study was possible only because many people were willing to give their time and share the benefits of their experience. A high degree of coöperation and assistance has been the general rule on the part of those consulted and in securing access to sources of information.

Almost a hundred people were formally approached in the course of the research. Informal discussions were held with many more. Some persons contributed so substantially that they justly deserve special mention. This is particularly true of Robert Grunsky, Executive Director of the California Metal Trades Association, Anthony Anselmo, Executive Secretary of the local Joint Executive Board of Culinary Workers, Bartenders, and Hotel Service Workers, Goldie Krantz, Administrator of the Welfare Fund of the International Longshoremen's and Warehousemen's Union and the Pacific Maritime Association, and Avram Yedidia of the Kaiser Foundation Health Plan.

Among the persons consulted several times each in connection with the study were Marshall Kuhn, Assistant Director of Enrollment of California Physicians Service, William Scheuber, Executive Secretary of the Alameda-Contra Costa Medical Association, George Johns, Secretary of the San Francisco Labor Council, and Julian Friedman of the School of Public Health of the University of California.

In the early stages of the study the author benefited from par-

vii

ticipation in a course on the Organized Forms of Medical Care conducted by Dr. Edward S. Rogers, Dr. Charles Gardipee, and Mr. Friedman. A survey in connection with the research was ably organized by Ann McCrory and the data were processed by Walter Phillips.

During the period when the study was in preparation, encouragement and assistance were provided by Margaret S. Gordon, Associate Director of the Institute of Industrial Relations.

Joseph W. Garbarino

April 20, 1959
Berkeley, California

Contents

Tables

Chapter I | Introduction

During the past fifteen years something close to a revolution has been taking place in the wage-payment system of American industry. Although direct wage payments measured by hourly earnings have been rising rapidly and virtually continuously for the great majority of American workers, the more important manifestations of this revolution have been in the forms rather than in the amounts of employee compensation. The growing use of the more general phrase "employee compensation" as a substitute for the unadorned word "wage" or "pay" is in itself an indication of the extent of the changes that have been taking place. The implied contract existing between a worker and his employer that used to be said to include a "rate of pay" is now spoken of as involving a "system of compensation."

Once limited to the direct payment for time worked or output produced, the scope of compensation has spread in several directions. The two most important of these are: (1) pay for time not worked such as vacations, holidays, or for call-in pay, and (2) payments to aid the worker in meeting certain contingencies that may interrupt his income or result in additional expenses. Examples of income-interrupting contingencies are unemployment, old age, accident, and ill health; the last two of these are also contingencies that bring about additional costs for medical care.

The sums allocated to supplements to direct wages have been

growing rapidly both in absolute amount and as a percentage of total payroll. The problems of measuring the costs of these benefits (or even of defining them) are formidable, but the best evidence available suggests that in 1955 American employers paid their employees wage supplements averaging 17 per cent of their direct payments for wages and salaries. It has been estimated that such supplements averaged about 3 per cent in 1929 and about 6 per cent in 1938.[1]

Of the items entering into the Chamber of Commerce calculations, the contingency payments mentioned above account for some two-fifths of all expenditures for supplements, and these items have attracted most attention from observers. The contingency payments in 1955 were divided almost equally between those required by governmental regulation (e.g., unemployment compensation) and those extended voluntarily or as a result of collective-bargaining negotiations between company and union (e.g., health insurance). The growth of that part of the supplement system designed to provide economic security under nongovernmental auspices has been particularly rapid and has generated some of the sharpest criticism. One principal form of criticism has been the charge that the supplement system has been creating a "new feudalism." The other has been based on the evidence of financial malpractice that has come to light in the course of state and federal investigations of the operations of the system.

This study will be concerned with one part of the private wage supplement system, the provision of hospital and medical care through collectively bargained health plans. It will not be concerned with the problems of internal financial control nor with the charges that these programs limit employee freedom. Emphasis will be upon the fact that these collectively bargained health plans are part of a massive attempt to meet an important

---

[1] The U. S. Chamber of Commerce has pioneered the collection of valuable statistics on wage supplements biennially since 1947. The 3 and 17 per cent estimates are from its figures. The data show that for 124 identical companies replying to its survey over the entire period, supplements increased from 15.1 to 21.7 per cent of total payroll between 1947 and 1955. This is substantially higher than the over-all figure used in the text for several reasons, the most important probably being that the larger companies with more complete benefit programs tend to respond more readily to surveys of this type. U. S. Chamber of Commerce, *Fringe Benefits—1955*, Washington, 1956, pp. 29, 34. The 6 per cent estimate is by Melvin Rothbaum in G. Taylor and F. Pierson (eds.), *New Concepts in Wage Determination* (New York: McGraw-Hill, 1957), p. 316.

social problem largely through a voluntary, privately administered program. The negotiated plans have introduced an important new element—a group of powerful economic organizations that serve as the representatives of a large body of consumers of medical services. In effect, this has resulted in a significant change in the structure of the medical market.[2]

It will be shown that the inclusion of medical care as an issue in contract negotiations has substantially increased the speed of an evolution in the conditions under which medical services are performed and, in addition, has turned this evolution into new channels. This process has affected the system of pricing medical services, the prices of the services, the level of total medical expenditures, the distribution of income among segments of the medical profession, the structure of medical organizations, and, in general, the entire network of relationships between the organized groups involved.

Labor economists are fond of describing collective bargaining as a process of accommodation between two organizations, the union and the business firm. For reasons that will be discussed later, bargaining over health insurance programs has increased the use of collective bargaining as a decision-making process and has introduced some of the forms and techniques of bargaining into a different set of organizational relationships. The problem of developing new methods and terms of accommodation has confronted unions, labor councils, employer associations, state and county medical associations, insurance companies, and the medical service organizations. Some of the issues that have arisen and some of the methods of dealing with them will be analyzed in this study.

Health Insurance as Private Social Security

Since the end of World War II the American social security system, developing in an environment marked by both federal and state governmental activity as well as aggressive and imaginative

---

[2] As the work of an economist interested in industrial relations, the subject is viewed from the standpoint of economic analysis and limited use is made of the jargon and apparatus of economics. Use of impersonal concepts such as the "market for medical services," "bargaining agencies," and "medical industry" serve to point up the emphasis on the economics of medicine. From this no inference should be drawn that the personal and humanitarian character of the medical care problem is unrecognized or is being deëmphasized.

private organizations, has changed in some significant ways. Governmental programs have not been static, particularly in the areas of protection against income loss due to old age or disability, but the private programs have expanded greatly and most of the significant innovations have been introduced under nongovernmental sponsorship. The flood of developments resulting from a dozen years of almost continuous activity has often been described as a "system of private social security." Pretentious though this phrase may sound at first hearing, it takes on meaning when account is taken of the more than twenty billion dollars of reserves in private pension plans, the more than one hundred million persons covered by some form of voluntary health insurance, and the approximately two million workers currently enrolled in private supplements to state unemployment compensation.

Under the catch phrase, "fringe benefits," a term which includes all forms of nonwage items of remuneration as well as the programs usually thought of as social security measures, the personnel specialists of unions and management have expanded the simple wage contract of the pre-World War II period into a complex "package" of payments and services. In addition to pension, health, and unemployment benefits, the prerequisites of a job today may include such diverse items as scholarship funds for the children of employees, prepaid legal services, access to vacation resorts at reduced rates, low-interest loans for the purchase of automobiles or houses, employer contributions for the purchase of stock in the company, low-cost housing projects for pensioners, and dental care for workers' children. The social scientist[3] who called advertising and the installment plan "the two most fearsome social inventions since the discovery of gunpowder" should have added a third, the tax-deductible contribution to an employee benefit fund, to his list.

Although the array of benefits devised is an impressive tribute to the ingenuity of industrial relations experts, major emphasis in the private economic security system has been in two broad areas: (1) the replacement of income lost through the effects of old age, disability, or unemployment; and (2) the financing of medical care required because of nonoccupational accidents and illnesses.

---

[3] Daniel Bell in W. Haber, *et al.* (eds.), *Manpower in the United States* (New York: Harper, 1954), p. 19.

This study is concerned with certain developments in the second area—the provision of medical care. In some respects this is the most interesting aspect of the nongovernmental economic security programs being carried on at the present time. Two of the more important reasons for this are the absence of a governmental program for medical care for the general population and the tendency for issues in medical economics to extend beyond the immediate financial problem to include questions of medical organization and philosophy. (It has been suggested, for example, that many advocates of group as against individual practice as a method of medical organization are influenced by the fact that this method is most suited to some types of prepayment programs.)

Because governmental programs for old age and survivors insurance and unemployment compensation are well developed, private activity in these fields has been designed to supplement this broad publicly administered base. In the case of medical care, however, no governmental program has been established up to this time although proposals for a publicly administered system of health insurance have been put forth repeatedly. The voluntary health insurance movement, with its rapid growth in the past dozen years, has been advanced as the best example of the ability of "welfare capitalism" to forestall the necessity for the continued development of the "welfare state." Here is an example of a private program attempting to serve as a substitute for, rather than a supplement to, a public program. Important and influential groups in the economy are committed to making this substitute work well enough to make a comprehensive state system unnecessary. Included among these groups are the medical and auxiliary professions, the medical service organizations, the private insurance industry, the great majority of employers, and a small but fairly substantial minority of union officials. This lends a special significance to efforts to maintain voluntary health insurance as the primary vehicle in the financing of medical care.

The second reason cited for the special interest attaching to the health insurance movement, the tendency for the interested organization to go beyond financing to the organization of medical care, stems from the nature of the particular benefit involved. Cash benefits paid to a worker under a pension or an unemployment compensation plan may be spent for any one of the tremendous variety of items making up the American family budget. Family differences in spending habits and the multitude of types of producers and suppliers involved make it difficult to mobilize the purchasing power of such cash payments so as to influence methods of production or distribution of any single product or service.[4]

For medical care, however, an earmarked sum of money is made available through the prepayment mechanism of health insurance. This sum is to be spent for a narrow range of services performed by an easily identifiable group of suppliers. Prices of these services have been rising and one branch of the suppliers, the doctors, have for some years enjoyed the highest average annual income of any profession in the United States. Proposals to reorganize the medical "industry" have been commonplace in the political arena. These circumstances make it inevitable that a revolution in the way medical care is financed should raise the question of the wisdom of the way the existing system distributes the income involved. This is true even though the revolution is being carried out primarily under the sponsorship of friends of the old regime. The financing system being called into question is the traditional payment of physicians on the basis of fees set unilaterally by the doctor involved, functioning as an independent practitioner and charging each patient for each item of service as it is rendered. It is also usually regarded as part of the traditional pattern for fees for the same procedure to vary among the doctors of a community.

This issue would have been raised even if health insurance had not become a part of the fringe benefit package in collective bargaining. When the unions entered the process, it meant that a

---

[4] Difficult, but not impossible, since some unions and other organized consumer groups have established coöperative stores, arranged discount plans, and organized banks and credit unions to exert pressure on the retail distribution and finance industries. Next to medical care the most promising area of activity for unions as representatives of organized consumers may be the housing industry and its real estate and financing subsidiaries. Unions have already promoted tracts of individual houses and apartment developments—coöperative and otherwise—and are investigating large-scale participation in the mortgage market. The goal is to lower members' housing costs by reducing contractors' and developers' profits, sales commissions, "closing" costs, and financing charges. Limits to the potential activity of unions on behalf of their members as consumers appear to be set only by the boundaries established by other unions in defense of their own members in their role as producers.

group of consumers making up a very substantial segment of the market for medical care was being represented by skillful professional bargainers to whom group action in the pursuit of economic advantage is a way of life. By 1957 more than twelve million workers were enrolled in health insurance plans in which unions had a voice in policy arrangements. Since most plans provide for coverage of the worker's dependents as well, it is probably conservative to estimate that more than a quarter of all persons with health insurance coverage are in plans in which a union influences policy.

The situation created by introducing collective-bargaining agencies acting on behalf of large groups of consumers into what previously had been a market made up of individuals is the focus of this study. By 1958 health programs had been a subject of collective bargaining on a large scale for almost ten years. During these years, the suppliers of medical services, the insuring agencies, and the unions have been working out new relationships with varying degrees of success.

In the United States the supply of physicians' services is produced by a large number of small-scale units, operating in very localized markets and organized into small geographical associations. Under the proper stimuli, these associations have demonstrated a degree of flexibility and local autonomy considerably greater than they are often given credit for by their critics. As a result, although significant new developments in medical economics have occurred on a national level, the experience on the scale of the county, metropolitan area, and the state offers a much richer vein of relatively unexploited materials.

Some of the following chapters, particularly chapters ii and iii, concern themselves largely with subjects that are national in scope, such as the rising level of medical fees and the abuse of health insurance benefits. Although considerable space is devoted to general problems in chapters iv through viii, these chapters are primarily concerned with a review of the variety of organizations, the tactics and strategy of group bargaining, and the experiments in medical care arrangements that have resulted from ten years of welfare fund activity in the San Francisco Bay Area. In the concluding chapter, an attempt is made to distill a set of general propositions from the material analyzed earlier, to evaluate the net effect of union activity on health care systems, and to forecast the pattern of the future.

During the hearings of a Congressional committee, a member of the Board of Trustees of the American Medical Association answered a question as to whether certain types of medical care programs were to be found in California by remarking: "You have everything in California."

Although this statement is something of an exaggeration even in the limited field of medical care plans, enough diversity does exist to justify the statement that there are few other states in which an investigation into health plans and collective bargaining would be more fruitful.

Other Important Influences

The problem of organizing and financing medical care in the United States in general and California in particular is a complex one with a long history of controversy. At the outset of this study it was evident that it would be impossible to isolate the effect of unions and collective bargaining from that of other social and economic forces which were part of the changing medical care scene. In California, at least two other major forces have been shaping developments in medical economics during the period under examination.[5]

One of these forces is the political pressure for a compulsory health insurance program and the other is the economic pressure generated by one of the country's largest and most successful prepayment group-practice medical programs. Compulsory health insurance has been a state issue in California almost as long as it has been a national issue, going back to 1917. One proposal actually enjoyed the endorsement of the state medical society for one hectic year in the mid-thirties. More recently three bills were introduced in the legislature with the active support of former Governor Warren in the years 1945 to 1949.

Pressure of a different type has been placed on the physicians and hospitals of large areas of California by the growth of the Kaiser Foundation Health Plan. The Kaiser Plan is a medical serv-

---

[5] These additional social and economic forces are discussed more fully in chapter iv below.

ice plan offering comprehensive medical care to its subscribers through its own medical staff and in its own hospitals and out-patient centers. Growing out of the health service organizations set up for the isolated construction projects of the early Kaiser enterprises, the plan was opened to the public at the end of World War II. Growth has been rapid and sustained. By the end of 1956 the plan included more than 300,000 members in the San Francisco Bay Area with only a very small fraction of this number being employees of Kaiser firms. The southern California branch is approximately the same size. In addition, the plan operates on a smaller scale in the Portland–Vancouver area in Oregon and Washington.

Both the compulsory health insurance movement and the Kaiser Plan development preceded the important union health and welfare activity which began in 1949. Many of the countermoves adopted by the medical profession in response to these forces had been initiated by that date. Collective bargaining over health plans gave developments an urgency and a drive which had not existed before. For example, the California Physicians Service (CPS), often referred to as the first state-wide, physician-sponsored medical care program, was established in 1939 in large part as an alternative to the state health system then being advocated by Governor Olson. Although union pressure had no part in the 1939 decision except indirectly through support for the state plan, the present CPS program reflects this pressure in its income-ceiling structure, the variety of programs it includes, and certain important administrative practices. Not only did the unions reinforce the strength of existing trends but they advanced new alternatives, such as union health centers.

Like employers before them, the medical profession discovered that, to the unions, activity at the bargaining table is an alternative to activity in the halls of the legislature. Unsuccessful in attaining national or state health insurance, the unions turned to what John R. Commons has called the "private legislation" of the collective-bargaining process. Winning a voice in the disposition of funds for medical insurance through union-management contracts, unions could threaten to set up their own health centers or to enroll their members in the Kaiser Plan to secure bargaining leverage against the medical organizations. As a result of the interplay of these several forces, it is impossible to identify exact cause-and-effect relationships in the changing economics of medical care in the Bay Area. Fear of the competition of the Kaiser Plan, the desire to make voluntary health insurance work, and the policies of unions and employers all combined to make important modifications in the way in which medical care is produced, paid for, and distributed. Recognizing that opinions will differ as to the relative weight each element should be given, an attempt will be made in later chapters to outline the changes thought to be primarily the result of union-management activity involving health insurance.

Plan of the Book

In the chapters to follow the development of the theme proceeds along the following lines.

In chapter ii the structure of the medical market is examined at the national level and in the San Francisco Bay Area. The aim is to assess the position of the collectively bargained health plans in the medical market. In addition to indicating the place of labor-management health plans in the market structure of the nation, in the San Francisco Bay Area the size of the negotiated plan business relative to the total business of specific types of insuring agencies is portrayed.

In chapter iii attention is shifted to the functioning of the medical market. At the national level this involves the analysis of the behavior of the prices of medical care services. The focus in this chapter is on the degree of inflation of the prices of medical care and the forces that might account for the observed price behavior. In chapter iv the problem of the abuse of health insurance is examined.

The next four chapters examine the way in which the labor movement in the San Francisco Bay Area has attempted to utilize its bargaining position in relation to the medical industry and the insuring agencies to deal with the cost problems of health plans. These problems in large measure have grown out of the problems of rising prices and abuse discussed in chapters iii and iv.

The first of these four, chapter v, is a review of developments in California that have provided the environment in which the negotiated plans operate. Chapter vi outlines the industrial relations structure of the Bay Area since this structure affects the forms and channels that action can take. Chapter vii is a historical review of the succession of strategies employed by the labor movement in almost a decade of attempting to influence developments. Chapter viii is a detailed case study of the way in which a labor organization in one of the local communities drastically altered the balance of medical power.

Chapter ix concerns itself with a series of special problems, some of general significance, which have characterized the past decade of health plan developments in the local area.

Chapter x attempts to assess the implications of the experience reported in this study for the future of public and private health insurance and chapter xi discusses the role that labor-management plans are to play in that future.

Chapter II | *The*
Structure of the
Medical Market

In this chapter the structure of the medical market will be outlined, some of the changes that have occurred will be reviewed, and the place of collectively bargained health plans in that structure will be indicated. The emphasis will be on the private or nongovernmental sector of medical demand.

These qualifications are important since some of the most interesting and important questions bearing on the future of medical practice are concerned with changes that affect the supply of medical services. Questions such as the role of the hospital as a medical center and the place of specialization and of group practice are of major importance to the consideration of the organization of this supply. In addition, the growing part of the total market that seems to be coming under governmental influence, directly or indirectly, is outside the scope of interest of this study.[1] Without minimizing the importance of these areas of concern, attention will be focused on that part of medical demand represented by private individuals and nongovernmental organizations.

Within this context the most important structural changes that have occurred over the past two decades are the growth of health insurance as a method of financing medical care and the addition of

[1] For a discussion of these issues see M. M. Davis, *Medical Care for Tomorrow* (New York: Harper, 1955), chaps. 9–11, and two articles by Herman and Anne Somers, "Private Health Insurance," in *California Law Review*, Vol. 46, Nos. 3 and 4, August and September, 1958.

health insurance to the fringe benefit "package" in collective-bargaining negotiations. The introduction of widespread health insurance coverage has changed the distribution of the financial burden of medical care costs and has almost certainly increased the total amount of money available for the purchase of medical services. The inclusion of health insurance as one of the issues in collective bargaining has expanded the base of insurance coverage and increased its depth. Considered from the standpoint of market structure, the significance of both the health insurance movement and collective bargaining is that they have introduced organizations into what had previously been a market characterized largely by transactions between individuals—the physicians and their patients. For the most part, the insuring agencies have chosen to minimize the impact that their rising participation in medical care financing might have been expected to produce. Certain types of insuring agencies, such as group practice service plans, are inherently revolutionary in their approach to the organization of medical practice. The collective-bargaining agencies have attempted to be more aggressive, both in their relationships with the suppliers of medical services and with the insuring agencies themselves.

In the sections to follow the changes in the medical market that have occurred on a national level and in the San Francisco Bay Area will be outlined in order to arrive at some knowledge of the institutions now operating in what was formerly a comparatively unstructured market and to measure the breadth of the economic base from which they operate.

Size and Structure—The National Market

Considered in terms of total dollar expenditures, the medical industry is an impressive part of the national economy. The Department of Health, Education, and Welfare estimates that private expenditures for medical care in 1957 amounted to a total of approximately fifteen billion dollars.[2] This is about two-thirds of the value of all residential construction during 1955, the record-

---

[2] In order to minimize the necessity for tedious documentation in the body of the text, methods of estimating various elements of the market, the citing of sources and the discussion of their validity are presented in Appendix A; 1956 will be used as a base year since, at the time of writing, it was the most recent year for which complete statistics were available.

breaking year in the building industry. In 1950, the Census showed that about 1.6 million persons were employed in the medical services.

Of the total private expenditure for medical care nearly 8.5 billion dollars was spent for hospital services and the services of some 190,000 practicing physicians. Most of the rest (6.5 billion dollars) was spent for dental care, other professional services, and drugs and appliances. Since for the most part, health insurance provides only for hospitalization and some physicians' services and excludes the other categories of expense, only this segment of total private expenditures will be considered. In the discussion to follow it is important to remember that public or governmental expenditures are disregarded as not being relevant to the subject matter of this investigation.

Hospital and physicians' services would be regarded by most people as the core of the medical industry. Expenditures on these two types of services have been growing at the same rate as the other categories, making up 57 per cent of all private medical expense both in 1948 and 1957. Increases in the expenditures for these "insurable items" have been accompanied by and perhaps to some extent caused by the rapid growth of health insurance over that period. The number of persons with some form of health insurance rose from over 60 million in 1948 to about 116 million in 1956, while the benefits paid through insurance increased by almost six times as the scope of insurance coverage broadened and the average money payments increased. As the percentage of the population covered by some form of health insurance grew and the coverage widened, insurance benefits became a factor of greater importance in the medical market. "Third-party expenditures," as these payments are called, provided a growing percentage of physicians' incomes and paid for a larger proportion of hospital services. Nationally, more than a quarter of the income of physicians (from private sources) came from insurance benefits in 1957 compared with about one-sixteenth in 1948. Over the same period the proportion of hospital services paid for by insurance doubled, with more than half of the total expense being covered in 1957.

These figures indicate that, to an increasing degree, the individual consumer of medical care has been financing his spending indirectly through the insurance mechanism. The amounts channeled through "third parties" by this method have grown rapidly both absolutely and relative to total expenditures on the services usually insured. These figures also suggest that the organizations concerned might be able to exert considerable influence on the functioning of the medical market if they chose to exploit the full potential of their market position. Viewing the situation in this way suggests the question: Who are these third parties and what role do they play in the medical market?

The Insuring Agencies

For convenience the insuring organizations are divided into three categories: the familiar commercial insurance companies, the medically sponsored insurance plans, and the "independent" plans. Commercial life insurance companies write about five-sixths of the commercial group policies. Medically sponsored plans include the Blue Cross and the Blue Shield companies as well as some other plans, which, though they may not be formal members of these organizations, have the same type of sponsorship and function in the same pattern. As the designation indicates, the distinguishing characteristic of these plans is a more or less formal link with the hospital associations or the county or state medical societies. The independent plans are a heterogeneous collection, usually relatively small in membership, which have been brought into existence under widely differing auspices. Sponsored by industrial companies, colleges and universities, community organizations, governmental bodies, unions, coöperatives, and individual hospitals or doctors, these groups operate under a wide variety of organizational forms and furnish a wide variety of coverages to their members. The three largest independent plans are the Health Insurance Plan of Greater New York, the Kaiser Foundation Health Plan on the West Coast, and the United Mine Workers health plan. These three plans cover about half of the more than five million members of this type of health system. The Mine Workers system covers about 1.5 million persons, or about 30 per cent of total enrollment. At the other extreme are the small groups of physicians who acquire independent plan status by agreeing to furnish care on a prepayment basis to small groups of subscribers. Although these independent plans include in total less than one-twentieth of the combined coverage of all health insurance, they have been a center of controversy within the medical profession.[3] This stems from the fact that their usual method of operation is group practice coupled with prepayment or in the language of controversy—the "closed panel" of physicians.[4] As a result of the economics of this form of organization, many of them have devised unorthodox financial arrangements for paying physicians such as capitation (flat sum per member) or direct salary. The type of conflicts within the medical profession that result are described in chapter v in relation to the Kaiser Foundation Health Plan.

Relationships between organized medicine and the independent plans are characterized by a marked inconsistency. The degree of conflict seems to be related to the type of sponsorship, the size of the eligible group of members, their income level, and the date of establishment of the plan. A plan sponsored by an industrial organization, established in the fairly remote past, and serving a small, limited membership of low income seems to have the best chance of leading a noncontroversial existence.

Independent plans are of interest in their medical as well as in their economic aspects because they typically offer a broader range of medical care to their members than the usual Blue Shield or insurance company plans. As a factor in the medical market the independent groups have grown somewhat faster than health insurance as a whole, but except in certain geographical areas their small size limits their economic importance. (This small size also helps to explain their relatively large percentage growth.) Difficulties in extending their type of coverage are formidable and may be increasing. Favorable economic conditions which permit the luxury of relatively expensive methods of medical care and the opposition of the medical profession make it unlikely that the direct role of these plans will greatly increase in the immediate future. Nevertheless, their influence is very important. They set a standard of coverage that many groups find desirable as a goal and they offer an example of a workable pat-

---

[3] See for example the decision in *Group Health Cooperative of Puget Sound v. King County Medical Society* (1951), 139 Wash., 541.

[4] The UMW plan could be regarded as an exception to this although the mineworkers do utilize this method and seem to be moving toward increasing emphasis on it. See chapter iv below.

tern of medical practice under nonmedical sponsorship for possible emulation by organized groups, particularly labor unions. In addition, in those areas where they operate, they often provide bargaining leverage against the medical profession and the insurance companies.

Quantitatively, the health insurance business is dominated by the commercial insurance companies and the medically sponsored health plans. Together they account for about 95 per cent of all coverage and, unless a major revolution in medical economics occurs, something like this overwhelming concentration of business is likely to continue. Within this over-all figure, however, changes in relative position of some consequence are occurring.[5]

The modern era of health insurance began in 1932 with the establishment of the hospital plans that were the forerunners of the national Blue Cross system. By 1939 commercial insurance companies were active in both hospital and surgical insurance and some medical societies were launching experiments with more comprehensive surgical and medical care coverage. By the end of World War II all branches of the health insurance business were flourishing in terms of numbers of persons covered. In 1946 Blue Cross still dominated the hospital insurance field with about twenty-four million persons enrolled while the insurance companies had a total of about fourteen million (these figures are not corrected for duplication; i.e., one individual may have been covered by more than one policy). By 1949 the commercial companies had overtaken Blue Cross. They have been widening their margin steadily ever since. By 1957 Blue Cross–Blue Shield coverage had grown to about fifty-five million but insurance company coverage had risen to about seventy million.

If surgical and medical care insurance are combined and considered separately from hospital insurance the picture is somewhat different. In 1946 the insurance companies had the major part of the business with some 10.6 million persons covered compared to about 4.4 million in the "Blue" plans. Unlike the pattern for hospital insurance, however, the medically sponsored plans have been growing more rapidly than those of the commercial insur-

---

[5] Throughout this discussion emphasis will be placed on the numbers of persons with *some* coverage without regard to the scope of that coverage. It is important to remember, however, that very wide variations in scope do exist, particularly in the individual policies of the commercial insurance companies.

ance companies. By the end of 1957, their coverage had grown to over forty-five million persons while the insurance companies had enrolled about sixty-seven million.

To sum up, as of 1957 commercial insurance companies did a majority of the business in both hospital and surgical expense insurance. The medically sponsored plans have been losing ground in hospital insurance but have been gaining in both surgical and medical expense insurance.

The fact that the medically sponsored plans cover a minority of the insured policy holders might be thought to have important implications for the practice of medicine. As far as their relations with the consumers and the producers of medical care are concerned, however, both the insurance companies and the Blue Cross–Blue Shield type of organization concentrate on acting as a mechanism for modifying the system of financing medical care without disturbing the organizational structure of the practice of medicine. Some of the Blue plans have modified the pricing practices of the medical profession and of the hospitals for that part of the latter's business covered by this form of insurance. Unlike the independent plans, however, both of the dominant forms of health insurance have accepted the existing pattern of medical organization.

Collectively Bargained Plans

Turning to that part of the national medical market which is represented by collectively bargained plans, a special form of "third party" activity, we find another example of rapid growth.[6] Isolated examples of negotiated health and welfare programs of limited scope have existed as far back as 1926 when the Amalgamated Association of Street and Electric Railway Employees won an employer-financed sickness and life insurance plan from the Chicago Rapid Transit Company through the decision of an arbitrator. This union continued to negotiate this type of benefit until in 1943 it was reported as having been included in more than 200 contracts. In 1939 the Amalgamated Clothing Workers of America converted an unemployment insurance fund, established

---

[6] Actually, since most such plans purchase insurance from one of the insuring agencies described earlier, they are really "fourth parties" in the medical market.

through collective bargaining in 1923, into a social benefits fund which included health insurance in its benefit structure. In spite of this pioneering activity, in 1942 the Bureau of Labor Statistics was able to find "relatively few" formal plans in effect.[7] By 1946, the first period of rapid growth had occurred and the BLS reported that "at least 600,000" workers were covered by health plans. Since that time growth has continued with the most impressive surge of membership occurring between 1948 and 1950 when coverage went up from about 2.7 million to more than 7 million. By the end of 1954 it was estimated that 12 million workers and 17 million dependents were enrolled in collectively bargained health plans. Since this date the growth has been slow, with the 1956 figure estimated at "in excess" of 12 million.

This increase should not be viewed as a net addition to health insurance coverage since many of the persons brought under bargaining agreements probably had been enrolled in some other form of coverage previously. The drive for plans financed through the bargaining process in many cases meant replacing a union-sponsored voluntary plan, an employer-sponsored plan, or individual coverage by a negotiated arrangement. In addition to these qualifications, there is no correction for duplication in the statistics of negotiated plans. Duplication of coverage is likely to be particularly prevalent in this type of coverage. A fairly substantial number of the American families in which both husband and wife work outside the home undoubtedly have both wage earners enrolled in plans which give dependents automatic coverage. If the negotiated plan coverage is expressed as a percentage of the national total for all health insurance, we find that more than a quarter of all health insurance is financed through collective bargaining in whole or in part. Although no method of estimating the size of benefit payments produced by negotiated plans is readily available, it is apparent that their impact on the medical market is very substantial. There is no question but that collective bargaining over health insurance has substantially increased the number of persons covered and raised the level of their insurance coverage, at least in dollar terms.

---

[7] Preceding material is from H. Baker and D. Dahl, *Group Health Insurance and Sickness Benefit Plans in Collective Bargaining* (Princeton: Princeton University Press, 1945), pp. 16–17.

Like health insurance generally, the rate of growth of negotiated plans has been slowing as the larger part of the potentially eligible population is enrolled. The three major forces propelling the collectively bargained plans forward were: (1) wage controls during World War II and the Korean emergency which permitted fringe benefits to be increased while acting to retard direct wage increases; (2) the pattern-setting impact of the United Mine Workers' Welfare and Retirement Fund which, in the days when John L. Lewis was a potent factor in collective bargaining, opened up a whole new range of bargaining possibilities; and (3) the court decisions requiring employers to bargain on health and welfare issues to meet Taft-Hartley Act requirements. Under the impetus provided by these events, negotiated plans grew to cover about 70 per cent of the employees working under collective-bargaining contracts. Although steady growth in the breadth and the depth of insurance coverage will probably continue, the spectacular surge of the last decade is not likely to be repeated. With the "principle" established, attention may now be turned to improving the functioning of the plans.

In summary, in 1957 about two-fifths of the 8.5 billion dollars of private expenditures for hospital and physicians' services was provided through health insurance. About seven-tenths of the total population had some form of insurance with hospitalization coverage most common. The majority of this group (54 per cent) were covered by insurance company policies. The medically sponsored plans insured about 42 per cent and the independent plans about 4 to 5 per cent. As to trends in coverage, independent plans have about held their small fraction of the business over the past several years, the commercial plans have overtaken and have been growing relatively faster than Blue Cross in hospital insurance, and the medically sponsored plans have been gaining on the commercial companies in surgical and medical care insurance. More than a quarter of all the health insurance in effect in the United States is financed through labor-management negotiations.[8]

---

[8] These statements are couched in terms of numbers of persons covered. Measured by expenditures for benefits, the proportional distribution presents a somewhat different picture. The medically sponsored plans and the insurance companies paid out almost the same percentage of the total insurance benefits in 1956 (45 and 47 per cent) whereas the independent plans paid out 8 per cent. Variations

There are a number of special elements stemming from the large and growing role of the negotiated plans. First, most of the holders of this coverage feel that this large block of insurance "was not sold, it was bought," with the resulting implications for selling methods and costs. Second, the decision to buy was not an individual decision but a collective one channeled through institutions—the union and the business enterprise. As noted elsewhere, this means that more-or-less knowledgeable representatives of at least some of the insured public exist. It also means that there has been a remarkable growth of what the insurance industry calls "100 per cent groups." In the usual group insurance situation it is very unlikely that all of the eligible population will participate in the program. It is customary to set a minimum percentage of those eligible (usually 75 per cent) which is required to enroll before a program will go into effect. This requirement grows out of the basic theory of group insurance. In its simplest form, the theory holds that if a high percentage of a large number of persons gathered together for purposes other than that of securing insurance enroll in an insurance program, the enrollees will approximate a cross section of the population with respect to their insurability. Along with other safeguards, this enables the insurance company to do away with tests of insurability, such as physical examinations. Coupled with the employer contributions to financing, collective bargaining has led to an extension of coverage to groups that might never have been reached by the usual selling techniques. In addition to reaching many individual companies and union locals that were at best marginal customers for a group insurance program, collective bargaining and the 100 per cent feature has meant including a large number of individuals who would have been extremely unlikely to have participated voluntarily in any insurance plan. As an illustration of these effects, one of the results of the growth of health plans in the Bay Area has been to create a problem of securing patients for the teaching hospitals. The former main source of supply had been nonpaying

from the percentages in the text reflect the differences in adequacy of coverage of the various types of plans—the most comprehensive are independent plans, followed in order by the medically sponsored and the insurance company programs. (*Social Security Bulletin*, December 1957, p. 50.)

patients, many of whom now have insurance coverage. In a sense the collective-bargaining method has been a semicompulsory substitute for compulsory health insurance. Although there are many groups in the population outside the reach of any feasible extension of collective bargaining, the introduction of health plans as a fringe benefit has undoubtedly made the attempt to create a successful national program of voluntary health insurance more successful than it otherwise would have been. Because of certain features of the American collective-bargaining system, the union movement has developed what amounts to a private fiscal system able to levy a form of "tax" to support this sort of a welfare program. The most important of these features are the device of the union shop, which makes union membership compulsory for from two-thirds to three-fourths of the production work force in American industry,[9] and the concept of exclusive bargaining rights that acts to limit the alternative systems of representation available to the workers in a bargaining unit. It is paradoxical that the union movement has been one of the most vocal of the organized groups supporting compulsory health insurance while at the same time it has furnished the vehicle most likely to make a voluntary system work well enough to forestall any full-scale national health scheme.

Size and Structure—The Bay Area Market

Analyzing the Bay Area medical market is both harder and easier than dealing with the national market. Data on health insurance in general are much more sparse for small local areas than for the nation at large but for collectively bargained plans, the primary area of interest here, the information available is more accurate and comprehensive than the national data.

Rather surprisingly, a smaller percentage of the total population in California is covered by health insurance than in the nation. (Strictly speaking, this is true only of hospital insurance, the most common type.) In 1955 about 54 per cent of the state's population had some form of health insurance coverage. No data exist

---

[9] It should be noted that this system appears as compulsion only to the minority (usually small) of workers who would not have joined the union voluntarily. It is, however, exactly this sort of minority that compulsory health insurance would be designed to include.

for any regional division smaller than the state, but in the discussion to follow the Bay Area rate of coverage has been assumed to be 10 per cent greater since urban areas usually have higher proportions of insurance coverage. This is almost inevitable because the characteristics of group insurance make coverage of small, dispersed units difficult.

Turning to an analysis of the Bay Area market, the information available indicates that something under half (perhaps 45 per cent) of those persons with some health insurance coverage were enrolled in a plan negotiated through collective bargaining in 1955. This would mean that almost 30 per cent of the population of the area was in negotiated plans. If this estimate is accepted as characteristic, the potential consequences for the structure of medical demand are obvious. The curious reader may wonder if this estimate couched in terms of numbers of persons can be translated into a statement about the proportion of money income of the medical profession that is generated by these plans. Any such attempt can only be a tentative one but, on the basis of assumptions detailed in Appendix A, it appears that something over twenty cents of the average dollar of income of the doctors in the Bay Area may come from negotiated health plans. Note that the percentage of persons in negotiated plans is greater than the percentage of income generated because all medical expenditures of insured persons are not covered by insurance.

There are a number of major differences in the structure of the negotiated plans in the Bay Area as compared with the national pattern. First, in the Bay Area a higher percentage of all health insurance in force is financed by collective bargaining (45 as against 27 per cent). Second, the employer pays the full cost in a much higher percentage of the bargained plans. In 1954 the employers paid the full cost of only 62 per cent of the nation's negotiated plans studied by the Bureau of Labor Statistics while in the Bay Area nine of ten plans were financed wholly by the employer. As time goes on, this differential is being reduced as more national plans shift to employer financing. Third, it seems to be more common in the Bay Area for the collective-bargaining contracts setting up health and welfare plans to specify the amount of the employer's contribution rather than to specify the schedule of benefits to be provided. In the Bay Area at the end of

1955 an estimated 75 per cent of all workers covered by negotiated plans were working under contracts that stipulated an employer contribution. Although comparable data are not available for the nation, the importance attached to the problem of disclosure of employer costs during the congressional debate on welfare-plan legislation in the summer of 1957 suggests that explicit contributions of this kind are less common. Fourth, collectively bargained plans not only make up a larger percentage of all health insurance in force in the Bay Area, but a much higher fraction of the workers in unionized firms is covered by negotiated health plans. In fact, except for the unlikely possibility of a major increase in the size of the labor movement in the Bay Area, the saturation point in coverage is near since almost nine out of ten workers under contract are enrolled in some form of plan. Nationally, the figure is about 70 per cent. Further activity in the health and welfare field will not be lacking, however, since there is a continuing problem of adequacy of benefits and extension of coverage.

Returning to the problem of the position of the negotiated plans in the over-all health insurance market, three questions arise: (1) How have the negotiated plans distributed their business among the insurance carriers? (2) How large a part of the Bay Area business of each type of carrier is represented by the membership of the negotiated plans? (3) Are there key plans that can be regarded as potential or actual leaders in relationships among the various organizations in the medical market?

Data necessary to answer the first two questions are summarized in table 2.1.[10] Although a number of heroic assumptions had to be made to arrive at these figures, in their final form they probably give the broad outlines of the situation as it existed in 1954, the date of the most comprehensive local survey of health and welfare plans. Since that time, in addition to a substantial general expansion of coverage, the principal change which had occurred up to mid-1958 was the transfer of a large segment of the health plan membership of the San Francisco Joint Board of Culinary Workers from commercial insurance to the California Physicians Service. Although this probably raised the CPS proportion of the

---

[10] For fuller discussion of the character and the role of the various collective-bargaining groups and medical service organizations mentioned in this section, see chapters v and vi below.

TABLE 2.1

THE NEGOTIATED HEALTH PLAN MARKET IN THE BAY AREA, 1954

	Type of insurer			
Item	Insurance companies	Blue Cross	CPS	Kaiser
Percentage distribution of negotiated plan membership among insurers[a] ...	65	19	5	12
Negotiated plan membership as percentage of insurer's Bay Area business	21	30	16	22

SOURCES: Estimates explained in Appendix A.

[a] The most important change since 1954 is a rise in the CPS share of the total with some drop in the insurance company share arising from a shift by the Culinary Workers from commercial insurance to CPS.

total and lowered the commercial insurance share, the latter still accounted for close to two-thirds of all negotiated plan membership. Blue Cross was probably still in second place with less than one-third of the insurance company coverage but with half again as many negotiated plan members as the Kaiser Plan in third place.

More interesting than the questions of the distribution of the business among the carriers is the degree of importance that attaches to the negotiated plan business of each of the insurers in the local market. The estimates of the proportion of the total membership of each type of carrier enrolled in collectively bargained plans runs from a high of 30 per cent for Blue Cross to 15 per cent for CPS with Kaiser and the insurance companies both at about 20 per cent. This relationship provides the first clue as to the bargaining leverage which the unions might be able to generate against a particular type of plan. Presumably the union's bargaining position would be stronger the larger the percentage of the insurer's total membership enrolled through collective bargaining. A little reflection reveals the need for qualifying this initial approach. With either Blue Cross, CPS, or the Kaiser Plan the unions would be dealing with a single decision-making unit of a limited size. For the Kaiser Plan the Bay Area membership is about half of the entire membership; Blue Cross operates throughout northern California and probably has at least 60 per cent of its total membership in the Bay Area; CPS operates state-wide and has about 30 per cent of its membership in the Bay Area. It would seem possible for the union movement to mobilize state-wide support for a particular health and welfare policy, but, even if this possibility is ruled out, a united policy in the Bay Area alone would create significant pressure against all three of these organizations.

The situation of the commercial insurance companies is different. Most of the insurance is underwritten by national companies which write more than one line of insurance and do only a small part of their total business in the Bay Area. Furthermore, the total negotiated plan coverage is divided among a number of companies so that the leverage of the unions against an individual company is further reduced. Fortunately for the unions, however, the multiplicity of companies contributes to competition for business. This competition gives a plan with a large total number of members considerable bargaining power even when this number is small relative to the national total of policyholders. In addition to the competition that exists among the insurance companies themselves and with the other types of insurers, a large union-management plan has the potential threat of self-insurance available.

Another reason why the bargaining strength of a particular union cannot be measured simply in terms of numbers of members is because the desirability of the union as an insured group depends in part on its insurance claim experience. A union group with a record of high and unpredictable insurance costs is not in a strong bargaining position to use the prospect of securing its business as a lever in negotiations with insurance carriers.

Major Negotiated Plans

This examination of the anatomy of the medical market would be incomplete if the negotiated plans were treated as a single unit in themselves. In fact unity of action for the various labor-management health plans has been the exception rather than the rule. In chapter iv the structure of the union movement is sketched briefly and a few area council labor bodies are identified as having been active in health and welfare matters. The most comprehensive of these, the San Francisco Labor Council, is limited to part of the geographical area and is the most restricted in its ability to act on behalf of its members. Machinery for effective decision-making in the Bay Area union movement, as in the rest of the nation, is concentrated in the national unions (e.g., the Teamsters Union, the Steelworkers, etc.) and their regional subdivisions. Although the San Francisco Labor Council has tried to function as a rallying point for the bargaining strength of the unions of the locality, identifying the more effective pressure points requires an examination of the size distribution and the strategic location of the individual negotiated plans.

No census of negotiated health plans giving details on identifiable individual plans has ever been made public. In the course of this investigation it is certain, however, that some knowledge was secured about the larger plans in the area so that a fairly accurate estimate as to their size can be made. In table 2.2 eight of

TABLE 2.2

ELIGIBLE MEMBERSHIP OF THE LARGER BAY AREA HEALTH PLAN
GROUPINGS BY TYPE OF INSURER, 1956 [a]

Grouping	Type of insurer			
	Insurance	Kaiser	Blue Cross	CPS
Total without dependents ..	45,000	24,000	24,000	20,000
Total with dependents	112,000	60,000	60,000	50,000
Teamsters	36,000			
Construction Laborers	9,000			
ILWU		14,000		
Joint Board of Culinary Workers		10,000		
Carpenters			15,000	
S.F. Retailers Council			9,000	
Joint Board of Culinary Workers				12,000
Butcher Workmen				8,000

[a] Figures are very rough estimates secured from officials of the groups or from the insuring organizations. Where the organizations cover a larger geographical area than the Bay Area, the figures are estimated Bay Area membership. Culinary Workers appear twice because of the dual-choice program. Dependents estimated as 1.5 per worker.

the largest "plans" known to the writer are grouped by type of insurer carrier as of 1956.[11] Strictly speaking, several of the "plans" are not literally single administrative units. What are called plans for convenience in the discussion are sometimes actually many separate plans in a legal sense. They are spoken of as single entities on the ground that they are subject to a single controlling influence based on the local area and therefore form the base of power from which bargaining strength is generated in dealings with the insurance organizations and with the medical industry. For example, although the regional office of the Teamsters Security Fund includes thirty-two separate union-management trusts, it is meaningful to treat the Teamsters as a unit for our purposes.

Table 2.2 points up the dominant position of a handful of union groups in the negotiated health and welfare field. Leaving out the Retailers Council, the single employer association in the listing, the six union groups account for about 30 per cent of all the negotiated health plan membership in the Bay Area.[12]

By coincidence, the listing of the eight largest collective-bargaining groups includes the two largest groups in each of the types of insurers. This permits an assessment of the bargaining situation within each organization.

As might be expected, by this measure even the large unions' bargaining strength is least in the case of the commercial insurance companies. Even the formidable Teamsters Security Fund is a small part of all the commercial insurance coverage in the Bay Area. The Teamsters and the Construction Laborer's plan combined add up to slightly more than one out of every nineteen

---

[11] In this part of the discussion as elsewhere, a special meaning is attached to the concept of a health "plan" which ought to be clarified. As used in most of this study a "plan" may be either a single group of workers covered by a single trust agreement and/or a single insurance carrier, or it may be a group of plans covering closely related workers who are members of the same national union or employees of the members of a single employer association. For administrative reasons, there are more individual plans in a legal or statistical sense than there are decision-making units controlling the policies of the plans. Since interest here is on the interplay of policy decisions, the term has been given a more useful, if less exact, meaning.

[12] The Retail Clerks Union represents the great bulk of the membership of the Retailers Council plan and might have been included as such. The cutoff point adopted for table 2.2 was arbitrary—a number of other unions, notably in construction and in the metal trades, are close to the Butchers Union in size. The principal criterion for stopping at this point was that it happened to result in inclusion of the two largest groups for each type of carrier.

persons covered by health insurance. It should be noted, however, that the measure of bargaining strength of the unions in commercial insurance is not the proportion of the total insurance business controlled by a given union. As pointed out earlier, the insurance companies are in competition with one another and it is small comfort to a company which loses a profitable contract to know that some other insurance company has gained the business. The Teamsters Security Fund furnishes an example of how the assessment of the importance of the fund in the commercial insurance market is modified by considering this fact. About two-thirds of the Western Conference of Teamsters health insurance is currently underwritten by a single company, the Occidental Life Insurance Company, based in Los Angeles. The Teamsters' ability to influence the terms on which insurance is secured for members will be measured by the importance of this large amount of business to Occidental rather than to the industry as a whole.

When the other insuring organizations are studied, it appears that in each case the union business of the carrier is a substantial part of the total membership and that this union business is highly concentrated in a few accounts.

In the Kaiser Foundation Health Plan somewhere around 80 per cent of all negotiated health plan coverage is represented by the San Francisco Culinary Workers and the International Longshoremen's and Warehousemen's Union. These two unions alone account for perhaps 20 per cent of all the Kaiser members in the Bay Area.

In the local Blue Cross organization the Brotherhood of Carpenters provides well over 10 per cent of the total membership in the Bay Area. The Culinary Workers and the Butchers occupy a similar position within California Physicians Service. These concentrations of membership are of greater significance to the Kaiser Plan, Blue Cross, and Blue Shield compared with the commercial companies because they do no other type of business.

In summary, negotiated health plan membership amounts to a substantial part of the total health insurance business of all the insuring organizations with this circumstance being of greatest importance to the noncommercial insurers because of their localized, smaller operations and single line of coverage. In all cases, but particularly for the noncommercial carriers, the great bulk of negotiated plan business is concentrated in a small handful of unions.[13] As a result it seems reasonable to conclude that these unions occupy a strategic position in the health plan business because of their absolute size and relative importance to the carriers. In chapter ix it will be shown that this bargaining position has been utilized against the Blue organizations in at least one subject area.

Accepting the argument that the unions have been active representatives of their members' interest in health care and that the structure of the medical market gives individual unions a strategic bargaining position raises the question of the results that may be attributed to this activity. Later chapters recount in detail the tactics and strategy of the labor unions in attempting to convert their position in the medical market structure into bargaining advantage and describe some of the effects of this effort on the insuring organizations. Without going into the full story at this time we can say that the unions have contributed to: (1) the increase in the variety of coverages available from the insurers, including an increase in the scope of coverage; (2) the development or improvement of "grievance procedures" whereby complaints against the insurers or suppliers can be made effective; (3) the spread of experience rating from insurance companies to the medically sponsored plans (i.e., the practice of relating the premium cost of a particular plan to the benefit experience of the members of that specific plan rather than to the benefit costs for all members); and (4) the growing interest of the plans in the pricing mechanism of the suppliers of medical care.

Summary and Conclusions

The principal points made in this chapter can be summarized as follows:

1. Two major changes have occurred in demand within the national medical market in the past twenty years. Insurance of the

---

[13] For Kaiser and CPS a concurring note on the size distribution of the rest of their negotiated plan business can be added. In 1956 Kaiser probably had more than thirty other plans making up the 15 to 20 per cent of the negotiated plan business not provided by the ILWU and the Culinary Workers. In both CPS and Blue Cross, the two largest plans probably accounted for about half of their negotiated plan membership. CPS had the other 50 per cent spread over more than twenty-five plans. No data are available on the number of negotiated plans underwritten by Blue Cross.

costs of certain types of medical care has grown rapidly until about two-thirds of the population has some form of coverage. In turn that part of the market financed through insurance companies as "third parties" has been further structured by the growth of a form of organized consumer representation by unions and/or management. This "fourth party" intervention involves something like one-fourth of all persons with health insurance. At least one-sixth of the nation's population is enrolled in insurance systems financed through collective bargaining.

2. In the San Francisco Bay Area, we have estimated that negotiated health plans cover just under 30 per cent of the population in the market for medical care and provide perhaps one-fifth of the income of local physicians. The negotiated plan membership is highly concentrated in relatively few decision-making units. Eight of the larger groups account for about one-third of the estimated 360,000 primary subscribers.

3. In that part of the Bay Area medical insurance market financed through collective bargaining, almost two-thirds of the policies are underwritten by commercial insurance companies, about one-fifth are handled by Blue Cross, and the rest are divided between California Physicians Service and Kaiser Plan. A substantial part of each of the insuring organization's total Bay Area business is accounted for by negotiated plans. The size distribution of these plans and their distribution among the various insurers is such as to suggest that a small number of plans might be able to have substantial influence on policy, particularly for the noncommercial carriers such as the Blue plans and the Kaiser health plan.

The most significant conclusion of the analysis of the structure of the medical market pertain to the potential importance of the negotiated welfare plans in this market. Since the employers and the unions that determine the policies of these funds control a substantial part of the total flow of funds in the market, their decisions on a wide range of questions of medical economics could have far-reaching consequences. On the national level, this potential has remained relatively unexploited for a number of reasons, the most important of which have been the difficulty of dealing with a decentralized system of medical organizations and a lack of interest in or a reluctance to deal with the basic issues.

The principal exception to this statement is the United Mine Workers Welfare and Retirement Fund. The UMW Fund has encouraged the entrance of new doctors into its area of operations, has aided the development of group-practice clinics, and has built ten modern hospitals of its own. It has also studied the problem of abuse of benefits and attempted to control such abuse by requiring consultation before hospital admission is approved, by limiting the payment of surgical benefits to specialists, and by attempting to restrict the payment of medical benefits to approved physicians. (Some of these controls have been modified or dropped.)

Principally because of their weaker bargaining position, the major activity at the national level of most of the other unions has been to present their criticisms of current health arrangements to legislative committees and other governmental bodies. The data in this chapter suggest that a good deal of potential bargaining strength exists and, particularly if employers could be enlisted as allies, might eventually be utilized.

The foregoing analysis of the San Francisco Bay Area market has pointed up the strategic position of the negotiated plans in this metropolitan area, not only with relation to the medical industry but with relation to specific insuring agencies. In later chapters the proposition will be argued that certain characteristics of local areas in general and of the Bay Area in particular have made the application of this bargaining leverage more common and more successful.

Before going on to review the ways in which the market position of the negotiated plans has been utilized, the behavior of the prices of medical care and the problem of the abuse of health insurance will be discussed in the next two chapters. These two factors in combination—rising prices of medical services and the cost inflation stemming from abuse—have generated the pressure on the unions to try to capitalize on the bargaining strength that their market position might be expected to afford them.

Chapter III | *The Functioning of the Medical Market*

Concern with increases in the general price level in the United States has been virtually continuous for at least the past two decades. Since the Korean action touched off a period of general inflation, the behavior of the prices of medical care has received particular attention. Compared with the 1947–1949 base period of the Consumer Price Index, prices in the Medical Care category have increased more than any of the other major components into which the Bureau of Labor Statistics divides the index. Between 1953 and 1958 the increase in the prices of medical services was more than double the increase in the CPI as a whole.

Because the period since 1949 has also seen health insurance coverage—particularly for surgical and physicians' services—increase at a rapid rate, the possibility that the inflation in prices has been caused by the growth of health insurance has to be considered. If the case were proved, it would be a serious indictment of private health insurance. It would mean that not only had some of the protection that the insurance was intended to provide been eroded in value but also that the substantial part of the population without any insurance coverage had actually had its position worsened by the development of the system.

When that part of the health insurance movement represented by negotiated plans is considered, it is particularly noteworthy that one of the periods during which medical care prices have in-

33

creased most rapidly relative to the general price level has been coincident with the rapid spread of collectively bargained plans. As noted in chapter ii, the great bulk of this growth of bargained plans occurred between 1948 and 1954 when the number of employees covered (not including dependents) rose from 2.7 to 12 million.

Increases in the cost of medical care[1] are a burden for all patients and all types of health insurance arrangements, but they pose a particularly difficult problem for collectively bargained plans. A large number of these plans call for a specific employer contribution toward the cost of the insurance. The size of this contribution is a matter of negotiation directly or indirectly and becomes a part of the general collective-bargaining agreement. Since a great many of these agreements run for more than one year while the contracts with the insurance carriers are almost invariably on an annual basis, a difficult situation often arises. At the conclusion of the insurance contract year, the cost experience of the health plan may require either an increase in premiums or a reduction in benefits for future periods. The union must either accept a deterioration in the economic position of its members through lower health insurance coverage or higher employee contributions or it must attempt to secure an adjustment of the employer contribution outside the collective-bargaining contract. In practice the latter alternative is either impossible to achieve or must be traded away from the employer by a concession of some sort. Even when the insurance contract renegotiation coincides with the renegotiation of the collective-bargaining contract as a whole, the union is forced to dissipate some of its bargaining strength in order to maintain the real value of a benefit won in the past and regarded by the membership as finished business.

Some employers and some unions have tried to meet this problem by specifying a set of benefits rather than a specific monetary contribution in their contracts. While this provides for possible

---

[1] Increases in the prices of medical services cannot be taken as equivalent to increases in the cost of care in the general case. Over the long run, trends in prices and in cost may diverge because of changes in the quantity of care purchased that result from developments such as improved methods of treatment, increased or decreased utilization of services, etc. For short periods of time and in the context of this discussion this qualification is not crucial. See the later sections of this chapter for a discussion of the "productivity" of the medical industry.

adjustment of the employer contribution during the life of the collective-bargaining contract, the cost of this adjustment inevitably becomes a relevant factor in the eventual renegotiation of the contract and influences the final settlement reached at that time. To the union negotiator this situation often takes on the appearance of utilizing the union's bargaining position to win benefits for the medical profession and the hospitals.

For these reasons the almost continuous increases in the costs and prices of medical care have been of special significance to the collectively bargained plans. In this chapter emphasis will be placed on an analysis of the functioning of the medical market as evidenced by price behavior. Two related questions will be considered: To what degree and in what sense are the prices of medical services inflated? What is the evidence that the growth of health insurance has caused this inflation?

Are the Prices of Medical Care Inflated?

The first difficulty to be faced is that the answer to this question is undoubtedly, "Yes, but so are almost all other prices." For about a quarter of a century prices in the United States have been rising. One way of rephrasing the query would be to ask whether medical care prices have been rising more rapidly than some appropriate standard of comparison. The starting point for analysis is usually the Consumer Price Index (CPI) of the Bureau of Labor Statistics. Intended as a measure of the changes in the prices of the goods and services purchased by wage earner and clerical worker families in the large cities, the CPI is one of the nation's most carefully calculated and most closely watched statistical series. Prices are collected for about 300 items grouped into eight major categories, one of which is Medical Care. In terms of their effect on the index as a whole, food and housing are the most important categories. Combined, these two groups of items account for more than 60 per cent of the total variation in the CPI; the Medical Care category accounts for about 5 per cent of the change. The Medical Care category includes seven subgroups, only three of which are of immediate interest for purposes of this study. These are: physicians' fees, surgeons' fees, and hospital rates.[2] Since these

---

[2] The other subgroups are Dentists' fees, Optometric examinations and glasses, Group hospitalization premiums, and Prescriptions and drugs.

items form such a minor part of the entire CPI, their influence can be assumed to be negligible.

As in most statistical investigations of this type the time interval chosen influences the results of all comparisons. To give as complete a picture as possible in this study price behavior has been reviewed for several key dates. These dates are: an early prewar year (1935), an immediate postwar year (1946), the year marking the end of the first wave of postwar inflation and the beginning of the rapid spread of negotiated health plans (1949), a date that can be taken as approximating the beginning of the post-Korea period of price stability (December, 1952), and the most recent date for which complete data are available (June, 1958). Percentage changes for each of the related periods, 1935–1946, 1946–1949, 1949–1952, and 1952–1958, have been calculated for the CPI and selected component items and are reported in table 3.1.

TABLE 3.1

PERCENTAGE CHANGES OF SELECTED CPI ITEMS FOR SELECTED PERIODS[a]

Item	1935–1946	1946–1949	1949–1952	1952–1958	1935–1958
All Items	42.1	20.9	11.5	9.0	110.7
Medical care (excluding drugs)	26.1	20.0	14.3	23.3	113.2
General practitioners' fees .	23.3	12.5	10.2	23.4	88.6
Surgeons' fees	23.3	13.2	8.4	10.0	66.1
Hospital rates	55.6	50.6	26.4	42.6	319.5
Dentists' fees	28.9	18.8	8.5	15.9	92.5
Optometric examination and glasses	14.9	11.9	6.8	5.7	45.1
Shoe repairs	73.8	18.9	11.7	16.0	167.7
Domestic service	174.6	3.4	12.0	19.3	279.4
Auto repairs	20.4	17.5	12.4	21.8	93.4
Men's haircuts	86.1	21.4	21.5	27.1	248.4
Beauty shop services	100.2	2.6	4.7	19.6	157.2
Laundry services	31.1	22.8	12.5	19.3	115.8
Repainting rooms[b]	...	...	...	31.0	...
Repainting garage[b]	...	...	...	40.0	...
Refinishing floors[b]	...	...	...	17.4	...
Reshingling house roof [b] ..	...	...	...	32.2	...
Television repairs[b]	...	...	...	36.8	...

SOURCE: U. S. Bureau of Labor Statistics, *Consumer Price Indexes for Selected Items and Groups*, Washington, July, 1956; and *ibid.*, August, 1958.
[a] The 1958 figures are for June of that year.
[b] The base for these data is December, 1952.

As a start it may be noted that the Medical Care index and the CPI increased at about the same percentage between 1935 and 1958 but that the timing of the changes was quite different. Although lagging behind the CPI from 1935 to 1946, the Medical Care index increased at approximately the same rate until 1949 and then at a substantially faster rate up through 1958.

As in the previous chapter, the lack of correspondence between the movement of unit prices (daily rates in this case) and the movement of total hospital costs needs to be considered. In the area of hospitalization the relationship between unit price and total costs appears to be complex. Since the purpose of this chapter is the analysis of unit price changes, there is no need to go into the subject deeply. However, since the rise in hospital rates has been so extreme, some discussion of the interconnection between rates and the costs of hospitalization to a health plan may be helpful.

It is often pointed out that any analysis of the impact of daily rate changes on hospital costs needs to consider the shorter average duration of hospitalization currently required for many illnesses and surgical procedures as compared to previous periods. On the average, the cost of hospital care for specific incidents of illness has been held down by the trend toward shorter periods of hospitalization. Unfortunately, at the same time the rate of utilization of hospital services (as measured by admissions per unit of population per unit of time) has been increasing. In addition, another factor tending toward higher costs has been present in the increasing importance of medical services performed in the hospital (laboratory tests, etc.) and not included in the daily rate. It can be seen then that total hospital expenditures are influenced by four major factors. They can be increased by the rising daily rates, decreased by the reduction in average length of stay, increased by the rise in rates of utilization, and increased by the rising costs of hospital "extras."

To make analysis more difficult, some of these factors are interrelated. For example, one of the reasons why the average stay for all admissions combined has been declining is probably because some part of the increased utilization is accounted for by admissions for relatively less serious medical problems. Again, one of the reasons for the higher daily rates is the shorter stay for specific types of cases, particularly surgery, since the days of hospitalization eliminated were the "low-cost" days in terms of the amount of care required by the patient.

It is interesting to note that of the three factors influencing total hospital costs that we have identified in addition to daily rates, two tend to increase costs still further while only one acts to decrease total costs. This suggests that the common practice of using the trend in hospital rates as an index of what is happening to over-all hospital costs of a health plan as a whole may actually understate the rise in costs that has taken place. In order to make a rough check of this possibility, the increase in per capita private expenditures for hospital care between 1948 and 1956 was calculated. It was found that these expenditures had increased 96 per cent.[3] Between these dates the CPI indicated a rise of 70 per cent in hospital rates. Although this method cannot be regarded as producing conclusive results, it suggests that, if the increase in population is taken into account, changes in rates may be a fairly accurate barometer as to changes in costs.

Analyzing the reasons for the rapid inflation of hospital rates and costs is a complex problem that will not be undertaken here. The justification for this decision is the fact that although the behavior of hospital costs is a very important problem to health plans, the greater part of the ire generated by their dramatic increase has been directed at the doctors. This seeming paradox can be resolved by pointing out that of the four factors influencing costs—daily rates, length of stay, rate of admissions, and cost of extras—only the first is completely under the control of the hospital. The rate of admissions and the average length of stay are the result of decisions made by physicians; the hospitals and the doctors share the responsibility for the number and cost of extra services that are performed. While hospital rate increases have been the subject of severe criticism, the effectiveness of these attacks has been reduced by the critics' difficulties in identifying the villain in the cast of characters. The vast majority of hospital beds are under the control of nonprofit or governmental organizations, many of them run by religious groups and virtually all of them in chronic financial difficulties in spite of their high daily rates. Hospital administration does not seem to be an outstand-

---

3. Estimates of the population of the United States for each year were divided into private expenditures for hospital services exclusive of expenses for prepayment. Data from *Social Security Bulletin*, Vol. 20, No. 12, December, 1957, p. 4.

ingly lucrative profession, wages are a constant problem in the recruitment of nurses, and the unions themselves can testify that hospital service workers are among the lowest paid of the nation's labor force. Criticism is further tempered by the fact that hospital rates are public information and are charged uniformly to all patients—a substantially different pricing system from that followed by doctors.

The inflation seems to stem from a number of causes. The more obvious of these are the increases in the prices of goods and services purchased, the increases in labor costs of all types, the changing patterns and methods of medical treatment, the higher rates of utilization of hospital services, rapidly rising construction costs, a rising standard of desired physical facilities, and a shift in the source of financial support from taxes and philanthropy to charges to patients.[4] Even without more conclusive evidence, it may safely be ventured that at least some of these factors have been affected by the existence of health insurance in a manner that tends to stimulate the cost inflation.

Analyzing of the indexes for general practitioner and surgical fees discloses a quite different pattern of behavior. Over the twenty-three year period general practitioners' fees rose somewhat more rapidly than surgeons' charges but neither of them matched the rise in the CPI. Examination of the four subperiods into which the period has been divided shows that during 1949–1952 increases in fees of the general practitioner almost duplicated the CPI rise and that during 1952–1956, a period of somewhat greater price stability, fees increased substantially. Surgeons' charges increased somewhat less rapidly than general practitioners' fees during 1949–1952 and at only about two-fifths of the latter's rate of increase during 1952–1956, but this latter rate was still slightly in excess of the CPI increase.

At first glance some of the data on general practitioners' and surgeons' fees would seem to lend support to the hypothesis that the growth of health insurance has contributed to a general inflation of fees. The Health Insurance Council reports, for example,

---

[4] For a good general survey of the problem see Herbert E. Klarman, "The Economics of Hospital Service," *Harvard Business Review*, September, 1951, pp. 71–89.

that the rapid growth in insurance for physicians' services began in 1948. Rises in the index of general practitioners' fees began to match CPI increases for the first time at about that date and began outstripping them shortly thereafter.

Before passing final judgment on this issue, however, the following points should be considered.

1. The only time period during which general practitioners' fees rose faster than the CPI was during 1952–1956. This was not due to an acceleration of the rate of fee inflation over the rate of increase in previous years but was due to a reduction in the rate of increase in consumer prices generally. The average annual rate of increase in fees was little higher than during 1949–1952 and was actually somewhat lower than during 1946–1949. The slowing of the rate of increase in living costs was principally due to a drop in agricultural prices and, to a lesser extent, to drops in the prices of some manufactured goods such as appliances and television sets. While the stereotype of the country doctor may be consistent with accepting a broiling chicken as a fee, there is nothing in the pricing mechanism for physicians' services in general to lead us to expect any simple short-run relationship between food prices and house calls.

This last point raises the whole question of the suitability of comparisons between the fees for physicians and surgeons and the package of consumer goods and services included in the CPI. Doctors' services are in the nature of personal services rendered to their patients, and in their economic character they resemble other forms of personal services such as those provided by barbers and domestic servants. The amounts paid for services of this type lead a dual existence. They are simultaneously prices to the consumer and, for the most part, income to the suppliers. The largest element in the price of most services performed by individuals is a wage, salary, or other form of income to the supplier.

Although there are many occasions when the price aspect of these services is crucial, consideration of the income aspects of the payments for physicians' services suggests that an analysis such as this ought to include a comparison with the payments for other services in which wage or salary payments are a major part of total cost. The CPI includes indexes for a number of such items;

table 3.1 includes data on the price behavior of eleven of the items that most obviously include a large element of labor cost. Between 1952 and 1958, the period during which fees of general practitioners outran the CPI, the prices of six of the eleven services increased an average of about 20 per cent less than fees. The other five items increased an average of over 40 per cent more than fees. Since during this time period surgeons' charges rose only about two-fifths as much as general practitioners' fees, all eleven of the miscellaneous services increased in price much more rapidly than did the surgical index.[5]

An approach similar to the one used here has been taken by a staff member of the Bureau of Labor Statistics in assessing the behavior of the indexes for fees of general practitioners and surgeons in an article in the *Monthly Labor Review*. This study emphasized that the prices of services generally had lagged behind commodity prices in the first half of the postwar decade and then regained their previous relative position in the last half of the decade. The explanation suggested for this behavior is that prices of services are "characteristically slow in responding to general economic developments. . . ."[6] The price behavior of a selection of the "more important service items" was presented and physicians' and surgeons' fees were found to have increased least of a list of ten items for the period 1936 through 1956.

The reasoning behind this hypothesis relies on some assumptions as to the nature of the pricing process of service industries and emphasizes a different set of attributes of these industries as compared with the industries producing physical commodities. In the study reported here the similarity between medical care and the personal service occupations or industries has been stressed whereas Langford has defined services as including public transportation and movie admissions since they represent industries that provide an intangible product. Such an approach is perfectly legitimate and yields a result even more favorable to the pricing practices of the medical profession than did the method

---

[5] Note, however, that the prices of auto repairs are often cited as an independent example of the inflation-producing effects of insurance.

[6] E. A. Langford, "Medical Care in the Consumer Price Index, 1935–56," *Monthly Labor Review*, Vol. 80, No. 9, September, 1957, p. 1053.

used here. There is a fundamental criticism, however, of the technique of comparing price movements of services to those of commodities. It implies that there is some "normal" relationship between the prices of services and of commodities but this appears to be of dubious validity. Nevertheless, for the time period studied, Langford's analysis does reinforce the conclusions arrived at in this section.

2. A different approach reinforces the suggestion that caution be exercised before judgment is passed on the question of a generalized insurance-induced fee inflation. If the availability of insurance benefits induced the raising of fees for insured services, it would be logical to expect the extent of the fee inflation to be directly related to the extent of insurance coverage. Insurance for surgical procedures has always been much more common than insurance for physicians' services; insurance for dentists' services is almost nonexistent.[7] On the basis of the effect of insurance alone, we would expect to find that the charges of surgeons had increased the most, followed by charges of general practitioners and charges by dentists. Unfortunately for this hypothesis, the data show that the actual price behavior was quite different. Of these three types of professional care, surgeons' fees increased least both for the 1935–1958 period as a whole and for 1952–1958. On the other hand, dental fees increased most for the period as a whole. Dentists' fees rose two-thirds as much as physicians' fees for 1952–1958; their rise outstripped the rate of increase in the surgical index for the period by about 60 per cent.

As a final comparison, it should be noted that the prices of optometric examinations and glasses, a service on the fringe of medical care, rose least over the whole time span. Increases were least between 1952 and 1958.

There is no way of knowing whether, in the absence of health insurance, the prices of physicians' and surgeons' services would have behaved more like those of the optometrists or those of the dentists (or those of the television repairmen). The evidence does indicate, however, that the conclusion that health insurance has been the cause of a general inflation of major consequence in the

---

[7] In 1956, for example, about 101,000,000 persons had surgical coverage but only about 65,000,000 were insured for physicians' services, according to the Health Insurance Council.

prices of professional medical services is at least open to question.

This type of analysis cannot be carried out for the Bay Area separately since the BLS cannot provide the component parts of the Medical Care index for the cities included in the price survey. For what it is worth, the medical care component of the general San Francisco index behaved approximately the same as the national index from 1947 through 1958.

Medical Care Prices in California

It is possible to extract some information on the economics of medicine in California and the Bay Area from a variety of informal sources. Although the limitations of the data must be kept in mind, a rough measure of price changes in California can be secured by examining some of the fee schedule material that has been developed during the lifetime of CPS. The original unit value fee schedule of CPS was published in the CMA journal, *California and Western Medicine,* in November, 1939. Converting this schedule into dollars by the use of the "ideal" unit value of $2.50 permits us to compare this schedule with the 1955 schedule. Neither of these schedules was established by a scientific sampling of the state's doctors, but both represent fees that the physician-members of the plan agreed to accept as full payment for a potential membership which might have included up to 90 per cent of California's population.[8]

In table 3.2 those items of medical service included in the general practitioners' and surgeons' fee listings of the CPI have been shown at their 1939 and 1955 prices according to the contemporary CPS schedules. If the picture revealed by this material is accepted as representative, the charges for the services priced by the BLS for the general practitioners' index have risen roughly in line with the national average while surgical fees have gone up less than the national average.[9] A review of several of the more com-

---

[8] In 1939 CPS claimed that the $3,000 family income ceiling for full payment would cover 90 per cent of the population. For 1955, the CPS Schedule B, which has a family income ceiling of $6,000, was used. In all probability this figure would not include 90 per cent of the 1955 population but it is not likely to have fallen far short. If the 1939 schedule at a $2.50 unit value was higher relative to the average fees actually charged than the 1955 schedule, this would have a tendency to understate the rate of fee increase.

[9] If the individual items in table 3.2 are weighted by the BLS weights reported in the *Monthly Labor Review,* May, 1957, p. 601, the simple arithmetic average

TABLE 3.2

CPS Fees, 1939 and 1955, for CPI Items

Item	1939 [a]	1955	Per cent increase
General Practitioners' Fees			
Office Visit	$2.50	$4.00	60
House Visit	3.75	6.00	60
Obstetrical Care	85.00	150.00	76
Surgeons' Fees			
Appendectomy	125.00	150.00	20
Tonsillectomy	50.00	65.00 [b]	30

SOURCE: 1939 figures, *California and Western Medicine*, November, 1939. 1955 figures, California Physicians Service, Fee Schedule "B," January 1, 1955.
[a] Converted from "units" to dollars at $2.50 per unit.
[b] Fifteen years and under, $50; over fifteen, $65.

mon surgical procedures in the two schedules suggests that, while the figures for appendectomies and tonsillectomies understate the rise in CPS fees for surgery generally, even after allowing for this fact the CPS surgical fee schedule has not fully reflected the increase in charges reported by the BLS.

Hospital rates in the city of San Francisco also appear to have risen roughly in line with the national figures as well. Between May, 1946, and November, 1957, the men's pay ward daily rates for fifteen San Francisco hospitals rose an average of 183 per cent, a figure which happens to be exactly equal to the rise in the national index for men's pay ward rates from 1946 to March, 1957. The San Francisco rates seem to have lagged behind those of the rest of the nation prior to 1951–1952 and to have increased somewhat more rapidly since then, but the differences in the date of collection of the data make relatively small variations in the rate of change unreliable.[10]

---

of the relatives for general practitioners' fees shows an increase of 72 per cent (nationally, 67 per cent) and an increase for surgical fees of 25 per cent (nationally, 55 per cent). For weights and the national data, see the *Monthly Labor Review*, May, 1957, p. 601; and September, 1957, p. 1055. This weighting system is not entirely precise but is satisfactory for our purposes.

[10] Average daily rates for 15 identical hospitals were $7.37 in November 1946, $13.13 in October 1951, $14.90 in March 1952 and $20.83 in November, 1957. The 1957 data were secured by telephone from the hospitals; the earlier figures are from E. R. Weinerman, *Labor Plans for Health*, San Francisco Labor Council, 1952, p. 29.

To sum up the foregoing discussion:

1. The movement of the CPI Medical Care component has been strongly influenced by the behavior of hospital rates and hospitalization insurance premiums. In the postwar period the rise in hospital rates has been very rapid compared with prices generally and is not easily explained. There seems to be no way of assessing the exact effect of the widespread existence of hospital insurance on rates but it is very difficult to believe that the result has not been a more rapid increase in daily rates and on total costs than would otherwise have occurred.

2. In the case of physicians' services there is good reason to exercise caution in estimating the inflationary impact of health insurance on the *general level* of charges. Fees appear to have risen somewhat less than the prices of other services in which labor costs are important. Furthermore, the degree of fee inflation is not correlated with the degree of insurance coverage for the various categories of professional service.

Some Demand and Supply Considerations

It might be argued that most of the nonmedical services used in comparisons of this kind are furnished by groups of workers who are organized for the purpose of achieving increases in their wages and therefore, by implication, doctors must have undertaken some sort of similar action to do as well as they have. Assigning causal factors for price behavior is a notoriously difficult job, but in their defense doctors can point out that the increase in effective demand for their services has probably been greater than for any other service used in the comparisons (with the possible exception of that furnished by television repairmen). The Department of Health, Education, and Welfare has estimated, for example, that total private expenditures for physicians' services increased about three-fifths between 1949 and 1957.

The impact of an increase in effective demand on the price of a service or commodity depends in large measure on the ease with which the supply of the service can be increased. The problems involved in increasing the supply of physicians are well known and will not be detailed here. According to the American Medical Directory the total number of physicians in the United States increased about 13 per cent or from 201,000 to 227,000 between

1949 and 1957. (Because of the rate of growth in population the number of physicians per 100,000 of population fell from 135 to 132 over this period.)

The economists of the American Medical Association have been at some pains to distinguish between the supply of physicians and the supply of physicians' services. It has been argued that the supply of physicians' services has increased much more rapidly than the supply of physicians. In other words, the productivity of the medical profession, like the productivity of the automobile industry, is believed to be rising. Frank G. Dickinson of the Bureau of Medical Economics of the AMA has calculated that the "quantity of service delivered per physician" from the period 1935–1939 to 1951 increased by 68 per cent, a figure that was conservatively reduced to 50 per cent for various technical reasons. Dickinson explained this change as resulting from "the greatly expanded use of nurses and technical assistants, the introduction of wonder drugs, improved transportation, the increasing proportion of patients seen in the hospital and office, and other increases in technological efficiency." [11]

It is instructive to apply techniques of analysis similar to those used by Dickinson to the period from 1949 to 1955. Briefly, the procedure involves estimating the change in the physical quantity of physicians' services by correcting the change in the total private expenditures for services by changes in the unit price of services as measured by the fees component of the CPI. The resulting estimate of quantity changes is then corrected for increases in the number of physicians to arrive at an approximation of the change in the quantity of services rendered per physician. Each of the measures used is a relatively crude statistical tool and, as Dickinson points out, the result can be regarded only as a rough approximation.

Carrying this procedure through for the years 1949 to 1957 with data from the Department of Health, Education, and Welfare, we find that total private expenditures for physicians' services increased 60 per cent, the price index of physicians' fees in-

---

[11] Frank G. Dickinson, "What We Get for What We Spend for Medical Care," in President's Commission on the Health Needs of the Nation, *Building America's Health* (Washington: 1954), Vol. IV, p. 19. For a discussion of this sort of approach by an observer skeptical of the validity of the results, see Seymour E. Harris' contribution in the same volume, pp. 3–16.

creased about 29 per cent, and therefore the total quantity of service apparently increased about 24 per cent. Since the number of physicians increased 13 per cent, this method of calculation suggests an increase in the quantity of service rendered per physician between 1949 and 1957 of about 10 per cent.

Since most of the factors proposed as explanations for the increases in services rendered per physician for earlier periods continued to operate from 1949 to 1957 (e.g., developments in new drugs and larger numbers of auxiliary personnel), the failure of productivity to increase more rapidly may seem surprising. At least a partial explanation can be found in changes in the rate of utilization of the "capacity" of the medical profession. In the measurement of productivity changes in industry it is well known that the behavior of the indexes in the short run reflects two major forces: (1) the effect of changing methods of production, and (2) the effect of changing levels of output (i.e., the effect of operating at different percentages of capacity). Increases in output from a level well below the capacity of an industry or an economy are usually accompanied by larger-than-average increases in productivity since both factors are typically working in the direction of raising productivity. Conversely, as output recedes from capacity levels, the output effect tends to lower productivity while the effect of changing methods probably continues to work toward raising productivity. For this reason, attempts to measure changes in productivity resulting solely from improved methods of operation should make use of time periods for which levels of output are comparable, preferably at full capacity levels.

The capacity of the medical profession to produce services is difficult to analyze, but the profession undoubtedly went from a considerable underutilization of capacity prior to World War II to a very high degree of utilization in the 1950's. Without question, a large part, perhaps the major part, of the increase in quantity of services rendered per physician reported by Dickinson for the years from the period 1935–1939 to 1951 was due to the "output effect" rather than to the "methods effect." The more rapid rise in the prices of physicians' and surgeons' services that occurred in the 1950's compared with earlier periods is exactly the behavior an economist would expect to result from the impact of increasing demand on an industry operating at capacity. Common observation and the comments of doctors both testify to the fact that capacity levels of operation have been characteristic of the medical business for the past several years at least. As evidence on this point, the Journal of the AMA has reported Department of Commerce figures of 56 hours worked per week by physicians in 1949.[12]

Interpreting the statistical data as representing the impact of a one-third increase in monetary demand on a supply of medical services which increased one-fifth as much is only one possibility. As an alternative explanation, one could argue that fees were increased independently of the increase in demand and in increase in private expenditures resulted since the demand for most medical service is inelastic. In all probability, the statistics reflect a combination of these two developments. If so, it would be impossible to come to a clear-cut conclusion on the basis of this kind of a review. Whichever hypothesis is adopted, the existence of health insurance probably can be said to have contributed to the raising of fees. If the increased fees are believed to be a result of the increase in medical demand, some part of the increase in demand must be the result of the widespread coverage of health insurance. If the fee increase resulted from other factors, health insurance provided some of the funds to support the higher level of fees. In either case, the growth of health insurance influenced the final result.

From this analysis of the functioning of the medical market the most significant conclusion seems to be that, except for hospital rates, the degree of fee inflation has probably been overestimated in the public mind compared with prices in general and the prices of other services in particular. By contributing to a more rapid expansion of monetary demand for medical services than would otherwise have occurred, the growth of health insurance probably exerted some inflationary pressure on the prices of medical services (perhaps a substantial increase in the case of hospitalization). In the light of the price comparisons noted and the lack of correspondence between the pattern of fee increases and the pattern of insurance coverage, however, the evidence does not support the belief that the spread of insurance by itself has had a major inflationary effect on the prices of medical services.

---

[12] *J.A.M.A.*, Vol. 156, No. 5, October 2, 1954, p. 502.

Chapter IV | The Problem of Abuse

Throughout the previous chapter attention was concentrated on the impact of health insurance on the prices of medical services paid by the general public. The men responsible for negotiating and administering health and welfare plans are concerned about medical fees and hospital rates in general but they are also concerned with the special problem of the "abuse" of specific provisions of specific insurance plans.

Insofar as abuse results in an increase in the prices for medical services, its existence would have an effect on the price indexes discussed in the previous chapter. Many forms of abuse increase *costs* of treatment, however, without directly affecting the *prices* of individual units of service. Their effects lie outside of an investigation directed solely at an analysis of prices. Indirect effects on prices do exist and may arise from the increase in demand for physician and hospital services associated with abuse of insurance. The increase in demand may raise the price of the limited supply of services and create a need for expanding the capacity of the medical industry at rising cost levels. Some forms of abuse such as the raising of fees for insured patients involve price effects directly but these consequences are probably limited to a minor fraction of the total medical market and therefore are likely to affect national or regional indexes only to a limited extent. Whether prices in general are affected or not, particular health

plans may experience a substantial cost impact from abuse, however, and therefore an analysis of abuse separate from an analysis
of over-all price behavior is needed.

"Abuse" of a system of prepaid insurance is a term which has
many ramifications and which means different things to different
interest groups.[1] For purposes of this study abuse of an insurance
plan refers to the creation of claims for services that either would
not have been rendered at all or that would have been rendered
at a lower cost to an uninsured patient in similar circumstances.
This definition views abuse from the standpoint of the negotiator
or administrator of a health plan concerned with the cost of medical services for covered members. From other points of view the
concept of abuse takes on added dimensions. Legislative investigations of the U. S. Congress and of some state commissions have
directed attention to irregularities in the handling of funds collected for health and welfare purposes. Staff specialists of some
major unions have concentrated attention on the sharp practices
of some of the insurance companies relating to commissions and
rebates, on pricing techniques in formulating bids, on the practice
of making unrealistically low initial bids for contracts, and on a
tendency to include items on the fringe of medical care while
neglecting some basic elements of coverage.

The medical profession has complained about relatively low
fee schedules that are sometimes represented to the customer as
providing full coverage, about listing below-average benefits for
medical procedures that occur frequently while listing above-
average benefits for cases that occur rarely, and about the exclusion of coverage for certain types of service that the profession believes should be included on medical grounds, e.g., internists'
services. Insurance companies and medical groups sometimes use
abuse of insurance to mean the overutilization of coverage by patients who "like to be doctored" or who have "hospitalitis." They
also complain about the inclusion of items in coverage which are
not "insurable" in the sense that they do not represent large, in-
frequent, unpredictable expenditures but are items that they

---

[1] For an excellent description of forms of abuse by patients, doctors, and hospitals along with a discussion of problems of definition, see Malcolm G. Taylor,
Health Insurance in Canada (Toronto: Oxford University Press, 1956), pp. 168–
182.

believe should and could be budgeted for by the patient, such as physical examinations.

Not only are different groups interested in different aspects of the problem of abuse but in some cases they hold opposing views as to whether a particular practice should be classified as abuse or as a proper function of insurance. For example, labor-union representatives often feel that providing for payment of frequent, small medical bills of their members is a perfectly justifiable use of the prepayment machinery of health insurance while insurance representatives often describe this as a distortion of the functions of insurance.

The particular aspect of abuse that will be stressed here includes the points that are regarded by union leaders as the most important phases of the problem presented by their relations with the medical industry. Rightly or wrongly, most union representatives would probably agree with Michael Davis that ". . . The major problem of controlling the unnecessary use of services under health insurance plans with fee-for-service payment arises from the physicians, not from the patients." [2]

The existence of abuse is difficult to prove or to quantify but the most important types appear to be the following:

1. The performance of medical procedures or the rendering of medical services that are included in the insurance contract but that would not ordinarily have been performed if the patient had not been insured. Abuse of this kind involves, among other things, the performance of unnecessary surgery and diagnostic procedures that are more elaborate than customary or that repeat tests previously performed. The prevalence of this type of abuse may increase both the costs of hospitalization and the costs of medical and surgical benefits.

2. Excessive multiple visits for doctor's care in the office, home, or the hospital or unnecessarily prolonged hospital stays. This could be regarded as a variation of the first form of abuse but it can be differentiated on the ground that the need for medical service is genuine but the quantity of care actually provided may be out of proportion to that required according to customary standards of practice. This excessive care may result from the

---

[2] M. M. Davis, *Medical Care for Tomorrow* (New York: Harper, 1955), p. 332.

desire of the patient for service or the desire of the doctor for income but it may also be encouraged by the benefit structure of the health insurance contract. When the first visit or the first two visits are excluded from coverage in cases of illness, reporting a greater number of visits (actual or feigned) may either relieve the patient from any direct charge or increase the doctor's income.

3. Unnecessary hospitalization ordered for the performance of a medically necessary service that could have been performed on an outpatient basis. This hospitalization may be ordered for the convenience of the patient or the doctor or to permit a claim to be filed for a procedure that is not covered by the insurance contract except as an incident to hospitalization (e.g., diagnostic laboratory work).

4. The charging of fees higher than those that would have been charged for the same service to an uninsured patient in similar circumstances. This is a special kind of "abuse" since the insurance carrier or the welfare trust fund may not suffer financially if their liability is limited by an indemnity fee schedule. The victim in this case is usually the patient himself who is asked to pay out-of-pocket charges in addition to the insurance premiums paid by him or on his behalf. (But note that the existence of out-of-pocket payments by patients by itself is not necessarily a proof of the existence of this kind of abuse but may be an indication of an inadequate fee schedule or of the acceptance of the principle of coinsurance.)

These four forms of abuse could be summarized briefly as follows: (1) The provision of unnecessary medical services, (2) the provision of excessive amounts of necessary services, (3) the provision of a necessary service in the hospital when it could have been performed outside, and (4) the charging of excessive fees for services. The use of words like "unnecessary," "customary," and "excessive" emphasize the subjective nature of much of the abuse problem. The boundary line between abuse and good medical usage varies as between doctors in a single geographical area, as between groups of patients, as between areas, and also as between different periods of time. These varieties of abuse do not exhaust the charges levied against the medical care industry by the welfare fund managers and the insurance carriers but they are the most important forms of the problem.

It is worth emphasizing once more that although some types of abuse noted above involve the costs of hospitalization, both admission to the hospital and the length of stay are in the hands of the patient's physician. As a result all four of these types of abuse generate resentment that is directed primarily against the doctor even though, in many instances, the doctor himself does not profit financially from the practice. Perhaps the high and rising level of hospital daily rates could be cited as the quantitatively most important "abuse" of all in the eyes of many administrators but, as noted in the previous chapter, this is a general complaint difficult to personalize.

In defense of the doctor, it should be pointed out that in some forms of abuse (e.g., hospitalization for noncovered services and excessive doctors' visits) the patient may either be a willing collaborator or in some cases the originator of the pressure for the occurrence. A patient who knows that laboratory procedures in connection with a diagnosis will be performed at his own expense as an outpatient in the doctor's office may be quite insistent on having his doctor arrange for his admittance to a hospital. If no insurance benefit is paid for the first two office visits for an illness, a patient may suggest a claim for more visits than are medically necessary on condition that he not be billed for the first two and thereby "get something out of" his health insurance. Instances where a working wife has exerted pressure to keep her sick husband in a hospital until the weekend are not unknown. Physicians should refuse to participate in these practices and probably most of them do so. It must be recognized, however, that this may mean losing the medical business of a patient and his family to a more obliging colleague in order to protect an insurance company against a possibly unwarranted claim. Considering the common attitude toward insurance benefits and insurance companies, it is not surprising that some doctors succumb to temptation and to the pressures of competitive practice. Other forms of abuse originate with the doctor or the hospital. Even though these practices may be limited to a minority of the representatives of the medical industry, the effect on costs of specific plans can be substantial.

Unfortunately relatively few reports of systematic investigations of charges of abuse are generally available. Since suspected cases of abuse involve the medical experience of individual health plan members and individual physicians, administrators are reluctant to make them public. Insurance companies, the medical service organizations, and some health plan administrators regularly perform medical reviews of claims but they do not publish their results. The "grievance committees" of the county medical societies almost certainly attract only a small proportion of total complaints and they are usually concerned with only one form of abuse—overcharging. Diligent reading and personal contact can turn up isolated anonymous anecdotes of abuse but no general conclusions can be drawn from material of this type.

Some indication of the scope of the problem can be secured from two types of evidence. A reading of the medical and hospital journals will turn up fairly regular pleas from the commercial insurers and the supporters of Blue Cross and Blue Shield that are directed to an unidentified minority of physicians responsible for excessive medical costs. Union officials are much more outspoken about this form of abuse, of course, but the frequency and strength of the appeals from within the medical industry itself gives them a ring of validity not possessed by complaints from the other aggrieved parties.

Two examples of the evidence as to the prevalence of abuse taken from the publications of the medical profession in the Bay Area are cited below:

The other important situation now facing us is the apparent increasing incidence of elevating medical fees in the case of patients covered by insurance carriers. (From the report of the Distribution of Medical Care Committee in the *Bulletin* of the Alameda-Contra Costa Medical Association, November, 1952, p. 38.)

In view of the repeated increases in the cost of hospitalization in every recent year, it is most important that physicians restrict hospitalizations to those which are truly essential. If physicians abuse Blue Cross, if they hospitalize under Blue Cross coverage patients with conditions which are rightfully excluded from the Blue Cross contracts, there will be no alternative other than to increase Blue Cross rates. (Letter to the Editor from the medical director of the local Blue Cross in the *Bulletin* of the San Francisco Medical Society, October, 1951, p. 4.)

In the December, 1952, issue of the *Bulletin* of the Alameda-Contra Costa Association a fairly typical article appeared asking the coöperation of member-doctors in limiting abuse of Blue Cross. Examples of obvious cases of outright abuse were cited in detail.

According to this article, three problems were most important: (1) hospitalization under a false diagnosis or for services not covered by the insurance provided; (2) undue prolongation of stays in the hospital; and (3) unnecessary hospitalization. The greatest single problem area concerned the enforcement of the clause in the contracts prohibiting hospitalization for diagnostic services while permitting such tests to be carried out if they were incident to a hospital admission for other purposes.

During the previous year articles similar in tone had appeared in the Alameda-Contra Costa Association *Bulletin* (April, 1951) and in the *Bulletin* of the San Francisco Society (October, 1951). These articles all stemmed from Blue Cross sources and did not include any quantitative estimate of the over-all importance of abuse.[3] They usually concentrated on the citing of extreme cases of abuse, a typical one involving "a man who was hospitalized early in 1950 and contracted a hospital bill of almost $60 for which almost $100 was for x-ray studies and almost $300 for laboratory tests. The only procedure which might have actually required hospitalzation was a biopsy which established a diagnosis."

Indication that abuse by doctors was not limited to the 1951–1952 perod and that on occasion the profession was ready to take stern remedial action is provided by a report of the San Francisco Society's Insurance Mediation Committee that in 1956 one doctor was expelled from the Society for "repeated" cases of overcharging during the previous year.[4]

In addition to statements like the above, a number of attempts to measure the prevalence of abuse in a quantitative manner have been carried out for particular health plans in certain localities. Since these studies represent isolated situations their results cannot be extrapolated to provide conclusions as to magnitude of the problem in the total population of health plans with any de-

---

[3] That Blue Cross found this a national problem is illustrated by an article by Kenneth Babcock, M.D., "The Excessive Use of Blue Cross Benefits," *Hospitals,* July, 1952, pp. 49–51. A commercial insurance company spokesman covers much of the same ground in A. B. Halverson, "Abuse of Health Insurance," *Best's Insurance News, Fire and Casualty Edition,* July, 1956, pp. 83–89.

[4] *Bulletin,* San Francisco Medical Society, January, 1957, p. 33.

gree of certainty. They are, however, informative in their own right. They seldom are fully reported as research papers but appear in speeches, letters to editors of medical journals, newspaper stories, and personal interviews. Not only is there a general reluctance to reveal available information of this kind but almost all of the attempts to arrive at a quantitative measurement of abuse suffer from another difficulty. Medical practice still has many characteristics of an art rather than a science. It is difficult for a third party to assess either the medical wisdom or the medical necessity of the services performed through a review of the case. Differences of opinon among fully qualified persons may exist with regard to proper care and hindsight sometimes reveals the existence of honest errors of judgment. Because of these facts and because physicians, the persons best qualified to make an assessment of the situation, have personal, organizational, and professional interests in the results of any investigation, only the most glaring instances of abuse are likely to come to light. The difficulties facing an administrator who tries to deal with marginal cases of abuse have been explained by Dr. Warren F. Draper, Executive Medical Officer of the United Mine Workers Welfare and Retirement Fund as follows:[5]

To solve our problems of unnecessary hospitalization, undue length of stay, unnecessary surgery, services of inferior quality and the like, we are asked to prefer specific charges of wrongdoing against individual physicians which, if proven, will enable the medical society to take appropriate action. Such a course is impossible for us to follow except in flagrant instances of misconduct.

The difficulties which we have with individual physicians are seldom of a character to warrant the filing of specific charges. Unnecessary hospitalization, unnecessary surgery, and the other procedures mentioned all deal with various facets of medical treatment of patients and do not in themselves constitute unethical or dishonest conduct and therefore do not afford grounds for charges against individual physicians. Furthermore, organized medicine does not concede to any third party the prerogative of passing judgment on the treatment rendered by physicians, nor upon the necessity of hospitalization, length of stay and the like.

---

[5] Warren F. Draper, M.D., "Problems Encountered in the Operation of the United Mine Workers of America Welfare and Retirement Fund," *The Pennsylvania Medical Journal*, Vol. 58, December, 1955, p. 1336.

With these difficulties in mind some of the material available will be reviewed for illustrative purposes.

Unnecessary Hospitalization

One of the best examples of a conscientious attempt to estimate the extent of unnecessary hospitalization is a survey conducted jointly by the Michigan State Medical Society and Michigan Blue Cross.[6] The State Medical Society appointed a committee of physicians which carried out an analysis of "over 12,000 consecutive clinical records in 25 typical Michigan general hospitals." Dr. Harry Becker, medical director of Michigan Blue Cross, described the criteria by which the necessity for hospital care was judged as "very conservative." The data collected, the methodology used in the study, and the conclusions drawn from it were all reported to have been examined and accepted as accurate by statisticians, doctors, and hospital executives.

Dr. Becker worded the conclusions of the survey as follows:

This study tends to prove that in Michigan—and I have no doubt that the same holds true with minor variation elsewhere—over 28 per cent of all hospital admissions contained some element of faulty use. As one would expect, these "faulty admissions" were, of course, more frequent among "insured" patients. Blue Cross members misused their hospital stays in nearly 36 per cent of cases. Commercially-insured patients misused them nearly 30 per cent of the time, but patients paying their own bills showed faulty use in less than 14 per cent of admissions.

In terms of hospital days, 11,172 of these 76,238 days studied were considered to be unnecessary to the recovery, safety or to the reasonable comfort of the patient. Nearly one out of five days used by Blue Cross patients was not a necessary day. . . .

. . . One out of eight Blue Cross patients entered the hospital for laboratory or x-ray examinations, although hospital outpatient departments were performing similar examinations on similar patients every day. Over 18 per cent of Blue Cross patients remained in the hospital in excess of their need.

In discussing a single type of abuse, unnecessary prolongation of hospital stay, Dr. Becker made the following comments (note that they are not limited to insured patients but apply to all patients surveyed): "In our survey 1,556 patients out of a total of

---

[6] The following material is taken from Harry F. Becker, M.D., "Controlling the Use and Misuse of Hospital Care," *Hospitals*, Vol. 28, December, 1954, pp. 61–64.

12,102 stayed longer than good conservative medical judgment would consider to be necessary for them. The days of overstay in the 12,102 cases we examined were 5,231. If this proportion is projected to the state of Michigan as a whole such overstay costs nearly $5,000,000 a year in Michigan for bed charges alone."

The Michigan study suggests a number of conclusions. First, some amount of medically unnecessary hospital expense apparently occurs independently of the existence of insurance coverage. Second, the availability of insurance benefits appears to make it from two to two and a half times as likely that unnecessary hospital expenses will be incurred. Third, while the data are not couched in dollar cost terms, it appears that the cost of unnecessary hospitalization probably ranges from about 15 per cent of total hospital expense benefits in commercial insurance to close to 20 per cent in Blue Cross. (These conclusions, of course, are limited to circumstances approximating the conditions, including the types of coverage available, in Michigan in 1954.)

Further data on the extent of unnecessary hospitalization can be found in various reports of the experience under the United Mine Workers (UMW) Welfare and Retirement Fund. Because of its lay sponsorship, its size, and the length of time it has been operating, the experience of this largest of the collectively bargained programs has provided a substantial amount of material bearing on the problem of abuse. In using this information it is important at the outset to stress that the environment in which the fund operates creates certain special problems that are not directly pertinent to the operation of plans functioning in a different socioeconomic situation. Much of the fund's activity is concentrated in isolated, small communities among a relatively low-income population subject to the vicissitudes of a single industry with a fluctuating level of economic performance. The limited quantity and allegedly low quality of professional personnel, the inadequacy of physical facilities and community organizations and even of transportation networks have been continuing problems to the fund. In a high-income, diversified metropolitan area with a high level of professional care and physical facilities these difficulties are at a minimum. Many of the problems of the professional relationships and control of expenditures are common to the two situations, however, and we shall concentrate on those aspects of the program.

The Welfare and Retirement Fund is a massive operation that covered a potential of 1.5 million miners and their dependents in 1952.[7] Although the greater part of the fund's financial resources (derived principally from a royalty of 40 cents per ton of bituminous coal mined), is absorbed by pension costs, the expenditures on health benefits amounted to just under sixty million dollars during the fiscal year ending in June, 1957. Operating in twenty-six states including Alaska, the fund provides in-hospital medical and surgical benefits, outpatient care by specialists, and some drugs but does not cover routine home and office visits. As would be expected, the fund represents a complex system of medical care, including the operation of ten hospitals opened in late 1955 and 1956, as well as a variety of prepayment arrangements for both solo and group practice of medicine. Although the fund has never published a full-scale, detailed analysis of its surgical or hospital experience, reports of area studies have been made at the several AMA-UMW Conferences. Examples of the data on unnecessary hospitalization are noted below:

At the 1954 conference, it was disclosed that in West Virginia "with few exceptions, the length-of-stay of Fund patients in hospitals exceeds that of non-Fund patients. The length-of-stay exceeds that of patients owning Blue Cross coverage by from seventeen to twenty-five per cent, and is about twice that of patients paying their own hospital costs. . . ." (1954 Report, p. 14. This sort of comparison does not consider the possibility that uninsured patients may be underhospitalized.)

In the Pittsburgh area, criteria that were described as "extremely conservative" were used to study unnecessary hospitaliza-

[7] U. S. Department of Health, Education, and Welfare, *Management and Union Health Plans* (Washington: 1954). Most of the data to follow are taken from reports of a number of conferences held in the West Virginia area and attended by representatives of the UMW Fund and the state and county medical societies of the coal-mining region. The reports are published by the American Medical Association under the general title of "Report of the ⸺ Conference on Medical Care in the Bituminous Coal Mine Area." Copies of the reports of the Second (1953), Third (1954), and Fourth (1956) Conferences were provided by Dr. Warren F. Draper of the UMW Fund along with some other material. Data taken from these reports will be cited in the text as "195– Report, p. –." The first Conference (1952) was reported in *J.A.M.A.*, Vol. 151, No. 407, January 31, 1953.

tion in "8 commonly used" hospitals during 1953. Of 5,420 admissions, 586 or 10.8 per cent, involved unexplained or questionable hospital days. It was estimated that almost $100,000 of a total of $923,000 in hospital payments was "wasted" during this period. A similar group of eight hospitals was studied for a period in 1954 and showed an almost identical waste ratio, 10.7 per cent. (1954 Report, p. 19. For the methodology of these studies see the 1956 Report, p. 22.)

It is difficult to judge the extent to which these several studies are comparable in their methods and results and how representative they are of the hospital insurance experience of the whole body of health plans in existence. For what the data are worth, the results can be summarized as follows:

1. The Michigan study revealed that faulty admissions among Blue Cross subscribers appeared to be about two and a half times as frequent as among the population without health insurance.

2. The Michigan study suggested that about 20 per cent of all hospital days paid for through insurance were medically unnecessary.

3. The UMW Fund data from West Virginia indicate that the average length-of-stay in the hospital for patients whose bills were being paid by the Fund was double the average of patients paying their own expenses.

4. The UMW Fund data from the Pittsburgh area (which includes western Pennsylvania and Ohio) suggest that about 11 per cent of both the days of hospitalization and the dollars spent for hospital care for Fund patients were medically unnecessary.

Although these results are influenced by differences in medical practice, the characteristics of the population covered by the insurance, the benefit structure of the plans involved, and the methodology employed in developing the data, they give the broad outlines of the problem.

Excessive Physicians' and Surgeons' Costs

During the winter of 1951–1952, certain patient-members of the California Physicians Service in the Los Angeles area received copies of the following innocent-appearing letter:[8]

---

[8] The information on the investigation reported in the text comes from Paul D. Foster, M.D., "Robbing Peter to Pay Paul," *Bulletin,* Los Angeles Medical Association, March 6, 1952, pp. 251–252.

Dear Member:

May we please have four minutes of your time . . . and your help.

Like most companies we periodically conduct independent audits. At this time, in reviewing thousands of records, claims are selected at random to confirm certain items and to help authenticate our records.

So . . . will you please help us, and our auditing firm, by briefly answering the following questions:

1. Have you received medical care in the last six months?
2. If so, who was your physician?
3. What were the months during which you received care?
4. Approximately how many visits were made each month?
5. Please describe briefly in your own words, the nature of your illness or accident.
6. What type of treatment did you receive?

In spite of the language of the letter, the addressees had not been "selected at random" but had been carefully chosen from the roster of those members on whose behalf CPS had paid claims to their physician-members. The letters were sent to those patients who were judged "to have top-heavy expense records with a certain physician." If the answers to the questions listed above appeared to justify suspicion, a further investigation was carried out.

Partial results of the CPS investigation initiated in this fashion were published in an editorial in the *Bulletin* of the Los Angeles Medical Association under the title, "Robbing Peter to Pay Paul."

In a strongly worded indictment, the editor reported that he "had in his possession photostatic copies of files and conclusive evidence which show the fraudulent tactics being used by upwards of 20 doctors . . ." in order to increase their income from CPS. The types of fraud discovered fell into four major categories:

1. Billing CPS for surgery which was never performed or for house calls which were never made.

2. Billing CPS for major surgery which was actually of a minor nature.

3. Billing CPS for postoperative care never actually given.

4. The final "all inclusive" source of fraud was reported as involving X-ray work, laboratory work, and anesthetist labor that was never performed.

On the basis of the Los Angeles investigation it was estimated that throughout the state CPS was paying out approximately $100,000 a month for fraudulent acts such as those enumerated above. If this estimate is accepted as accurate, this would mean that about 7 per cent of the benefits paid for physicians' services was absorbed by fraudulent claims.

Dr. Foster's editorial created a considerable stir both inside and outside the medical profession. The story was picked up by a national news magazine and many of the newspapers of the state. However, as an example of the difficulty of tracking down facts about abuse, the *Bulletin* provided no further details on the investigation in future issues.[9] CPS further states that no official report of the results is available to the public.

As reflected in the title chosen for the original editorial, the profession's stand was that the issue of fraud affected the other doctor-members of CPS but not the general public since the diversion of these funds reduced the amount available for distribution to physicians. It was apparently on this ground that further publicity was restricted. The validity of this line of argument rests on the somewhat dubious assumption that the premiums for CPS contracts were not affected by leakages of money in these amounts.

The reader will note that the types of fraud revealed by this investigation were not included in our earlier enumeration of the most important forms of abuse of health insurance. This exclusion resulted from certain special characteristics of the CPS procedures that suggest that the typical indemnity insurance plan (or the current CPS plan) is less likely to suffer from this kind of activity. These characteristics were:

1. At the time of the incidents exposed by the investigation, CPS did not notify the patient of the payments for medical serv-

---

[9] Some interesting clues as to the reaction to the editorial can be gleaned from the following: The second issue of the *Bulletin* after the Foster editorial appeared carried a two-page statement by the president of the Los Angeles Medical Association as a special colored insert bound into the magazine. Entitled "The Recent Publicity About C.P.S.," the statement supported Dr. Foster's general position in more moderate language but in a generally defensive tone. In the next issue a box on the editorial page carried a statement defending the editor's practice of dealing with controversial subjects but announcing that, ". . . To avoid the sole responsibility for publications in the Bulletin, The Editor has requested the Board of Trustees—and will also request the Council—to form an Editorial Committee to pass on future material to be published." This move was described as an effort to provide "a better guarantee that our profession's 'best interests' are given wider interpretation by a selected group, rather than by just one man." *Ibid.*, April 17, 1952, p. 443.

ices made to doctors on their behalf.[10] The success of the practice of submitting fraudulent claims for medical care never rendered required that the patient (unless he were a collaborator) be unaware of the existence of the claim. This peculiarity of CPS accounting probably grew out of the unit value system of compensating physicians and is not characteristic of the claim payment system of insurance companies in general. As a result of the investigation CPS closed this loophole by instituting a practice of notifying patients of the bills paid to physicians for their medical care.

2. Only under CPS does the doctor agree to accept the amounts specified in the fee schedule as full payment for his services to patients with incomes under the ceilings. This means that a doctor who feels that the CPS fee for a specific procedure is inadequate is tempted to correct this presumed inequity by creating a false claim. When working under the much more common indemnity insurance schedule, the doctor can deal with what he feels to be an inappropriate allowance by levying an additional charge to be paid by the patient directly.

Combined, these two factors gave some physicians the incentive to file fraudulent claims while making it possible for them to do so undetected. This combination of circumstances is not characteristic of insurance plans generally nor of CPS since 1952 and hence this form of abuse is probably not of major importance at the present time.

We have included this report in this discussion of abuse since it illustrates one variety of the problem which occurred during the development of the modern health insurance movement. It also demonstrates that the cost of an insurance plan cannot be controlled simply by securing agreement to a maximum fee schedule without installing other control mechanisms. It further indicates something about the magnitude of one type of flagrant exploitation of an insurance program, in this case the "doctors' plan" itself. The existence of this kind of outright fraud suggests that other forms of abuse, some of them more subtle and more easily rationalized, are likely to be of considerable magnitude.

---

[10] Malcolm Taylor, *op. cit.*, p. 23, states that this is also the usual practice in the CPS-type of plan in Canada.

Entering a claim for medical services never rendered can be regarded as the extreme limit of the general problem of charging excessive fees. In its more usual form, however, the question of excessive fees for medical services is more complex and involves the slippery issue of defining the meaning of the term "excessive." There are two important meanings which could be given the concept of excessive fees. First, fees for a given medical service or surgical procedure could be regarded as excessive in an absolute sense. This means that the fees actually charged would have to be compared with some measure of the "fair" fee for the procedure in question. Second, fees might be tested, not with reference to a standard fee regarded as generally applicable to all or to the great majority of cases, but with reference to the fees charged to other patients in similar economic circumstances (which includes those with similar insurance benefits), or to the same group of patients at different times.

Both of these approaches are difficult to apply in specific cases due primarily to the lack of information on the experience of health insurance plans and the lack of accepted standards of "fair" fees. Even when the operating statistics of a particular plan are made available, problems arise because some patients in the same group-insurance plan have quite different levels of *family* income, may patronize doctors of varying degrees of skill, prestige, and specialty training, and because surgical procedures in the same medical classification differ in complexity.

These disparities can be minimized by careful choice of a group to be studied, by the use of relatively large numbers of cases of apparently similar type in arriving at average figures, and by giving weight only to substantial differences in results. With these cautions in mind, the surgical experience of a specific insurance plan is analyzed in the following section.

Surgical Fees—The CMTA Experience

The California Metal Trades Association (CMTA)[11] is an employer association of metal fabricators spread through northern California with its center in the Bay Area. The association in-

---

[11] The CMTA and its insurance program are described at greater length in chapter ix below. This section is partial evidence of the excellent coöperation furnished the author by the executive director of the Association, Mr. Robert Grunsky.

cludes about 350 employers, most of whom are of small size when measured by numbers of employees. About 300 of these employers are members of the association-administered health plan. The number of workers covered by the plan fluctuates between five and six thousand, most of them concentrated in the Bay Area. Since the larger employers in the association tend to be self-insured, more than half of the employees of member firms are not included in the CMTA plan. The principal common characteristic of the employers in the association is that they deal with related metal trades unions. The accidents of union jurisdiction have a great deal to do with the geographical scope of the various collective-bargaining agreements entered into by the CMTA. Although the data to be analyzed in this section cover the period from January 15, 1954, through November, 1957, the health plan is one of the older plans in the area, dating back to 1949. The program has always been of the indemnity insurance type.

In January, 1954, the CMTA plan provided surgical expense coverage to "employees" (defined as the entire staff of the member firms including all executives) and to their dependents. From January, 1954, through August, 1957, benefits were paid to employees according to a $350 surgical schedule; dependents' benefits were based on a $300 schedule.[12] Effective September, 1956, the surgical benefit schedules were equalized with the adoption of the $350 schedule for dependents. This pattern of developments permits us to answer a number of important questions, at least as far as this plan is concerned.

1. What has been the trend in average surgical fees over the period in question and can the level of fees be compared to some standard?

2. Is there any evidence that different surgical fees for the same type of operation were charged to employees and to their dependents during the period when the two subgroups were on different benefit schedules?

3. Did raising the schedule for dependents by one-sixth in Sep-

---

[12] This means that the maximum dollar allowance paid to employees for any procedure was $350; the highest dollar allowance paid to dependents was $300. This ratio (350/300) applies to each operation in the two schedules; in other words, the benefit paid for each operation in the $350 schedule was approximately seven-sixths of the benefit paid for the corresponding operation in the $300 schedule.

tember, 1956, result in an increase in the average surgical fees charged this subgroup for the same type of operation?

To sum up the issue, to what extent were the surgical charges under the CMTA plan influenced by the existence of the plan over-all, by the existence at the same time of two different levels of benefits for employees and their dependents, and by two different levels of benefits for the dependents at different time periods?

In analyzing the CMTA data for this purpose we shall concentrate the bulk of our attention on three time periods. The first six months for which records are available (January 15, 1954, through July, 1954) make up one period; the last six months prior to the change in the surgical schedule (March, 1956, through August, 1956) make up the second period; the last six months for which data are currently available (June, 1957, through November, 1957) make up the third period. Six months was chosen as the length of each interval as a compromise between two desirable characteristics. First, the period should be short so that the averages computed would be affected as little as possible by long-run trends in the way the charges behaved, and second, the intervals should be long enough to include a relatively large number of surgical operations to minimize the effect of small numbers of atypical fees. In our examination then, we shall be comparing the way the plan worked at three points in its career: at the beginning of the record, just before a substantial change in the benefit structure was instituted and during the most recent half-year prior to the time of writing and after the changes in benefits. The total time span involved is just under four years. Each of the questions suggested earlier will be considered in the sections to come.

Table 4.1 summarizes the over-all experience of the CMTA health plan for the three time periods under discussion. At first glance the table seems to suggest that average surgical fees were declining over the time span covered since the average fee fell from $154 in 1954 to $121 in 1957. While it is true that the cost to the plan of the average surgical operation declined, this was not the result of lower fees for the same operation in the different periods. The lower average fee simply indicates that the "operation mix" was changing in the direction of a higher proportion of low-fee operations. This is shown by the behavior of the average surgical allowance which is substantially independent of the level of fees charged, depending almost entirely on the changing distribution of high- and low-fee operations performed.[13]

TABLE 4.1

SURGICAL EXPERIENCE OF THE CMTA INSURANCE PLAN

Period	Number of cases	Average fee	Average allowance	Average difference	Percent of average fee paid	Per cent of cases, fee exceeding allowance
Jan. 1954– July 1954 ..	200	$154	$115	$39	75	72
Mar. 1956– Aug. 1956 ..	289	131	96	36	73	76
June 1957– Nov. 1957 ..	322	121	93	29	77	64

SOURCE: Compiled from data supplied by California Metal Trades Association. Dates are inclusive. Surgical schedule for dependents increased September, 1956.

Accepting the fact that the operation mix was changing, is there anything that can be said about fees for the same operations on the basis of table 4.1? There is a suggestion that surgical fees may have been rising between 1954 and 1956 to be found in the data reported in the last two columns of the table. It can be argued that the average fee charged should change in proportion with the way the average allowance changed. Buried in this statement is the implied assumption that the ratio between each actual fee and the corresponding schedule allowance is approximately the same for all operations or that differences in this ratio cancel out over large numbers of operations. If this assumption is accepted, average fees would be expected to decline at about the same rate as average allowances, the average difference in dollars between the two would become smaller, and the percentage of the average fee covered by the average allowance would be constant.

Table 4.1 reveals that the average difference did shrink between 1954 and 1956 but not enough to keep the percentage of the surgical bill covered by the indemnity from falling slightly. This analy-

---

[13] "Substantially" but not entirely independent since the actual amount allowed is never greater than the schedule specifies but may be less if the doctor's fee is less. In practice this is unimportant and the average allowance actually paid can be taken as practically equivalent to the average maximum allowance permitted. In only a small minority of cases were the actual fees charged (and hence the allowances) lower than the schedule permitted. For example, of the eighty-two tonsillectomies and the thirty appendectomies in 1954, in only one case of each was the actual fee less than the scheduled allowance.

sis indicates that surgical charges for the same operations may have risen slightly but such a conclusion can be only tentative. Between 1956 and 1957 the average surgical fee for all operations combined continued to fall, the average difference between fees and allowances fell sharply, and the percentage of the average bill covered rose. The reader is reminded, however, that the surgical schedule for dependents was raised between the dates cited and that data in table 4.1 reflect this fact.

It is possible to make a rough calculation of what the average allowance for 1957 would have been if the schedule of dependents' allowances had not been changed. Under the CMTA plan, dependents' surgery has accounted for slightly less than two-thirds of all operations on the average. When the schedule was changed in September, 1956, the allowances for dependents' operations were raised by one-sixth. Since about two-thirds of the operations had their allowances increased one-sixth, this is equivalent to an increase in all allowances of one-ninth ($2/3 \times 1/6$). This means that if dependents' allowances had not been raised, the average surgical allowances would have been about $83 instead of $92.61 and the percentage of the average surgical bill covered would have dropped to around 69 per cent.[14]

If these estimates are accepted as approximately correct, it implies that surgical fees charged members of the CMTA plan rose at an average rate of about 2 per cent a year over the four-year period from January, 1954, through November, 1957.

Roundabout calculations of this type are suggestive but the assumptions involved prevent them from being anything but approximations. The biggest stumbling block to greater accuracy is the changing operation mix which is revealed by the behavior of the average surgical allowance for the three periods. The best method for eliminating this effect is to compare the financial experience with a standard operation or set of operations. In practice this means falling back on an analysis of the experience with tonsillectomies and appendectomies (as does the Bureau of Labor Statistics in calculating the CPI). This procedure is justified by a number of factors: these operations are common enough so that meaningful averages can be calculated, they are relatively stand-

---

[14] Allowances can be calculated easily from the relation $x + x/9 = 92.61$ where x represents the average allowance under the old schedule.

ardized procedures, and they account for a very substantial part of total surgery.[15]

Data for dependents' tonsillectomies are presented in table 4.2 for the same three time periods represented in the earlier table. These data show a rise of about 10 per cent in the average fee for a tonsillectomy between 1954 and 1956. This is a rate of increase substantially in excess of the 3 per cent rise in tonsillectomy fees reported in the Consumer Price Index between March, 1954, and March, 1956.

The most interesting information contained in table 4.2 is provided by the apparent failure of fees to rise between 1956 and

TABLE 4.2

CMTA EXPERIENCE WITH DEPENDENT'S TONSILLECTOMIES[a]

Period	Number of cases	Scheduled allowances	Average fee	Range of fees
Jan. 1954– July 1954 ..	48	$45	$64	$35–100
Mar. 1956– Aug. 1956 ..	72	45	71	40–150
June 1957 Nov. 1957 ..	59	53	71	50–100

SOURCE: Compiled from data supplied by the California Metal Trades Association.
[a] Includes Tonsillectomies and Adenoidectomies.

1957. In September, 1956, the change in surgical schedules which became effective raised the allowance for dependents' tonsillectomies from $45 to $53. According to the table, none of this increase was offset in increases in fees over the next year. The entire amount went to the patient to reduce out-of-pocket expenses. In this instance, there is no evidence of an upward adjustment of fees as a result of the increase in indemnities.

Turning our attention to appendectomies, we can extend the

---

[15] For the CMTA plan, tonsillectomies and appendectomies accounted for 35 per cent of all operations in the 1954 period covered in table 4.1. This figure is somewhat higher than that reported from other sources. Information furnished by Mr. Harry Duncan of the Travelers Insurance Company, for example, shows that these procedures account for between 27 and 28 per cent of all surgical claims. This discrepancy is probably due to differences in family composition of the CMTA plan compared with the insured population generally.

analysis to another area. Since many fewer appendectomies than tonsillectomies are performed, the six-month time intervals used to this point have been abandoned in table 4.3 in favor of the longer intervals needed to include an adequate number of operations. For all appendectomies combined, the average fee for the 1955, 1956, and 1957 periods was almost stable at about $205 while the average fee for 1954 was about 5 per cent less. This pattern suggests that fees for appendectomies performed for CMTA patients behaved not much differently from those reported in the appendectomy component of the CPI. The latter showed a slight increase from March, 1954, to March, 1956, for the nation as a whole.[16]

TABLE 4.3

CMTA EXPERIENCE WITH APPENDECTOMIES[a]

Period	Number of cases	Scheduled allowances	Average fee
Jan. 1954–Aug. 1956			
Employees	24	$175	$205
Dependents	59	150	202
Nov. 1956–Nov. 1957			
Employees	16	175	205
Dependents	18	175	202
All Cases Combined			
Jan. 1954–Dec. 1954	30	150–175	196
Jan. 1955–Dec. 1955	28	150–175	205
Jan. 1956–Aug. 1956	25	150–175	207
Nov. 1956–Nov. 1957	34	175	204

SOURCE: Compiled from data supplied by the California Metal Trades Association.

[a] Dates are inclusive. Data not available for September, 1954, July, 1955, and September and October, 1956. Dependents' benefits increased September, 1956. (Range of fees 100–400.)

Appendectomies are distributed among employees and their dependents more evenly than tonsillectomies (almost all of which are performed on dependents). This permits an analysis of the fees charged employees as compared with those charged dependents during the years when the two groups received different

---

[16] Statements as to the behavior of CPI components in this section are drawn from U. S. Bureau of Labor Statistics, *Consumer Price Index: Price Indexes for Selected Items and Groups*, Washington, July, 1956.

allowances. During the almost three-year period prior to the raising of dependents' surgical benefits in September, 1956, there was a $25 differential in the indemnities paid employees and their dependents. The medical care cynic would have expected the fees actually charged to reflect this difference in allowances but table 4.3 shows the average fees levied on each group to have been virtually identical. After dependents' benefits were increased to the employees' level in September, 1956, the cynic would have expected average fees to rise to reflect the new higher indemnities. Once again, the data indicate that this did not happen. The average fee charged dependents during the year after the schedule change was exactly the same as the average fee charged during the previous three years.

Up to this point we have been studying the over-all trend of fees and comparing the fees charged different subgroups of the CMTA plan population. It would be useful if an evaluation of the absolute level of fees could be made, at least for appendectomies and tonsillectomies. As noted earlier, this introduces the question of the standard of comparison to be used. For the San Francisco Bay Area there is no generally accepted standard of fees, but in table 4.4 we have collected the fees listed for these specific operations by a variety of sources during the time span covered by the CMTA data.

TABLE 4.4

FEES FOR TONSILLECTOMIES AND APPENDECTOMIES FROM VARIOUS SOURCES

Source	Tonsillectomies	Appendectomies
CPS Schedule A (1956)	$42 or $63 [a]	$131.25
CPS Schedule B (1955)	50 or 65 [a]	150.00
CMA Relative Value Schedule at $5 per unit (1956)	75	175.00
ACCMA fee list (1954)	60 or 75 [b]	200.00
S.F. Medical Society (1953) ..	60 or 90 [a]	150.00
S.F. Labor Council (1957) ..	45	150.00

SOURCE: See text.
[a] The lower figure is for patients 15 years and under; the higher for those over 15.
[b] The lower figure—under 12 years. The higher over 12 years.

The schedules or lists from which these fees were drawn have had widely varying status within the medical profession. The last two schedules listed in the table, for example, have little or no status with any official body of organized medicine. They are included because they represent two schedules in the preparation of which organized labor attempted to participate. The San Francisco Labor Council schedule is one which was used by the council as a basis for a 1957 attempt to set up a panel of individual physicians in San Francisco who would agree to accept its allowances as full payment.[17] The "relative value" schedule (described below) was used as a base with certain modifications being introduced. This attempt enjoyed little success.

The fees identified as from a San Francisco Medical Society schedule were taken from an ill-fated schedule that was worked out as a result of negotiations between committees of the Society and the labor movement. In 1953 the fees were regarded by labor groups as relatively high for the under $5,000 income group for which they were primarily intended. Although discussions were held with insurance companies, CPS, and Blue Cross, the schedule never achieved full official status and can be regarded mainly as a historical curiosity. The other schedules in table 4.4 have some claim to being representative of average medical fees for some portion of the area's medical market.

Consideration of the absolute level of fees inevitably raises the question of the income level of the CMTA insured group. Since the health plan covers all executives as well as production and clerical workers, there is a wide range of income levels represented. Information as to annual family incomes is not available but the bulk of the plan membership probably had annual incomes between $4,200 and $5,400 as individuals during the time period studied.[18]

---

[17] See chapter vii for a fuller discussion of this incident.

[18] This statement is based on an examination of the hourly wage scale specified in collective-bargaining agreements in effect between the CMTA and the International Association of Machinists. Base rates in effect from 1953 to July, 1956, ranged from $1.67½ for janitors to $2.55½ for tool and die makers with 1 per cent increases going into effect on July 1, 1954, and 1955. From July 1, 1956, to July 1, 1957, the basic day-shift hourly rates ranged from $2.13 for janitors and to $2.95 for tool and die makers. But note that since some 300 firms are in the plan, a sizable percentage of the total membership would presumably be classed as "executives."

This estimate of income rules out the CPS Schedule A which is intended to compensate physicians for care rendered to persons with a family income below $4,200 in 1956. Eliminating Schedule A, along with the two schedules noted earlier as not having even semiofficial status with the medical profession, leaves us with three schedules from table 4.4 available for analysis:

1. The CPS Schedule B—a schedule of fees which member-doctors agree to accept as full payment for surgical services performed for CPS subscribers. This schedule was published in 1955.

2. The 1956 "Relative Value Schedule" (RVS) of the California Medical Association. This schedule was prepared on a state-wide basis after a three-year fee study. It is expressed in "unit values" rather than in dollars and has the effect of ranking the various medical procedures listed according to their relative position in the hierarchy of fees. These unit values can be converted to absolute dollar values by the use of a multiplier appropriate to the level of actual fees in a given locality. In table 4.4 a multiplier of $5 per unit has been used in arriving at the listed dollar fees.[19] Although it is very difficult, especially for a layman, to make meaningful comparisons between two fee schedules, the CMA schedule at $5 seems to be roughly 15 to 20 per cent above the $6,000 ceiling CPS Schedule B.

3. The 1954 Alameda-Contra Costa Medical Association (ACCMA) "median fee list." These fees were gathered through a survey of the membership which asked for the usual fee charged for the procedures included. They were intended to be maxima charged any patient regardless of income unless a higher fee was arranged in advance of the operation at the initiative of the doctor. In general these fees seem fairly comparable to those in the CMA schedule at $5 per unit and are therefore substantially higher than the CPS Schedule B. The ACCMA's survey was carried out in 1954 and the list was used until 1958 when it was replaced by the RVS.

If we accept the arithmetical averages of table 4.2 as being typi-

---

[19] The $5 multiplier for surgical fees might conceivably be challenged as too low for the Bay Area. At $5 per unit, however, the CMA schedule produces a maximum listed fee of $500 for something like 67 different surgical procedures. This large number is in part the result of the relatively complete enumeration of operations as compared with the usual schedules, but a substantial number of the same procedures are found in Schedule B at $400, the CPS listed maximum.

cal of CMTA experience, we have average fees of just under $70 for tonsillectomies and something over $200 for appendectomies. How do these figures compare with the three schedules from table 4.4?

In the CPS Schedule B the tonsillectomy average fee is differentiated by age group, but the CMTA average is considerably higher than either figure. Since a substantial majority of CMTA tonsillectomies are probably performed on children aged 15 or younger,[20] the average fee is probably 20 to 25 per cent higher than the CPS schedule would suggest. The CMTA appendectomy average fee of $200 is one-third higher than the CPS Schedule B item.

It should be pointed out, however, that the CPS fees are meant to be applied throughout the state and are not designed solely for the higher-cost metropolitan areas (although about two-thirds of all doctors practice in these areas). More important, physicians sometimes describe this level of fees as involving a "subsidy" provided to the profession's own health plan. As noted later, Schedule B fees and the accompanying plan of benefits were also set up to meet a competitive situation and are not intended to set limits to charges for other practice. The medical profession in California has consistently refused to permit the CPS schedules to be regarded as implying any definite relationship to indemnity insurance schedules. The reader can judge for himself whether the differences between the CMTA average fees for these operations and the fees in Schedule B should be accepted as a measure of the "subsidy" contributed to CPS by Bay Area physicians. The writer personally doubts that surgical fees charged in the open market to families with an annual income below $6,000 in 1955 were 20 to 25 per cent higher than the CPS fees accepted as full payment for families at this income level. If this doubt is justified, then the CMTA average fees were above the appropriate charge for this particular group.

Shifting to the Relative Value Schedule (RVS) and the ACCMA fee list raises the question of the proper form of the aver-

---

[20] Since adult employees accounted for only 11 per cent of all tonsillectomies during calendar 1954, it can be assumed that adult spouses accounted for no more than 10 per cent of the tonsillectomies included in table 5.2. Since children over 18 are no longer classed as dependents for insurance purposes, only a minority of the remaining 90 per cent of the cases were likely to have been from 16 through 18 years of age (CPS Schedule), or even from 13 through 18 (ACCMA list).

age to be used in comparisons. The RVS was computed by using both median and modal figures while the ACCMA list of monetary values was based on median fees.

In compiling fee schedules the use of a modal or median fee is probably preferable to an arithmetic average. Both of these figures can be computed for the CMTA cases for comparative purposes. For all the tonsillectomies in table 4.2 both the median and the mode of charges were $75. The median and the mode of the charges for appendectomies were both $200.[21]

Comparing these figures with the CMA schedule, we find that the CMTA median charge of $75 for tonsillectomies is the same as the RVS at $5 per unit. The CMTA $200 appendectomy median is about 15 per cent above the corresponding RVS fee. When the ACCMA fees are used for comparison, the situation is reversed. The appendectomy median charge for the CMTA equals the fee specified by the association while the median fee for tonsillectomies is the same as the listed fee for adults but certainly more than the *average* association fee would be for the appropriate combination of adult and children's operations.

Measuring CMTA charges against the RVS and the ACCMA fees raises the issue as to whether the fees in the schedules should be regarded as applicable to the CMTA group or whether, on the average, lower fees might be appropriate.[22] There is no way of answering this question.

---

[21] A fee is the median fee if there are as many higher fees in the array as there are lower fees. The modal fee is the one occurring most frequently. In tables 4.2 and 4.3 the familiar arithmetic average was used.

For the three periods in table 4.2 the successive median fees were $65, $75, and $75, with 78 of all 179 tonsillectomies at $75. For all periods combined as well as for each subperiod separately, the median fee for appendectomies was $200, with 47 of 117 operations performed at this rate. The concentration of the charges at the median was so great that only about one-tenth of the tonsillectomies and about one-fourth of the appendectomies were above their respective medians.

[22] The critical reader may wonder if the relatively high average fees for CMTA plan members did not result from high fees charged "executives" and low fees charged production and clerical workers. To check this possibility, information as to the occupation of the subscriber was available for 25 appendectomies for which the charge exceeded the $200 median. In only three cases was the operation performed on an "executive" or a member of an executive's family. The other cases involved production or clerical workers. There were, however, eight other cases for which no occupational data were available. It has been estimated that a liberal definition of "executive" might include as many as 20 per cent of the plan membership, though this seems rather high. In this plan there seems little indication of an "ability-to-pay" fee system.

As a final note, in the course of discussing the ACCMA system, some observers expressed some skepticism as to the reliability of "usual fees" collected by the questionnaire method from doctors who know the results will be related, however remotely, to fee determination. In the absence of any evidence to the contrary, however, the above analysis has accepted the ACCMA list as represented.

Evidence as to the absolute level of fees has been presented in lengthy detail to enable the reader to reach his own conclusions. In the opinion of the author, the members of the CMTA group are probably being charged somewhat higher fees than the same persons would have been charged as uninsured individuals. The difference may not be large—perhaps on the order of 10 per cent.

Since published analyses of this kind are relatively rare, the CMTA experience will be summed up in some detail:

1. Over the almost four-year period of the study, the operation mix changed substantially so as to reduce the average surgical payment by about 20 per cent.

2. There appeared to be a rate of increase in fees for dependents' tonsillectomies of about 2 per cent annually. Fees for appendectomies increased more slowly at an annual rate of about 1 per cent. For both operations increases were concentrated in the first half of the period.

3. During the time period when subscribers and dependents were on different benefit schedules, there was no significant difference in the actual fees for appendectomies charged the two groups. After dependents' allowances were raised to the same level as subscribers, no change in actual charges for dependents was observed.

4. Although the average charge for dependents' tonsillectomies rose slowly during the first three years while the insurance indemnity for this operation remained unchanged, there is no evidence that fees were increased to take advantage of the increased allowances introduced during the fourth year.

5. Considering the best evidence available as to the level of fees for tonsillectomies and appendectomies in the community, the charges to CMTA patients seemed to have been somewhat higher than would have been expected in view of the estimated income level of most of the plan members.

In short, the CMTA analysis shows little evidence that the existence of the insurance plan could be charged with increasing fees actually charged between 1954 and 1957. It does raise the possibility that in previous years and in the early years of this study, fees had been adjusted upward from the level that a group of patients such as this might have been expected to pay.

Unnecessary Surgery

It is generally accepted that a good deal of unnecessary surgery is performed in the United States with or without the added incentives provided by the existence of surgical coverage under health insurance.[23]

In his article Williams defined unnecessary surgery "as an operation which is not supported by careful clinical reasoning and judgment, and not confirmed in diagnosis by any disease actually found." He reported that of all major surgery, the appendectomy was the most often done and the most often abused. A reading of some of the literature concerning unnecessary surgery suggests that a group of several operations involving the female reproductive organs would probably be the next most serious source of abuse.

Detection of unnecessary surgery usually is the result of the work of a "tissue committee" formed from the staff of a hospital.[24] Either as part of a special study or as a continuing review as one item in a "medical audit" of hospital operations, the tissues or organs removed are examined for evidence of disease and as a check on techniques of treatment and accuracy of diagnosis. Of course, a pathologist's report that tissue removed was normal does not necessarily mean that the operation was performed for financial gain. Records of this type for particular surgeons or hospitals do, however, provide the basis for comparative analysis and possible remedial action when certain standards are exceeded.

---

[23] See the remarks of Dr. Paul Hawley, director of the American College of Surgeons, in *U. S. News and World Report*, February 20, 1953; and the article by Greer Williams, "Unjustified Surgery," *Harper's Magazine*, February, 1954. At the time he wrote the article, Mr. Williams was public relations director of the American College of Surgeons.

[24] For a description of the make-up and functioning of such a committee together with some of its findings and the results of remedial action, see H. V. Weinert and R. Brill, "Effectiveness of Hospital Tissue Committee in Raising Surgical Standards," *J.A.M.A.*, Vol. 152, November 8, 1952, pp. 992–996.

Reports of investigations of this type are not plentiful. Some information has been published by the UMW fund and an example or two will be reviewed at this point.

At the 1952 AMA-UMW Conference, the fund's Executive Medical Officer stated that one investigation revealed that the pathological report of 54 appendectomies confirmed the diagnosis in 25 cases and reported normal appendices in the other 29. One physician who performed 11 appendectomies during the period investigated had only three diagnoses confirmed by the pathologist.[25]

At the 1956 Conference it was reported that the fund found that over a three-year period in one hospital 60 Caesarean sections were performed by two surgeons in a total of 315 deliveries. This represented a rate of 19 per cent. After the fund submitted this information to a committee of the medical profession for review, action was taken that resulted in a drop in the rate from 19 to 3.5 per cent.[26]

As in the other forms of abuse, agreement is general that the bulk of real abuse results from the activities of a minority of physicians. This statement is often made in defense of the medical profession and the material reviewed for this section bears out this contention.

Examples like these can provide no basis for any sort of guess as to the prevalence of this type of abuse. They have been presented to illustrate the nature of the problem and to outline the form a system of control would have to take to be effective. Compared with other forms of abuse, this type is more directly a medical problem and less an economic problem. Insofar as unnecessary surgery can be reduced, it would be desirable to do so even if the economic cost of such surgery to the patient, to a health plan, or to society as a whole were zero.

Excessive Services

This is a catchall category of abuse intended to cover problems such as excessive doctors' calls—either at home, in the office, or

---

[25] Paper presented to the 1952 Conference on Medical Care in the Bituminous Coal Mine Area by Warren F. Draper, M.D., *Views and Suggestions*, p. 5. A copy of the paper was furnished by Dr. Draper.

[26] 1956 Report, p. 16. For other examples from UMW experience see p. 20 in this Report; and pp. 16–17 and p. 21 of the 1953 Report. See also the articles cited earlier in this section.

in the hospital—unnecessary or duplicated laboratory tests, unneeded injections, and the like. Because of the difficulty of policing services of this kind and because of the high total costs generated by their abuse, many of these items have been excluded from coverage by most health insurance plans. As an alternative to exclusion they have been subjected to specific controls such as the requirement that the patient pay full costs up to a certain amount before insurance reimbursement begins (the "deductible"), or that the patient pay part of the cost of each service received (coinsurance). A different approach has been to limit the liability of the insurance plan to a certain maximum number of visits or dollar amounts of service.

There is no dearth of examples to show that complete coverage of all medical needs of this type can result in heavy financial drains. Of the organizations mentioned in this chapter, both the California Physicians Service and the United Mine Workers Fund originally covered home and office visits and later abandoned this coverage as too expensive. (CPS has since reinstated this coverage with controls against abuse.) It is easy to confuse discussions of how expensive it is to provide this type of care through insurance with the likelihood of massive abuse. Furnishing these forms of coverage would be expensive even if abuse were kept at a minimum. On the basis of the experience of the Windsor Medical Services, a health plan with comprehensive coverage, it has been estimated that adding complete outpatient care by physicians to in-hospital medical benefits more than doubles the cost of physicians' care to the plan, even with a low level of abuse.[27]

When the desire to keep premium costs down is added to the admittedly difficult problem of control of abuse for these kinds of service, the typical insurance administrator has tended to retreat from this form of coverage to the more "insurable" items of medical care such as hospitalization and surgery. It can be argued that

---

[27] S. J. Axelrod and R. E. Patton, "The Use and Abuse of Prepaid Comprehensive Physicians' Services," *Amer. J. Pub. Health,* Vol. 42, May, 1952, p. 570.

The Windsor (Canada) Medical Services is a very successful example of a large plan sponsored by a medical society on a community basis offering complete medical care with a minimum of administrative and financial restrictions and paying doctors on a fee-for-service system. The WMS utilizes a control procedure of medical committee review of physicians' claims and has experimented with statistical control methods. See C. A. Metzner, S. J. Axelrod, and J. H. Sloss, "Statistical Analysis as a Basis for Controls in Fee-For-Service Plans," *Amer. J. Pub. Health,* Vol. 43, September, 1953, pp. 1162–1170.

the relatively small sums involved in each separate claim for out-patient medical care made it inefficient and unnecessary to use the insurance mechanism for payment of these expenses. Without going into this controversy at this point, it can be noted that the desires of consumers, the pressures of competition, and increasing experience have all combined to bring about a cautious expansion in the area of outpatient medical care and laboratory services in recent years.

Although there is no way of knowing the extent of abuse in the usual health plan stemming from these sources, the Windsor plan provides an important clue to the potential in expanding services in this area. The physicians' reviewing committee in WMS concentrates on bills submitted for multiple services rendered in the home, office, or hospitals. In 1950, Axelrod and Patton reported that the total amount of the bills for these services was reduced by about 6 per cent as a result of medical review.

This gives no indication of the amount of abuse of this kind that would exist in a plan with a different structure of benefits or method of operation and with no control or a different control system. It does indicate the relatively low level of abuse that can be achieved when conditions are favorable. Important among these conditions are physician coöperation and local control.

Abuse and "Closed-panel" Plans

Throughout this chapter the discussion of abuse has been carried out in the context of the cash indemnity insurance plan without comprehensive coverage and with a fee-for-service method of payment. Some comment on the character of the abuse problem in the comprehensive "closed-panel" plans is in order.

Most of the forms of abuse described in earlier sections are confined largely, if not wholly, to indemnity plans of limited coverage. If a health plan provides outpatient care and diagnostic and laboratory work outside the hospital, the pressure for unnecessary hospitalization is greatly reduced. In fact, if the plan operates its own hospitals there is a positive incentive to minimize hospitalization costs. Methods of reimbursing physicians, such as capitation or salary, that make income earned independent of the quantity or type of service rendered tend to eliminate fraudulent claims, excessive fees, and unnecessary services as sources of abuse. We would expect abuse stemming from these factors to be minimized in a health plan that provided comprehensive service, operated its own hospitals, and paid member-physicians by salary or capitation. The enthusiastic supporters of this type of plan often remark that they benefit from keeping people well rather than from treating the sick. In their more exuberant moments they sometimes draw an analogy to the apocryphal Chinese medical system in which the physician is said to be paid only while the patient remains healthy.

Human frailty being what it is, the possibility of abuse is not entirely absent in this form of medical organization. For one thing, abuse for which the patient is responsible may still occur. Some patients may demand excessive amounts or inappropriate types of service and the plan must provide for the control of these practices. (One of the most difficult problem areas is the control of home calls.) Also, since many of these plans draw a substantial part of their total income from incidental fees and extra charges, the plan's income (as distinct from the physician's) is not entirely independent of the quantity of service rendered. In general, however, these issues are of much less importance in comprehensive, physician-panel plans than they are in those referred to as the indemnity type.

To offset these advantages, these plans are peculiarly susceptible to another class of problems that, from the standpoint of the patient, can be regarded as special forms of abuse. This requires expanding the notion of abuse to include medical care that is inadequate with respect to the quantity or the "quality" of care.

The concept of quality of care occurs frequently in discussions of prepayment group-practice plans and is used in a variety of meanings. In a fundamental sense the quality of medical care is a general medical problem and is related to the ability and motivations of the medical profession and the physical facilities and other supporting elements (auxiliary personnel, drugs, etc.) that make up the medical care industry. The particular concern of the prepayment group-practice plans with the issue arises from the possibility that this organizational form is especially vulnerable to a deterioration of quality in some sense.

Perhaps the basic quality problem facing the typical panel plan is the recruitment of capable physicians in the face of the antagonism of the bulk of the private practitioners in the area. In varying degrees the physician-members of such plans usually are faced with a loss of status among their professional peers. Critics of these plans often allege that the well-known opposition of their colleagues to this kind of practice deters all but substandard doctors from accepting such appointments in the usual case. They claim that the better doctors who do enter such plans are often disillusioned with the actual conditions of practice they encounter and leave for private practice. On the other hand, the defenders of the plans argue that group practice of this type is the best guarantee that a satisfactory level of physician ability can be achieved since it subjects the participating doctors to the continuous scrutiny of their colleagues. The members of the panel are originally selected by other physicians and their day-to-day performance is known to their fellows and can be influenced by professional standards. In contrast, the doctor in private practice is selected in the first instance by a layman, the patient, and is relatively free from professional review of his practice.

There is no way of knowing how the average level of ability of the medical staff of a panel plan compares with the average for the other physicians in the area. The mechanism of group practice would seem to be *potentially* capable of guaranteeing that the group average would be at least as high as that of the community. Whether the recruits available for such plans in the face of professional opposition are such as to permit this potential to be realized is a question that must be considered on a case-by-case basis.[28] Under existing conditions the *possibility* of "abuse" exists in that the members of an insured group may receive care of a quality below the average of the community. It should be noted that this possibility would be reduced if the medical profession attitudes toward this type of practice were to be modified.

[28] The growing concern with the malpractice problem in solo practice also suggests that the issue is not as clear-cut as some partisans would indicate. It should be pointed out that there are advantages to physicians in group practice involving such things as work schedules, low costs of practice, association with colleagues, stability of income, etc., to offset the loss of independence. Defenders of the panel plans also insist that preventive medicine and group practice organized by specialties are themselves an important extra element in the quality of care. For a recent and generally favorable statement on the quality of care in group-practice plans, see the report of the American Medical Association, Commission on Medical Care Plans, special ed., *J.A.M.A.*, Jan., 1959, especially pp. 48–53.

In addition to the problem of recruiting physicians of average ability, the structure of the panel plans may make them particularly susceptible to abuses of quality. In one sense the members of such a plan are "captives" (of the plan, not necessarily of particular doctors), and the very features that eliminate the abuses of overservicing and overcharging tend to encourage other forms of the problems. The physicians as individuals are insulated from economic pressures to render service that satisfies the patient in convenience, quantity, or quality. Professional ethics must bear the entire burden of enforcing standards. Probably no panel plan is ever without a minority of patients who complain about "assembly-line" medicine, waiting for service, hasty and perfunctory treatment, inaccessibility of preferred physicians, and inadequate concern for patient welfare. Although these problems exist in solo practice as well, they are probably present in accentuated form in panel plans.

This situation has led many organized groups, particularly labor unions, to ask for some form of "consumer control" over panel-plan administration. In general, this is an attempt to impose on the medical staff some type of administrative control directly responsive to the consumer-members of the plan as a supplement to professional self-discipline. As a minimum this involves seeking a voice in scheduling hours of operation, setting work loads, and investigating of complaints. It may also mean an attempt to participate in allocating the income of the plan, including a part in setting the remuneration of physicians and plan executives. The success of member organizations in achieving this kind of control has varied from plan to plan. In some of the larger plans, including the Kaiser Plan, the consumer representatives have achieved little or no success. Particularly when the physician-members are dependent on the plan for all or the great bulk of their income, they are chary of lay participation in fundamental decisions. Some prominent examples of "unenlightened" personnel policy of unions in their role as employers have undoubtedly reinforced this reluctance.[29]

---

[29] Examples are the labor problems of the AFL-CIO with its organizers and the attempts of the Teamsters Union to prevent its office employees from joining unions of office workers in some areas.

At the present time, the competition of other forms of medical care, combined with professional self-discipline, is the best protection against abuse of all types in the various systems of organization.

Conclusions

It would be desirable at this point to make a firm estimate as to the financial magnitude of the losses stemming from all forms of abuse of indemnity health plans. However, the fragmentary nature of the evidence available, its ambiguous character, and its dependence on the special circumstances of different health programs and methods of investigation, make any estimate little more than guess-work. But it does seem both possible and helpful to try to set some limits within which, on the average, the correct figure for costs of abuse would fall.

At any point in time, the figure certainly is greater than zero and almost certainly less than 100 per cent of the medically justified cost of providing benefits. In the best of possible worlds, it probably cannot be reduced below somewhere between 5 and 10 per cent of the true benefit costs. A little more tentatively, there seems to be little reason to believe that, in the usual case, abuse increases costs as much as 50 per cent. Narrowing the range from the 10 to 50 per cent bracket greatly increases the chance of error and the likelihood of differences of opinion. As a tentative conclusion, it is suggested that the abuse figure for the average plan at any point in time probably falls between 15 and 30 per cent of the true medical costs that would be appropriate to the plan. We need to remember that no insurance system—governmental or private—can eliminate all questionable benefit payments except at an administrative cost that might exceed the costs of accepting the inevitability of some abuse. This would indicate that benefit costs might possibly be reduced from 10 to 20 per cent if all forms of abuse were reduced to the practicable minimum.

More important than a quantitative estimate of the magnitude of abuse is the conclusion that stems from consideration of the impressive variety of potential abuses that have been detailed in this chapter. Considering only broad categories and without exhausting all the possibilities, we have discussed unnecessary admissions to hospitals, prolonged stays in hospitals, fraudulent claims, excessive fees, unnecessary surgery, and excessive services, both in and out of the hospital. The implication inherent in this review of the scope and complexity of potential abuses is that any system of control must be comprehensive and must touch on all aspects of medical practice if it is to be effective. Steps toward implementing a satisfactory system of control have been taken but progress has not been remarkable for its speed. It is debatable whether the medical profession alone is both able and willing to accept the responsibility of devising and operating a control system that will be medically and politically acceptable. The drive of various organized groups, particularly labor union groups, for "consumer representation" in various strategic areas of medical practice (e.g. hospitals) and in the "nonprofit" insurance plans arises from a recognition of the complexity of the over-all problem. In a later chapter, we shall review the efforts of the labor movement in the San Francisco Bay Area to take a first step toward participation in the control system—joint agreement on schedules of fees.

It might be wondered whether pressures that might result in the revolutionizing of medical practice are justified in the light of the estimated figure of 10 to 20 per cent of improvement in the control of abuse cited above. This view is an oversimplification of the problem for at least two reasons. First, the tentative estimate in this section was made in the light of existing methods of medical practice, the existing range of insurance benefits, and the existing system of payment. If these assumptions were abandoned and the basic system of predominantly solo practice, limited benefits, and fee-for-service payment with fees set unilaterally by individual doctors were changed, the context of the discussion would be completely altered. Second, even if major modifications of medical practice are ruled out, the estimates in this section were carefully described as applicable "at any point in time." The importance of this qualification comes from the relative character of many forms of abuse. With the widespread coverage of health insurance and in the absence of an effective control system, the existence of the insurance almost certainly exercises a subtle but pervasive influence on the standards of accepted prices and accepted practices. Abuse is difficult to define at best and in many cases its identification involves comparisons with customary practice. Over time, these standards are themselves influenced (not entirely for the worse) by the existence of insurance and the definition of abuse is subject to a kind of erosion. The existence of this kind of long-run effect helps to make some control necessary.

Chapter V | Factors Influencing Health Plans in California and the Bay Area

In Edward Bellamy's *Looking Backward, 2000–1887*, there is the following remarkable prediction of medical practice as it might exist more than a hundred years after the time the book was written.

"When you want a doctor," I asked, "do you simply apply to the proper bureau and take any one that may be sent?"

"That rule would not work well in the case of physicians," replied Dr. Leete. "The good a physician can do a patient depends largely on his acquaintance with his constitutional tendencies and condition. The patient must be able, therefore, to call in a particular doctor, and he does so just as patients did in your day. The only difference is that, instead of collecting his fee for himself, the doctor collects it for the nation by pricking off the amount, according to a regular scale for medical attendance, from the patient's credit card."

With some four decades yet to elapse before the effective date of Bellamy's forecast, the system he described some seventy years ago may yet be placed in operation. His work is not quoted here as a possible model of a national health system, however, but to illustrate that some of the current issues in the organization and financing of medical care have a long history in the United States. Serious proposals to meet the problems noted in the excerpt have been advanced over the past several decades. Prior to the 1930's the issue was joined over the question of the role of government—

federal and state—in the medical care system. With the introduction of nongovernmental health insurance in the 1930's the possibility of a further set of alternatives was introduced. The early forms of the health insurance movement were attempts to provide a noncompulsory system of insurance, sponsored by the hospital industry and the medical profession, as a substitute for governmental action. These programs resembled the governmental proposals with which they were competitive in their benefit structure and their financial mechanisms. In the 1940's commercial insurance companies entered the field on a large scale with a somewhat different approach. Also in the 1940's a number of large-scale experiments in group practice were launched which attempted to go beyond the financial problems of the medical consumer to change the organizational structure of medical practice.

When the negotiated health plans were started in the 1940's, they began operating in an environment that included the long-standing agitation for a governmental health system, a large medically sponsored program of private health insurance, a flourishing commercial insurance variation of the private system, and, in some areas, one or more of the controversial "independent" plans offering a quite different medical care system. The reactions of the trustees of the welfare funds varied. Faced with the problems of abuse noted in the last chapter, some of them tried to manipulate the competitive systems of protection so as to maximize the medical benefits available to their members. For the success of their operations, they were dependent on the strategic leverage generated by their place in the market structure as outlined in chapter ii.

In California a full complement of the competing medical care systems was available by 1946. Compulsory health insurance at the state level had been a serious political issue for more than a decade. It enjoyed the very active support of Governor Earl Warren, a political leader of formidable stature. Blue Cross organizations were active in both northern and southern California and the state Blue Shield plan, California Physicians Service, had been in operation since 1939 as the first state-wide, profession-sponsored medical insurance plan. The Kaiser Foundation Health Plan, one of the largest independent plans in the nation, was opened to the public in 1946 and was operating in the San Francisco and the Los Angeles areas.

An understanding of the position of the negotiated plans in 1949 and the early 1950's requires a knowledge of the background of the more important organizations and movements peculiar to California and the Bay Area. In this chapter some of the most important features of the medical scene will be described and their interrelations traced. In no case is there an intention to give the complete historical background of the growth of a particular institution. Those features that are necessary to explain the development of the health insurance movement prior to the inauguration of large-scale union-management programs in 1949 will be stressed. The situation as it existed at that date in the San Francisco Bay Area will be the bench mark from which later discussion will proceed.

Compulsory Health Insurance in California

No discussion of developments in voluntary health insurance can ignore the role played by the long-standing campaign for a governmentally sponsored compulsory health system.[1] In addition to the well-known proposals for national health insurance, the medical profession in California has had to contend with a series of home-grown state plans which have rivaled the national program in local importance and more or less paralleled it in timing. Two state commissions endorsed the principles of state compulsory health insurance in 1917 and 1919 at the time of the first wave of serious interest in the subject. During the prosperous twenties activity in the field died out, but was renewed with the advent of the Great Depression. By 1934 a number of surveys and legislative committee studies of the cost and distribution of medical care were under way in California. The most ambitious of these was the California Medical-Economic Survey, a research project financed jointly by the California Medical Association (CMA) and the federal and state governments at a combined cost of al-

---

[1] Material for this section was taken primarily from M. M. Davis, *Medical Care for Tomorrow* (New York: Harper, 1955), pp. 219, 274, 368–369; Don Jensen, "The Development of the Health Insurance Movement in California," unpublished M.A. thesis, University of California, 1939; and "Health Insurance, the C.M.A. and the Governor," *California Medicine*, April, 1950, pp. 256–8.

most $100,000. In January, 1935, the CMA received a preliminary report on the results of the survey which foreshadowed a recommendation for a system of compulsory health insurance. Financial support for the project was withdrawn by the CMA but a final report was completed by the staff and submitted in October, 1936. After considerable delay the report was released to the public in a form that drew the fire of survey director Professor Paul Dodd of the University of California, Los Angeles as having been drastically edited and with many of the conclusions and recommendations omitted. Following a bitter controversy, the original version of the completed report was published independently in 1939.[2] Included was a recommendation for a system of compulsory health insurance.

Legislative proposals did not wait on the report of the survey. A State Senate committee, working on a bill for introduction in the 1935 Legislature, approached the CMA for assistance and endorsement on the grounds that such legislation was "inevitable." At a special two-day meeting in March, 1935, the House of Delegates, the governing body of the CMA, endorsed the compulsory approach "for certain population groups" and appointed a special committee to assist the Senate committee in drafting a compulsory health insurance bill. Voting on the resolution endorsing the proposal was close and the minority report was later described by the CMA journal as having "sounded the beginnings of a voluntary health insurance plan . . . which flowered four years later into California Physicians Service." The bill resulting from this sequence of events was unpopular with all concerned, including the proponents of compulsory insurance. A "spontaneous" organization of doctors rallied opposition to the bill within the CMA to such effect that at the 1936 meeting of the House of Delegates two of the backers of the original resolution publicly recanted their position. Other supporters of the endorsement were reported as having been retired from office by their constituent medical societies. Thus ended the revolt of what a national medical publication described at the time as "Our Rebel West."

In 1939 Governor Culbert Olson, whose administration (1938–

[2] P. A. Dodd and E. F. Penrose, *Economic Aspects of Medical Services* (Washington: Graphic Arts Press, 1939). Describing the earlier version as "completely censored," Dodd and Penrose stated that ". . . It represented an open breach of promise and commitments," p. 272.

1942) has been called California's New Deal and who represented the first break in a half century of Republican executive control, introduced a new health bill. By this time the CMA had ready at hand the profession's own voluntary plan, California Physicians Service (CPS). Launched in February, 1939, and a center of in-tramural controversy at regular intervals since, CPS has been the vehicle through which the medical profession has sought to dem-onstrate the absence of a need for compulsory insurance and to influence the development of commercial health insurance. Mem-bership in CPS was originally limited to persons with an annual income of $3,000 or less. This group was offered fairly comprehen-sive coverage on a service basis with relatively low premiums.[3]

Backers of compulsory health insurance had argued that the low-income worker would not or could not purchase health insur-ance on a voluntary basis. In line with this reasoning, both the 1935 health insurance proposal and Governor Olson's 1939 bill had provided for compulsory inclusion of workers with less than $3,000 annual income in the plan.[4] CPS was designed to provide the voluntary equivalent of the compulsory state system at mini-mum cost while retaining physician control of the system.

Failure of the Olson program in the legislature did not end the threat from the governor's office. Olson was replaced in 1942 by Earl Warren who was to introduce a succession of compulsory insurance measures during his eleven years in office. In contrast

---

[3] A note on definitions: A health plan is usually described as comprehensive in coverage if it includes home and office visits, laboratory procedures for treat-ment and diagnosis outside the hospital, maternity care, and some elements of "preventive" medicine such as physical examinations, in addition to the more usual hospital, surgical and in-hospital medical benefits. CPS originally included all home and office visits and physical examinations.

A service plan provides its subscribers with benefits described in terms of the service or treatment required. This is in contrast to the indemnity plan which provides cash payments for specified procedures and services. Payments may be more or less (usually less) than the actual cost of securing the service.

[4] The Olson proposals provided for full coverage of hospital and medical care for the families of persons covered by the Unemployment Insurance Act who were earning less than $3,000 annually. Free choice of physician was to be provided with the doctors being remunerated on a capitation basis (a fixed sum per patient on each doctor's "panel"). Financing was to be by employer, employee, and state contributions.

The later Warren bills differed in that coverage was extended to governmental employees at all levels, income limitations were dropped, financing was to be based only on employer and employee contributions and the doctors were to be paid on a fee-for-service basis according to a schedule to be fixed by the ad-ministrators of the system.

to the earlier versions, coverage was broadened and the income limitation was dropped. Warren-sponsored bills were introduced in 1945, 1947, and 1949 but in each case they were blocked in committee and did not get to the floor of the legislature. The seriousness of the situation faced by the doctors was pointed up by an attempt to force one of the bills out of committee which was lost by a vote of 39–38. Only 41 votes were needed for an absolute majority of the Assembly. Although Governor Warren had been reported by medical representatives as saying, "California will have a system of state prepaid medical care insurance before I leave office as governor . . . ," no such system existed when he moved from Sacramento to the United States Supreme Court at the end of 1953. His successor, Goodwin J. Knight, made occasional references to health insurance but formulated no specific proposals. The CMA interpretation of his attitude may be inferred from a remark in the journal of the association on his assumption of office, "The change is certainly welcome. . . ." [5]

In this brief review attention has been limited to bills enjoying active administration support. Throughout the entire period under discussion the California branches of both major labor federations existing at that time as well as a variety of other groups consistently advocated passage of a compulsory health bill and advanced legislative proposals to this end. Against all of these efforts the medical profession argued that the need could be met and was being met by a system of voluntary health insurance. While the comparative legislative calm of the past several years is in part the result of the relatively conservative temper of the times, it is also due to the experiment in voluntary health insurance currently being conducted on a massive scale. Over 1,100,000 workers, representing an estimated 85 per cent of those covered by collective-bargaining contracts in California, were enrolled in negotiated health insurance plans in the spring of 1956. As early as 1951 it had been estimated that over five and a quarter million persons making up about 50 per cent of the total population of the state were covered by some form of health insurance.[6]

---

[5] *California Medicine*, Vol. 79, No. 6, December, 1953, p. 455.

[6] Figures for collective-bargaining coverage are from California Department of Industrial Relations, *California Industrial Relations Reports*, San Francisco, March, 1956, p. 3. The estimate for the total population is from the President's Commission on the Health Needs of the Nation, *Building America's Health* (Washington: 1954), Vol. IV, p. 336.

Unless the present voluntary program continues to expand in scope and in coverage and unless a fairly high level of member satisfaction is maintained, the compulsory health insurance movement is unlikely to be held at bay. The five bills vigorously backed by the governors of the state in the fourteen years from 1935 to 1949 testify to the political strength of the concept. Realization of this fact helps to explain the very considerable efforts the medical profession has made and currently is making to adjust to the demands of the present situation. With the election of the second Democratic governor of the twentieth century in 1958 and with the state legislature under Democratic control for the first time in an even longer period, this issue may again become of major importance.

The Kaiser Foundation Health Plan

The Kaiser Foundation Health Plan[7] is a system of prepaid medical care offering comprehensive coverage on a service basis. It operates in the San Francisco Bay Area, the Los Angeles area, and on a limited scale in Portland, Oregon, and Vancouver, Washington. As of January, 1956, the plan had a total of 511,000 members; 302,000 were in the Bay Area, 186,000 in southern California, and the remainder in the Portland–Vancouver area. Unless otherwise noted, in the discussion to follow attention is centered on and figures are quoted for the Bay Area, where the plan was founded in its present form and activities are still centered. In this region the plan utilized the services of slightly over three hundred physicians as of January, 1956, and operated five hospitals and eleven

---

[7] Basic data for this section were secured from *Available Health Plans and Group Insurance*, Hearings before the Committee on Interstate and Foreign Commerce, House of Representatives, 83rd Congress, 2nd session, 1954, Part 6, pp. 1134–1450; and *Plan for Health*, the monthly bulletin of the Kaiser Foundation Health Plan, issues of December, 1955, January, 1956, and November–December, 1957.

Structurally, the Kaiser organization involves four separate entities; Kaiser Foundation, a charitable trust providing facilities and funds for teaching, research, and charity; Kaiser Foundation Health Plan, a nonprofit trust which enrolls members, collects dues, maintains records, and contracts for hospital service and medical care from (1) Kaiser Foundation Hospitals, a nonprofit corporation operating the hospitals and medical centers, and (2) Permanente Medical Groups, the physician members of the plan, organized as independent doctor-partnerships. Detailed information on the internal organization of the plan can be secured from the transcript of the congressional hearings cited above. In this study the term Kaiser Plan will be used to refer to the whole complex of organizations. (Until 1953 the name "Permanente" was used rather than "Kaiser.")

outpatient centers. The background of the plan is an interesting chapter in medical economics.

In the United States it has been a common practice for employers in isolated areas of the country to assume responsibility for the medical needs of their employees. Industries in which this pattern has existed include mining, construction, lumbering, and the railroads. In the 1930's the Henry J. Kaiser enterprises followed this practice on a number of construction projects in the western states, utilizing the services of Dr. Sidney Garfield as administrator. From what was at first the treatment of industrial injuries of the employee, a system of comprehensive medical care financed on a prepaid basis and including the dependents of the worker has gradually evolved.

During World War II the Kaiser management operated a large shipyard at Richmond, at the beginning of the war a town of modest size located on the east shore of San Francisco Bay. The shipyard drew a flood of workers into the area from all parts of the country. At the peak of activity the yard employed over 80,000 workers, many of them lodged in temporary war housing in and around Richmond. Although Richmond was part of the San Francisco–Oakland metropolitan complex, Kaiser decided to utilize the medical care pattern developed on the construction projects in this new setting.

A hospital was purchased in Oakland and a prepaid medical care plan was inaugurated under the direction of Dr. Garfield. Membership was limited to workers at the shipyard. With dues of fifty cents a week the plan built up to a peak membership of more than 70,000 workers in 1944, accounting for a very high percentage of the labor force at the yards.

As the war drew to a close, employment at the shipyard dwindled rapidly. With the eventual total abandonment of the yard in prospect, the question arose as to the fate of the health plan and the Oakland hospital. Since many former employees remained in the area there was some pressure from this source to continue the plan. In July, 1945, with membership down to about 15,000, the plan was thrown open to the general public with the intention of continuing it on a long-run basis. From this point, the plan began a steady and rapid growth, reaching a membership of approximately 60,000 by the spring of 1949. This date coincided with the introduction of negotiated health plans on a wide scale.

In the subsequent rise of Bay Area membership to 310,000 at the end of 1957 the growth of negotiated health plans played an important but not the major role. In addition to the fundamental fact that the Kaiser Plan satisfies an important segment of medical demand, the mushrooming growth since 1949 is primarily the result of a major expansion of hospital and medical center facilities in both northern and southern California. In the Kaiser system of operation the member not only must secure his medical care from a doctor who is a member of the plan (the characteristic feature of the "closed panel" plan), but he must also be hospitalized in a plan hospital. Though on occasion the plan has leased hospital accommodations, in general, expansion of the membership in a given geographical area or entrance into a new area depends on the acquisition of hospital as well as outpatient facilities. Both the CMA and Mr. Henry J. Kaiser agree that the problem of financing facilities is the major obstacle to further important expansion in membership.[8]

Medical benefits under the Kaiser Plan are on a service basis and are comprehensive enough to cover an estimated 85 to 90 per cent of all the medical expenses of the member who uses the services to which he is entitled. The "standard group coverage" includes doctors' care in the home, office, and hospital, all surgery, 111 days of full hospitalization including drugs, physical therapy, maternity benefits, allergy and pediatric service, physical and eye examinations, and X-ray and laboratory services. Major exclusions are mental disease, tuberculosis, and contagious disease requiring special facilities. Kaiser uses a system of extra charges and "inci-

---

[8] "The demands for this comprehensive type of medical, surgical and hospital coverage far outstrip the speed with which facilities can be financed and built." Testimony of Henry J. Kaiser, *Available Health Plans* . . . , p. 1344. Mr. Kaiser testified that in "several cases" membership in the plan had been closed (p. 1370). At the time of his testimony (January, 1954) the Kaiser Foundation was completing a $10 million construction program, $5.5 million of this amount being financed by private borrowing.

President Arlo A. Morrison, speaking before the CMA House of Delegates, said, "The competitive position of C.P.S.-Blue Shield as it relates to closed panel groups (especially the Kaiser Health Foundation) is largely dependent upon the funds available for the expansion of facilities." *California Medicine,* June, 1955, pp. 423–424.

dental fees" to control usage and provide revenue. (Examples are the one dollar charge for each outpatient visit and the partial charges made for maternity service and the removal of tonsils and adenoids.) A charge of approximately one-half private rates is made for home calls. On the standard contract dependents receive essentially the same range of services but must pay more and larger extra charges.

In addition to the standard group coverage, Kaiser offers four other contracts. These are: an individual contract with benefits equivalent to the dependent coverage on the standard contract, a group contract in which dependents receive the same benefits as the subscriber, a group contract in which some incidental fees are eliminated, and a "supplemental" contract designed to convert the more usual commercial insurance or Blue Cross–Blue Shield contract into comprehensive coverage. At least the last two and possibly the last three types of contracts can be said to be a direct result of union-management health plan negotiations and will be discussed at some length at a later point.

This is not the place for a detailed review of the relationships between the Kaiser Foundation Health Plan and the organized medical profession in California. Although the character of the relationship differs among the various medical associations involved and with the same associations over time, the range of variation is quite small, running from active hostility to an armed neutrality. Gaining admission to the county medical societies has been a continuing problem for Kaiser doctors. Since the foundation operates its own hospitals, however, this has eliminated a major disability often attached to nonmembership, exclusion from hospital staff privileges.

The basic element in the opposition of organized medicine is the economic competition of a group-practice arrangement coupled with its own prepayment plan. In combination these techniques threaten the existing system of medical practice. This problem is magnified in the Kaiser case because the original impetus for the plan came from an industrial organization proud of innovations in production techniques in shipbuilding and which was headed by a man who proposes his health plan as a general pattern for the "new economics of medicine." In addition, premium charges in the past have been kept at relatively low levels.[9]

From the standpoint of medical economics, the linkage of group practice and a prepayment plan has the effect of narrowing the market for medical care in which the individual practitioner sells his services. A decision to take advantage of the insurance mechanism to prepay your medical bills is at the same time a decision as to identity of the supplier of the service. This is true since a typical condition of this type of prepayment contract is that service be secured from a doctor in the group.[10]

In the case of the Kaiser Plan, an expansion of facilities is not staffed by doctors who already have successful practices established in the locality. Although some of the staff may be recruited from doctors who are practicing in the area or who otherwise would have entered practice in the area, on balance the entrance of the plan means a net addition to the total supply of medical services in the local market. Under these circumstances the established doctors see every person who joins the Kaiser Plan as a potential or actual patient who is lost to them for the duration of his membership. Even if all the Kaiser staff were recruited from men with local practices, the remaining independent practitioners would resent their former associates competing through the medium of a group-practice prepayment plan particularly when it offered benefits on the service basis. Kaiser's impact on medical practice in a specific community is described in chapter viii in

---

[9] Throughout its life Kaiser Plan premiums for comprehensive coverage have been roughly comparable to the rates for the most limited coverage of the alternative programs available in the area, most of which offer no assurance that additional charges of an unknown magnitude may not be made. At the end of 1957 charges were $5.50, $10.00, and $13.20 for family units of one, two, and three or more. (Standard group contract.)

[10] In theory there is no reason why a medical group could not sponsor a prepayment plan that permitted the subscriber to go outside the group for service and have a cash indemnity paid to him or to his doctor on his behalf. This is not the usual practice. It converts the integrated health plan into two segments, a medical group and an indemnity insurance company which contracts with the medical group for an unknown part of its business. This involves forecasting not only the total utilization of medical care by the plan members, but also the way in which the membership divides this care between the two parts of the plan. But see the CPS arrangement described in the next section for an approximation to this situation. A New York plan, Group Health Incorporated, has a variation of this system.

which the expansion of the Plan into Pittsburg, California, is described. Although the Pittsburg case is an extreme example, it illustrates a situation in which a minimum of one-third of the total medical demand of the community was diverted from independent practitioners to the Kaiser Plan almost overnight. Moreover, the score or so of doctors practicing in Pittsburg, a town with an estimated population of not more than 15,000 at the time, realized that the opening of an outpatient clinic, backed by the resources of a new seventy-bed hospital nearby, meant that Kaiser literally had the capacity to monopolize the medical business of the community.

It would be unjust to imply that medical opposition to the Kaiser operation is based entirely on economic self-interest. Many members of the profession are skeptical of the true independence of the physician-members of the Permanente medical groups because of lay administration, of the turnover of staff, the quality of some of the professional personnel, and the work-load and methods of operation of the Plan. The epithets of "corporate medicine" and "assembly-line methods" appear in discussion of the system. Suggestions have been made that the self-sustaining character of the hospital operation—bank-financing for hospital construction is one of the plan's accomplishments—is possible partly because the professional staff is "exploited" in terms of work-load and remuneration.[11]

In rebuttal, Kaiser states that doctor's incomes are comparable with those of like training and experience in private practice, that the ratio of physicians to membership ranges from one to 1,000 to one to 1,300, ratios regarded as acceptable for sizable groups, and

---

[11] In the past decade the journals and bulletins of the state and county medical societies have published dozens of discussions and statements of opinion on the Kaiser Plan. One of the most thorough can be found in an editorial in *California Medicine*, June, 1953, pp. 66–67. The editorial states that "There are at least 35 former Permanente doctors now in private practice in the East Bay area alone." Although the Kaiser Plan does not release turnover data, Mr. Kaiser testified in January, 1954, that it was "comparatively small" and Dr. Garfield reported that only one partner had left the organization. (*Available Health Plans* . . . , p. 1372.)

To acquire partnership status "from the ranks" requires two years on salary and two years as a junior partner. The proportion of full partners to total staff is not available. Salary for "a new man coming out of medical school" was quoted as "in the vicinity of $900 a month." (*ibid.*, p. 1376) Partners were reported as earning as much as $35,000 a year net income (*ibid.*, p. 1373). In 1953 the medical groups received 40.7 per cent of the premium dollar for professional services (*ibid.*, p. 1359).

that group practice permits higher quality of care at greater convenience and economy to the doctor and the patient. It is claimed that the integrated health plan approach permits comprehensive coverage without sacrificing professional independence and that the integration of medical and hospital care permits more efficient hospital and medical center operation.

Much of the battle against closed-panel groups such as the Kaiser Plan has been carried on under the slogan of "free choice of doctor." This phrase simultaneously emphasizes a major weakness of the closed-panel system and the concern of the independent physician with access to the medical market of the community. Panel groups respond that the choice of the group as a whole is a valid exercise of free choice on the part of the patient. This argument has been effective enough to cause a shift in medical society emphasis from the initial exercise of the right of free choice to the right of a dissatisfied patient to change his choice. On this score the closed-panel prepayment plan is vulnerable since a member who is dissatisfied with the treatment of an existing ailment and goes outside the panel for treatment loses the benefit of his insurance. The medical societies have attempted to estimate the magnitude of this practice in connection with the Kaiser Plan through a survey of their members, but have never released the results.[12]

As a practical matter, most of the questions at issue between the medical societies and the Kaiser Plan depend on intangible elements which cannot be measured statistically. Since the burst of Kaiser expansion in late 1953 and early 1954 when the Walnut Creek and San Francisco hospitals were opened, relationships have taken on the character of a sort of "competitive coexistence." Beneficiaries of the competition have been the consumers of medical care as Kaiser has improved its services and the medical service organizations have broadened coverage, raised income ceilings, and developed more flexible programs without any observable deterioration of either the economic or professional standards of the medical profession. Uneasiness as to the future is more pronounced along the frontiers of Kaiser's service area as the doctors in local communities brace themselves for the next wave of expansion. Even here the profession is coming to realize that expan-

---

[12] Some fragmentary data on this problem are presented in chapter ix below.

sion is not the deadly blight on their practice it may appear to be at first impact. It is difficult to imagine a more severe blow than that suffered by the medical community of Pittsburg in 1953, but the 1953–1954 directory of the county medical society revealed more physicians in private practice than were listed in the 1952 directory.

The present state of apparent equilibrium depends on a number of factors, any one of which may change on short notice.

1. To this time Kaiser expansion has been extensive rather than intensive, that is, growth has come principally through opening up new geographical territory rather than through the enrollment of a rapidly increasing percentage of the population in a given area. Whether this is an inherent characteristic of the Kaiser operation, a deliberate policy decision on the part of Kaiser, or simply the result of circumstances is an important unanswered question. In no community does Kaiser have more than slightly over one-fifth of the population enrolled.

2. Expansion has occurred in a time period and in a geographical area marked by a rapidly increasing population, enjoying high and rising levels of income and willing to devote a substantial portion of that income to improving their standards of medical care.

3. Developments of the past several years in commercial indemnity insurance, the medical service organizations, and the medical profession have had the effect of increasing the attractiveness of the insurance programs offered by other agencies relative to the Kaiser program. The comprehensive character of Kaiser coverage and the "certainty of coverage" element have been two of the Health Plan's major advantages in the past. With broadened benefits, higher income ceilings, and the beginnings of effective medical society influence over fee charges, the differential advantage of the Kaiser Plan in these respects has been narrowing.

The term certainty of coverage refers to advance assurance that the patient will have all or a *major and predictable* part of his medical and hospital bills covered by his insurance benefits. Comprehensive health plans providing service benefits afford this assurance by definition. In order for cash indemnity plans to approach this status, the indemnity schedule must be closely related to community medical costs and fees must not be influenced by the availability of insurance payments.

It is in connection with the broadening of benefits that the negotiated health and welfare plans have had their impact. Leaders in the drive for certainty of coverage and comprehensive benefits, the unions have been able to make their bargaining position felt both within the Kaiser organization and in relation to the medical profession through their ability to influence, if not control, the disposition of their health and welfare money. Prior to the rapid growth of negotiated plans, about the most a health insurance plan or insurance company could hope for as a result of sponsorship by either employers or unions was the privilege of a payroll deduction or other assistance in the collection of premiums for members enrolling voluntarily and usually at their own expense. With the advent of bargained health plans, central bodies were created that collected regular payments on behalf of the great majority of the labor force and contracted with specific health plans for the business of the union members. Since the first requisite of bargaining strength is the existence of alternative courses of action, the unions' attempts to secure broader benefits and certainty of coverage from the insurance company programs and the medical service organizations were greatly aided by the existence of a competitive health plan (Kaiser) that included these features. Although at the end of 1956 no more than about 10 per cent of the total membership of negotiated health and welfare systems was enrolled in the Kaiser Plan, the possibility of other transfers was an ever-present threat to the complacency of rival plans.

So far as the Kaiser Plan was concerned, the approximately 10 per cent of total collective-bargaining coverage enrolled accounted for more than about one-fifth of the total membership. More important, approximately 80 per cent of that number or one-sixth of their entire membership in the Bay Area was drawn from two union groups.

The pattern of events which evolved as labor unions in the Bay Area attempted to improve their position in the health insurance field utilizing the Kaiser Foundation Health Plan as one vehicle of change forms the subject matter of chapter vii.

CPS—Background and Problems

A review of the evolution of the California Physicians Service[13] from its founding in 1939 is essential to an understanding of the reaction of the medical profession in the Bay Area to the pressures generated by the introduction of collective bargaining into the health and welfare sector. The purpose of this review is twofold: (1) to trace the interplay of conflicting philosophies about the profession's role in the financing of medical care as reflected in differences about CPS policies; and (2) to provide the groundwork for analyzing the way in which the resolution of these differences has been affected by external pressures, particularly those from labor and management.

In addition to accomplishing these main objectives the material to be covered will help to explain why California is one of the minority of areas in which Blue Cross, the hospital insurance organization, and Blue Shield, the physicians' medical service organization, are competitive rather than complementary to one another. The California Blue Cross plans and CPS are not entirely divorced from one another. Coöperation is still maintained in certain joint programs of Blue Cross hospitalization coverage and Blue Shield medical and surgical coverage arranged at the national headquarters of company and union for all U. S. employees, including those in California plants. However, with these exceptions the organizations go their own way. The Blue Cross systems offer not only the usual hospital insurance but also a complete indemnity-type medical and surgical insurance; CPS offers complete hospitalization coverage as well as the customary medical and surgical benefits.

The record of the development of CPS demands intensive scrutiny because it is in the area of medical and surgical services that the major problems in health and welfare programs arise. The Blue Cross organizations have their own internal problems and have been the focus of consumer complaints about inflation of costs. In general, however, the difficulties of the medical profession in charting its own course and in its relations with outside

---

[13] Material in this section is drawn from *California Medicine* (known as *California and Western Medicine* prior to July, 1946), the bulletins of the San Francisco Medical Society and the Alameda-Contra Costa Medical Association, and information furnished by officials of Blue Cross and CPS in the area.

groups have been more severe. Except for the ever-present problem of cost inflation, the organizational pattern of the hospitalization portion of health insurance has been stabilized in a form relatively satisfactory to both the hospitals and most of the consumers of their services. For physicians' services, on the other hand, the scope of coverage has been less satisfactory and the question of the exact organizational form which best meets the desires of the profession and the public has not been settled. As this survey will bring out, the CPS program in its original 1939 version was closer in many ways to the pattern desired by the union welfare spokesmen than is its present form. Responding to pressures from inside the medical profession during the next decade, the trend in CPS policies was toward a system of more limited coverage that was less desirable from the union point of view. In the fifties the profession has been forced to modify its position again in attempts to compromise the conflicts within its own ranks and with organized consumers. The positions of the parties to these compromises can best be understood in the light of their experiences in the hectic early years of experimentation with health insurance plans.

Development of Blue Cross and CPS

As is generally known, hospital insurance plans sponsored by individual hospitals and groups of hospitals were developed prior to the medical service plans and have become widely known as Blue Cross plans. Local plans of this type first made their appearance during the depression years of the early 1930's as a response to the dual problems of protecting the patient from major hospital expenses and of providing the hospitals with a reliable source of income. As originally developed, the plans provided hospitalization on a service rather than an indemnity basis and, while some of the plans have adopted an indemnification system, most retain their service benefit character. The Blue Cross organization itself is a network of these local and regional plans with the affiliated units retaining much of their autonomy and their corporate identity. The national organization establishes minimum standards for membership for the component associations, sets up requirements for the use of the Blue Cross symbol, and, most important, furnishes the vehicle for the geographical coördination of the separate plans and consequent interchange of service between plans. Services are provided through contracts with local hospitals; a high percentage of all American hospitals are affiliated with their local organization. Blue Cross has occasionally been referred to as the fastest growing voluntary movement in the country. Whether this characterization is accurate or not, the growth has been very rapid. Nationally, membership numbered about fifty million at the end of 1956.

In California, Blue Cross services are currently provided through two organizations, Hospital Service of California, (for the northern part of the state) and Hospital Service of Southern California. Throughout this study, unless otherwise noted, the term Blue Cross is used to refer to Hospital Service of California, the Blue Cross plan operating in the Bay Area.

Blue Cross began writing contracts in 1936 after several years of exploratory investigation. The initial impetus for the organization came from the Alameda County Medical Society which also furnished a major portion of the required financing for the plan. Originally operating only in Alameda County, the plan spread throughout all the counties of northern California. At the beginning of 1956 the total membership was approximately 635,000.

Within a few years medical societies in other parts of the country began to experiment with similar types of organizations for the provision of medical and surgical services. The local medical societies constituted themselves an organizational base for the writing of this coverage in order to have a program available that would be under physician control. Under the leadership of Dr. Ray Lyman Wilbur, who had been chairman of the pathbreaking national Committee on the Costs of Medical Care which functioned in the late twenties and early thirties, the California Medical Association organized the California Physicians Service, incorporating it in February, 1939. Although it was stressed that CPS was the first state-wide, physician-sponsored medical plan, the experience of a system operated in King County in the state of Washington was acknowledged as influential in devising the service.[14] As state and local medical societies across the nation

---

[14] County medical societies in Washington and Oregon pioneered this development as a result of a provision of the Workmen's Compensation Acts in those states. Employers were permitted to use compensation funds to contract directly

continued to establish such plans, the need for a national organization similar to the Blue Cross Commission became evident. In 1943 the American Medical Association announced a decision to form such a group and the Blue Shield Commission came into being. As in Blue Cross the local plans retained their identity and autonomy. The national group set minimum standards and acted as a coördinating body.

Total membership in CPS has fluctuated for reasons that will be explained later. The high point was reached in 1951 when membership exceeded one million. At the beginning of 1956 state membership stood at just over 700,000. Since this number was split almost equally between northern and southern California, it can be seen that northern California CPS membership was about 60 per cent of Blue Cross membership in the mid-fifties. Unlike the pattern in most other states, in California relatively few CPS members are also members of the Blue Cross.

Physician membership in CPS has always been on a voluntary basis for the individual doctor. It is difficult to be precise as to the exact percentage of California's practicing physicians who are members at any given time because of the difficulty of arriving at a firm figure for the number of doctors actually in private practice. It is safe to say, however, that a substantial majority of such physicians have been members throughout the plan's lifetime, with an estimated 90 per cent total for 1956. Total physician membership has grown from about 5,000 in 1939 to about 12,500 in 1956. Professional membership in CPS is not dependent on membership in the California Medical Association or a county society but is open to any licensed physician. Since 1946 the consumer member may also claim benefits from CPS for treatment by doctors (including doctors of osteopathy) who are not members of CPS.

In its early years CPS was governed by a Board of Trustees who were elected by some seventy-five "administrative members" who were in turn chosen by vote of the physician-members of the plan. Administrative members were not limited to medical doctors and have included several prominent nonprofessionals. At least one nonmedical man served on the Board of Trustees. In 1944 the

---

with the suppliers of medical care for services. To protect the traditional method of practice, county societies organized to provide these services and expanded into the area of general prepayment.

arrangements were changed and it was provided that the House of Delegates, the governing body of the California Medical Association, would also constitute the administrative members of the CPS. Lay administrative members-at-large were retained but they are now elected by the other administrative members of the House of Delegates. Insofar as this change has had any practical effect it has made CPS more directly responsive to CMA policies.[15]

As noted earlier, the content of the CPS program as well as its very existence was directly influenced by the compulsory health insurance bills introduced in the state legislature. As did the 1935 and 1939 legislative proposals, CPS concentrated on that portion of the population of California with family incomes of $3,000 or less as of 1939. Census data indicated that more than 90 per cent of all California families had incomes of less than $3,000 in 1939. For this group CPS offered a service benefit plan of broad scope. The plan covered ". . . Complete medical, surgical and hospital care for all illnesses and accidents, with a few specific exemptions such as mental cases, drug or alcoholic addiction, pre-existing ailments or results of lawless acts, at $2.50 a month. . . ." Also included were X-ray and other laboratory services as well as physical and premarital examinations.[16] This coverage was intended to be competitive with the proposed state system's plan for "complete" medical care as far as the employee was concerned. Dependent coverage was to be more limited and at extra cost.

For several years CPS operated in the national pattern as the companion plan to Blue Cross. Although CPS was organizationally independent of Blue Cross, it utilized the selling organization of the latter group and each of the two plans operated exclusively in its own medical jurisdiction. Difficulties soon arose, however, in part though not exclusively as a result of the disappointing financial results of the early years of CPS operation.

The Unit Value System

At the time of the organization of the CPS, the actuarial aspects of health insurance were unknown. The necessity of offering a

---

[15] Data on the original plan of control were secured from *California and Western Medicine*, April, 1939, pp. 289–294, 329–330; and on the 1944 changes, *ibid.*, June, 1944, pp. 329–331.

[16] *California and Western Medicine*, June, 1939, p. 449. Eighty cents of the $2.50 premium was for hospitalization coverage by Blue Cross. An alternative plan which did not cover the first two doctor's visits was available for $2.00.

plan that could stand comparison with the compulsory health measures under consideration led to the adoption of an ambitious schedule of benefits. Under the circumstances it is hardly surprising that, financially speaking, CPS fared badly compared with the expectation of its sponsors.

In essence CPS was an undertaking to provide a wide range of medical services in quantities that could not be forecast with precision in return for a set monthly premium per member. Since the total income generated by a group of a given size during the term of the contract was a fixed figure, some method of dealing with the variable element in the plan, the quantity of service required, had to be devised.

Two main alternatives were available. CPS could have adopted a schedule that listed the dollar fees payable to its physician-members for each of the services involved and paid each doctor periodically for the services rendered to subscribers. Since the premium fixed in the contracts would be based on estimates as to the degree of utilization of the services—estimates that might very well be too low—some method of dealing with a potential excess of claims over income would have to be provided. A simple method of doing this would be to accumulate reserve funds sufficient to meet a drain of this kind until the time when premium rates could be adjusted upward, the scope of benefits reduced, or some other remedial action taken. Adoption of this plan would mean that the money for such a reserve would have to be collected, usually by setting premiums high enough so that they would not only cover the expected claims and administrative costs but would provide a surplus for the reserve.

A second method of dealing with the risk involved in agreeing to provide an unknown quantity of service for a known total sum would have been to pay the doctors according to a flexible fee schedule. Under the flexible fee schedule the dollar fees for the separate medical services would vary inversely with the total amount of services performed in any accounting period. In other words, in a month in which a large amount of service was rendered, the dollar fees per service would be low and vice versa. Under this plan no reserve would be needed since the doctors would assume the risk of loss by agreeing to reduce their claims against the system when necessary to keep income and outgo in balance.

CPS adopted the second alternative. A fee schedule was developed for the medical services to be provided by the plan. Fees in the schedule were not expressed in dollars but in "units," a kind of synthetic currency for accounting purposes. Physician-members would build up claims against CPS as they treated subscribers and claims would be calculated in units.[17] After the books were closed for each month the total number of units would be divided into the total amount of money available to pay claims and the resulting dollar figure would be the "unit value" for the month. Under the first alternative described above, the reserve balance introduced flexibility in the total amount of money available in any month. Under the second alternative the doctors provided the needed flexibility through the unit value fee system.

In its essentials the unit fee schedule is simply a ranking of the various medical services showing the value of each item compared to each of the other items. For example, a tonsillectomy was "worth" ten times as much as the first office visit; an appendectomy two and a half times as much as a tonsillectomy. Needless to say, however, in assigning the number of units to each service, the designers of the schedule had a particular set of dollar fees in mind as a goal. The CPS schedule was drawn up on the assumption that ". . . Ideally, the unit has a value of $2.50."

A very important feature of the CPS system was that the doctors agreed to accept the fees generated by the unit value method as full payment for care rendered to plan subscribers. It was this feature of the plan which gave it a "service" rather than an "indemnity" character.[18] From the consumer's point of view benefits

---

[17] Samples of the numbers of units assigned to services were: first office visit, 2 units; appendectomy, 50 units; tonsillectomy, 20 units.

[18] The reader is reminded that a service plan contracts to provide services to subscribers whereas an indemnity plan contracts to provide dollar benefits. Unfortunately, considerable confusion in terminology exists in much of the discussion of these topics. For example, writers often contrast the service principle with the "insurance" principle, when the reference should be to the "cash indemnity" principle. Service plans may be conducted on a basis of adherence to insurance principles.

It is sometimes assumed that a service plan requires the use of a unit value, capitation, or some other unorthodox method of payment for doctors. Present CPS practice demonstrates that this is not true since, to subscribers with incomes under the ceilings, CPS is a service plan, while to the doctors CPS now pays on a fee-for-service basis according to fee schedules expressed in dollars.

As a further point, service plans are not necessarily "comprehensive" in coverage (i.e., including outpatient medical care and laboratory procedures, and some

expressed as services are desirable since the patient is assured that his insurance will cover the cost of the medical care provided in the policy. With a cash payment he faces the possibility that the actual fee for service may exceed the benefit paid.

As will be noted below, the decision to operate a service rather than an indemnity system was an important one. The issue was not decided by default since the problem was considered by the House of Delegates of the CMA in December, 1938, with the vote favoring service benefits. As the then-current philosophy was expressed in the CMA journal, "California Physicians Service is not an insurance company thinking in terms of dollars—it is a doctor's organizaton thinking in terms of service." [19]

In summary, CPS as originally conceived offered to families with incomes of less than $3,000 a comprehensive medical insurance coverage, with hospitalization arranged through Blue Cross, on an exclusively service benefit basis, with physician-members working under a unit value system of remuneration. By the 1950's each of these distinguishing characteristics had been modified or abandoned.

Early Years of CPS

In August, 1939, the California State Employees Association became the first group to sign a contract with the new medical care organization. At the close of the first accounting period, August 15 to September 30, the unit value was calculated and found to be approximately $1.30 rather than the hoped-for $2.50. Apparently in the belief that prosperity might be just around the corner, payment was actually made on the basis of a unit value of $1.75. Unfortunately, operating results did not improve and the unit value sank to 50 per cent of the "ideal" $2.50 figure by April

---

preventive medicine); conversely, comprehensive plans may be set up to pay cash benefits rather than services. Some of the more interesting experiments being conducted currently involve attempts to devise financially feasible methods of making indemnity plans more comprehensive.

Finally, the word comprehensive is sometimes used in two senses. Most often it refers to the range of different services covered. On occasion, however, it is used to refer also to the depth as well as the breadth of coverage. By this usage a comprehensive plan must not only pay *some* benefits for a wide range of items but must pay all or a large percentage of total medical costs. In practice, this distinction is usually important only where the dollar maxima or medical care or surgical procedures are exceeded in a complicated case.

[19] *California and Western Medicine,* October, 1939, p. 259.

of 1940. During the next summer and fall the rate inched up to $1.35 but the December, 1940, value was announced as $1.10 under the caption, "The Epidemic Has Struck!" An influenza "epidemic" was cited as responsible for the drop to what was to be the all-time-low unit value even though $2,000 from a stabilization fund was used to bolster December income.[20]

By February of the next year the unit value had risen to $1.25 where it was to remain for a full year. By the fall of 1941 the continued payment of fees that amounted to half the expected level began to tell. After October 1, the full-coverage contract was abandoned in favor of a policy that excluded the first two doctor's visits for any ailment from coverage and that raised rates for women members to reflect their higher utilization. The November issue of the CMA journal reported the "elimination of unsatisfactory groups . . ." and announced that increased attention was being given to the sale of new limited-coverage contracts stressing surgical and in-hospital medical benefits.

In February, 1942, the first official indication of physician discontent appeared. The Council of the Alameda County Medical Association (ACMA) passed a resolution "disapproving California Physicians Service as now constituted and operated. . . ." Its members were advised to resign. At the request of the CMA, this resolution was rescinded in May in the interests of "unity" after some resignations had occurred. The Sacramento society was reported as being "in the same position." Rumblings of discontent were also reported from the San Diego area.

During 1942 unit values fluctuated narrowly around $1.40. A steady improvement began the next year, culminating in March of 1944 when payments of $2.25, 90 per cent of the 1939 goal, were established. These were maintained for the next several years. It had taken four and a half years to reach this level.

Apparently the dissatisfaction revealed by the 1942 incident involving the Alameda County association was not eliminated by the progressive increase in unit values. The December, 1944, issue of *California and Western Medicine* included a copy of a letter signed by twenty-one Alameda members and addressed to all members of the CMA. For our purposes the important section of the letter dealt with an attack on the service character of CPS

[20] *Ibid.*, March, 1941, p. 143.

contracts. As an alternative the letter suggested that: "Insurance, ably managed, can protect the patient by partial reimbursement without injury to Medicine. . . . Let C.P.S. be changed to insurance—but pay it to the patient. Let the doctor decide whether the sum is adequate compensation in each case. . . ."

The letter went on to draw an analogy between the service benefit philosophy and socialism and to argue that: "Too prominent among the advocates of C.P.S. are doctors least affected by it, particularly doctors on salary at public and private institutions. . . . The essential in (Socialistic schemes) is the release of the patient from financial obligation to the doctor. An *agency* controls both cost to patient and fee to doctor and thereby obtains influence over both."

Defenders of CPS countered in the same issue with a letter signed by forty-four other ACMA members asking that CPS physician-members "keep an open mind on the subject" and recommending dealing with defects "in the democratic way and not through a revolution within our midst." The CMA Executive Committee also prepared a reply pointing out that the question of service benefits had been voted on twice (once in 1938 and the second time in connection with a resolution introduced by ACMA members at the House of Delegates meeting in May, 1944). The Committee also expressed the belief that "the people . . . do not feel that insurance cash reimbursement, leaving an exposure to additional bills, answers the problem of the cost of medical care. . . ."

In the interval between the 1942 protest and the above exchange, important events occurred in which the Alameda County group played a significant part. In 1943 the northern California Blue Cross, with headquarters in Oakland and with close ties to the ACMA, added medical and surgical coverage on a cash indemnity basis to its service hospitalization program. This departure from traditional Blue Cross practice was undertaken in large part as a result of requests from the Alameda foes of CPS. This meant that the hospital branch of the medical industry had made available a complete health insurance system which competed directly with the physician-sponsored plan for medical and surgical benefits. Since the Blue Cross selling organization had also been handling CPS previously, a difficult situation was created.

CPS reacted by adding a service hospitalization coverage to its own medical and surgical plan and what was to become an almost complete divorce of the two medically sponsored health insurance ventures began. Blue Cross in southern California continued to function as a partner of CPS until 1951 when the two agreed to go their separate ways. In both cases one of the results of the split was a substantial temporary drop in membership as most of the subscribers to the former combination Blue Cross–Blue Shield system chose one or the other alternative for all their coverage. Competition between CPS and the Blue Cross organizations in California is thus in large part the outgrowth of the dissatisfaction within the medical profession with the service benefit system and its related control over fees for service and doctor-patient financial relationships.

A "New Look" in CPS

After the 1944 flareup in the CMA journal the Alameda County association was threatened with expulsion from the state association.[21] More positive action was forthcoming, however, when at the 1945 meeting of the House of Delegates of the CMA a committee under the direction of Dr. L. R. Chandler was appointed to review the operations of CPS and make recommendations as to its future policy. Reporting to the 1946 meeting of the Delegates, this committee recommended major changes in the CPS program. Prominent among the suggested changes were proposals that:

1. Service benefits be retained for single individuals with annual incomes below $2,400 and for families below $3,000.

2. Membership be open to all persons regardless of income with the proviso that the individual doctor would receive the CPS fee for services to these patients plus an additional amount to be determined solely by the doctor and collected directly from those patients with incomes over the ceilings.

---

[21] Reported in the June, 1950, issue of the *Bulletin*, Alameda-Contra Costa Medical Association, p. 13. "This [ACCMA men as officers of CMA] presents a different picture than that of five years ago when Alameda County was threatened with expulsion from the State Society at a time when the emotional controversy over CPS was at its height. . . ." (In 1950 the Contra Costa County society merged with that of Alameda to form the Alameda-Contra Costa Medical Association.)

3. In the future, fee schedules be expressed in dollars and not in units. This appears to have been a matter of form rather than substance since the practical effect seems to have been to announce payments at 90 per cent of the dollar schedule rather than in unit values equal to 90 per cent of the desired unit value.

4. Patients be permitted to secure service from nonmember-doctors (including osteopaths) as well as CPS members. This proposal was adopted in spite of strong opposition to the recognition of doctors of osteopathy and to paying nonmember-doctors the going CPS rate without an agreement to limit their charges to that amount for patients below the income ceilings.[22]

Although the ACMA believed that its actions had called the Chandler Committee into being, and although it immediately "unanimously approved" CPS in its revised form, the new look in CPS left the basic issue unchanged. The ACMA's principal objection had been to the intrusion of a third party into the financial aspects of the doctor-patient relationship in order to make the promise of service instead of indemnity benefits effective. Under the new system no change whatever occurred in arrangements for patients with incomes below the ceilings. Removing the income limits on membership did include the acceptance of the indemnity principle for the above-ceiling groups. ACMA objectors may have felt that the major increases in family income which had occurred and were occurring would put a large and growing proportion of the population in the category to which the combination fee of the CPS allowance plus a direct charge would be applicable. Most interesting of all, the ACMA, whose leaders in 1944 had inveighed against the influence of a third party on the fee of the individual doctor, a decade later pioneered in publishing fees which, in the absence of prior agreement to the contrary or unusual complications, were to be the maximum fees for services rendered to all patients without qualification.[23]

---

[22] The full report of the committee together with the discussion and the action taken by the House of Delegates was published in *California and Western Medicine*, June, 1946, pp. 361 *passim*.

[23] It should not be inferred that ACMA's role in this situation was entirely the result of a talent for controversy. A former executive secretary of the association, Mr. Rollen Waterson, argues that a major part of the total membership of CPS at this time resided in the area served by ACMA. This was explained as the result of the tie-in with Blue Cross which, as noted, centered its activity in Alameda County. As a result this county society had most at stake in the operations of CPS.

If the ACMA "revolt" did not determine the shape of the revised CPS, what factors did? The analysis which follows cannot be documented specifically but should be regarded as the sum of impressions gained from a fairly thorough survey of the sources cited at the beginning of this section.

Most important among the changes were (1) the opening of membership to persons with incomes above the $3,000 ceiling with doctors permitted to establish their own fees for this group, and (2) the decision to pay claims on CPS presented by physicians who were not members of the plan. It appears that the first change was primarily the result of the new drive for state compulsory health insurance and the second the result of the opening of the Kaiser Foundation Health Plan to the general public.

Appointment of the Chandler Committee occurred at the May, 1945, meeting of the House of Delegates of the CMA. In January of that year, Governor Earl Warren, a more formidable foe than Culbert Olson, opened his legislative campaign for a compulsory health bill. Unlike the Olson proposals which included the familiar $3,000 ceiling on incomes of those eligible, the Warren bill had no income limitations. Under the circumstances, if CPS were to fulfill its role as a voluntary alternative to the state proposal, it would have to broaden its coverage of the population. In the face of the widespread opposition to service benefits for the lower-income members, it was difficult to propose eliminating the income ceilings altogether without introducing a new system of compensation. Addition of the modified indemnity feature for higher income members was the method adopted.

Two months after the Committee was established the Kaiser (then Permanente) Plan opened enrollment to the public at large. The traditional professional objection to plans of the Kaiser type has been based on the lack of "free choice of physician" inherent in the requirement that subscribers secure treatment from a plan doctor if their insurance is to be effective. The CMA found itself sponsoring in CPS a plan with some embarassing resemblances to a "closed panel" as long as subscribers could profit by their policy only when treated by physicians who were CPS members. The provision that all licensed physicians could, if they wished, become members of CPS at will satisfied the requirements of medical ethics. Since all doctors were not in fact members, however, the subscriber did not have completely "free choice." Paying CPS benefits to any physician who treated a CPS subscriber regardless of the physician's membership status left the medical profession free to criticize the "closed-panel" aspect of the Kaiser and similar plans without being open to the same charge themselves. This change also contributed to the need to express fees in dollars rather than units since nonmembers were not party to the unit value agreement.

Another factor that influenced the opening of CPS to all persons was one directly related to the main theme of this study. Under World War II wage regulation, health and welfare benefits could be added to the wage package at a time when direct wage increases were not permitted. The employer, employee, and union interest that resulted continued into the postwar era. Provisions for some sort of health insurance coverage began to appear with increasing frequency as an employer fringe benefit. Union and other employee organizations often evinced an independent interest which led to the establishment of many beneficiary groups without employer participation. If CPS were to participate in this growth it had to be able to enroll workers whose income might exceed the relatively modest income ceilings whether these higher-income workers were found as a minority part of the larger group or made up the bulk of a potential unit. This change also made it possible for CPS to deal with the phenomenon of the annual increase in money income which, since World War II, has come to be accepted almost as an inherent characteristic of the American economy.

Summary

This review of the background of health plans in California and the Bay Area has attempted to make several points in anticipation of the discussion to follow in chapter vii.

1. CPS originally had most of the characteristics union spokesmen feel to be essential in a health plan for the members. It was comprehensive in coverage, offered a wide choice of physicians, provided assurance through the service benefit system that the worker would not be faced with large additional charges, and was low-cost protection open to almost all of the working population.

2. Over the years, external and internal pressures forced a mod-

ification of many of these features. (*a*) The first adjustment was a narrowing of the coverage under the impact of high costs. Attempts to cover all home and office visits, diagnostic laboratory and X-ray procedures, and physical examinations were felt to be an unwarranted drain on the income of the fund. (*b*) Internally, the system met with two major types of objections. The unit value system left the doctor as the last man in line when the funds were distributed. Physician-members felt that they were underwriting losses while the other recipients of plan income, e.g., laboratories and hospitals, received stipulated fees in full. Low unit values in the early years made this problem acute.

Fundamental objections to the basic service benefit philosophy appeared, centering around the necessity for such a system to fix some pattern of fees for the doctors in order to permit the liabilities of the plan to be forecast. As a result the percentage of the population offered service coverage was curtailed by the failure to adjust the cutoff income ceilings for several years. For the increasing proportion of workers with incomes above the ceilings, a variation of cash indemnity benefits was adopted.

3. Most important of all, the very existence of CPS as well as its survival in the face of great difficulties, indicated an ability on the part of the medical profession to innovate and adjust in response to outside influences. While the degree of flexibility demonstrated by the profession was inadequate in the opinion of its critics, the CPS experience during these years foreshadowed other changes in medical practice to come, both inside and outside the framework of CPS.

After the revisions in CPS that stemmed from the Chandler report, relative calm prevailed until the introduction of large-scale negotiated health plans in 1949 set off another critical series of events.

Chapter VI | *The Industrial*
| *Relations Structure*
| *of the Bay Area*

Since a major part of the forthcoming analysis will be concerned with developments in a particular metropolitan area, it is necessary to review some of the salient physical and structural characteristics of the region. It is commonplace for students of metropolitan government and urban planning to emphasize the manner in which the fragmentation of political jurisdictions has shaped the way in which certain problems such as water supply or rapid transit have been approached. Both the geography and the political boundaries of the San Francisco Bay Area have also had an important influence on the structure of the private organizations that deal with medical matters in the Bay Area. For example, the multiplicity of separate counties (nine in our definition of the area) has meant that there is no single central labor council or local medical society with jurisdiction over more than a minor portion of the region. The physical barriers to the movement of population imposed by the bay and the surrounding mountains have affected the ability of health service organizations such as the Kaiser Plan and other proposed medical centers to serve whole sectors of the population. The impact of geographical barriers and of political subdivisions on the structure of the employer organizations and the national unions has probably been less marked, but it has still been of major significance. For these reasons the topography of the Bay Area is discussed at this point and some of the more important organizations with which we shall be concerned are described with reference to their geographical location.

Throughout California and a large part of the West Coast the term "Bay Area" has almost the status of an official place name. The central physical feature defining the area is, of course, San Francisco Bay, a body of water about sixty miles in length and five to twelve miles wide, with its long axis running in a north-south direction. (Actually this usage ignores a distinction observed by map makers—the northern third of this area is officially known as San Pablo Bay.) In this study the Bay Area will be understood to include the nine counties that border on this body of water.[1]

The bay connects with the Pacific Ocean on the west through the Golden Gate, a two-mile wide channel at about the half-way point of the western shoreline. The total population of the nine counties was estimated at about three and a quarter million in 1956. The two principal cities are San Francisco (800,000) and Oakland (450,000). San Francisco lies south of the Golden Gate at the tip of "The Peninsula," the arm of land making up the southwest shore of the bay. Oakland lies directly across the bay from San Francisco and is the center of the "East Bay," the two counties of Contra Costa and Alameda which make up the eastern shoreline.

The term "West Bay" is increasingly limited to the region south of the Golden Gate, including San Francisco and the entire length of the Peninsula. The rapidly developing area north of the channel is designated as the North Bay. No simple phrase representing the southern part of the Bay Area has yet come into general use although it is the most rapidly growing section both in terms of population and industrial expansion. This area's principal community, San Jose, is about one-third the size of Oakland.

In spite of the relatively static level of population and industry imposed on San Francisco by its strictly limited land area, "The

---

[1] From the southern tip up the west coast and around the bay, the counties are Santa Clara, San Mateo, San Francisco, Marin, Sonoma, Napa, Solano, Contra Costa, and Alameda. In defining the extent of the San Francisco–Oakland Metropolitan Area the Bureau of the Census uses a narrower basis, leaving out the counties of Santa Clara at the southern end and Sonoma and Napa in the north. For Census purposes, the city of San Jose in Santa Clara county is treated as the central city of its own standard metropolitan area.

City" remains the core of the region in the sense that it is the financial, trade, and entertainment center as well as the location of the headquarters offices of many business and labor organizations. With the medical schools of both the University of California and Stanford University located in the city, it is the medical center as well. (Stanford has, however, announced that it is moving its school "down the Peninsula" to its home campus in Palo Alto, Santa Clara County.)

San Francisco and Oakland are the local centers of medical politics as well as medical practice since the San Francisco and the Alameda-Contra Costa County societies are the second and third largest in the state (after the gargantuan Los Angeles County society). Total membership in the San Francisco society is approximately 2,000 while total membership in the Alameda-Contra Costa group is about 1,600.[2] Fast-growing Santa Clara County has the only other society of substantial size in the Bay Area with some 700 members.

Alameda County was the original stronghold of Blue Cross in California and retains the main offices of the northern California unit in Oakland. San Francisco houses the offices of the state medical association and the state-wide Blue Shield plan, California Physicians Service. The Kaiser Foundation Health Plan was originally organized in the East Bay and has its headquarters in Oakland, the site of its first hospital. It also maintains additional hospital facilities in Walnut Creek, Richmond, and Vallejo in the East Bay and San Francisco and South San Francisco in the West Bay. Kaiser operates medical centers in the southern sections of both the East and West Bay and at Napa on the eastern boundary of the North Bay. Lack of hospital facilities in the southern Bay Area and in the North Bay prevents major Kaiser growth in these sections at this time.

Employer and union organizations are also centered in the cities of San Francisco and Oakland. In San Francisco the San Francisco Employers Council functioned for many years as the "peak" association including among its members individual employers as well as operating as an "association of associations." In the early

---

[2] Contra Costa's society merged with the Alameda County society in 1950 at a time when its membership was a small fraction of Alameda's. The combined headquarters is in Oakland, Alameda County. The figures in the text are as of 1956.

1950's the council split into two divisions. One retained the original name and concentrated on providing negotiating services in collective bargaining to a membership group drawn from various industries. The other subdivision, under the name of the Federated Employers of San Francisco, concentrated on research, lobbying, and coördinating activities for its members. Most of the "industry associations," i.e., those organized primarily along industrial lines, such as the Pacific Maritime Association and the California Metal Trades Association, maintain their headquarters in San Francisco. In the East Bay the "general" association is the United Employers. Headquartered in Oakland, the United Employers provides both research and negotiating services to members in a variety of industries.

The structure of area labor organization follows traditional patterns. The usual complement of district councils, joint boards, and joint councils exists to coördinate the activities of the groups of separate nationals and locals with interests common to a single industry, such as the Building Trades and Metal Trades Councils. Since the overwhelming majority of workers in the Bay Area, particularly in San Francisco, are members of national unions that were affiliated with the American Federation of Labor prior to its merger with the Congress of Industrial Organizations, the San Francisco Labor Council for decades has been the dominant city federation in the West Bay. Across the Bay the Central Labor Council of Alameda County, the first metropolitan labor council in the country to complete a merger of AFL and CIO councils, is the largest general-purpose local labor federation and maintains offices in Oakland. Both of these councils have been active in the health and welfare area though utilizing different approaches. Relatively minor centers of organized employer and union activity are located in San Jose at the southern tip of the bay.

Special mention should be made of the independent International Longshoremen's and Warehousemen's Union which participates in an imaginative and aggressive health and welfare program covering the entire West Coast from its San Francisco headquarters.

In the following discussion of the industrial relations pattern of the Bay Area attention will be centered on the interrelationships of employers, employer associations, and employee organizations as they relate to the health and welfare issue. The object of the exposition will be twofold: (1) to outline the structure of labor-management relations in a way that will identify some of the decision-making units and demonstrate that the decision-making function in industrial relations in the Bay Area is diffused among many organizations, the great bulk of which are local or regional in scope and can adjust to local conditions; and (2) to support the view that among these organizations the local unions and councils of unions have actually been the dynamic element in health and welfare affairs.

When meaningful decisions are made at the local level by aggressive and inventive organizations, the variety of medical arrangements already described can be exploited fully in seeking solutions to problems.

When the unions are described as the dynamic element in health and welfare affairs, the intention is to emphasize their role in representing the consumer of medical care in the day-to-day operations of health plans. There is no intention of arguing that employers have been without influence in determining the form and content of the health care programs that have come out of collective bargaining. Neither is there an intention of arguing that the financial administration of the plans, the appointment of administrators, and the adoption of systems of financial control and operation have been dominated by the unions. In many plans a case could be made for this position but the area of internal administration is not the center of this study. Where the unions have made their most important contribution is in reviewing and evaluating the results of the medical care system established through collective bargaining. It is the unions that have pursued the problems of cost inflation, adequacy of benefits, new types of benefits, establishment of fee schedules, and the control of abuse most vigorously. Pressures for changes in the forms of medical organization and in the relationships between existing forms of organization have generally come from the union movement. It is in this sense that the unions are put forth as the dynamic element in health insurance matters.

As far as possible the argument will be bolstered by statistical documentation. In the nature of the case, however, certain statements regarding the degree of influence assigned to particular factors must be based on judgment and might well be challenged by another observer.

Role of the Single Employer

It is customary to describe the Bay Area as a region in which industrial establishments are small relative to other metropolitan areas (using numbers of employees as a measure of size). Figures on the median size of plants in manufacturing can be cited in support of this assertion. According to the 1947 Census of Manufacturers, for example, the median manufacturing establishment in the San Francisco–Oakland Metropolitan Area employed 5–9 workers. Of the thirteen metropolitan areas with 1950 populations of more than one million, only the three largest—New York, Chicago, and Los Angeles—had medians as low as San Francisco while the others were in the 10–19 range. Median figures are not entirely satisfactory for this purpose, however, since they are strongly influenced by the very large percentages of all establishments in the lowest (1–4) size class in all cities. Another way to make our point is by citing the numbers of establishments in the largest size class, 2,500 employees and over. At the beginning of the health and welfare cycle in 1947, the San Francisco–Oakland area had only four plants of this size, fewer than any of the other large metropolitan areas.

The picture is not changed by considering the multiestablishment firm, by concentrating on absolute rather than relative size, or by using current figures on firm size. Although comprehensive data for all companies in the region on a comparable basis are not readily available, evidence collected by the local Chambers of Commerce suggests that no manufacturing firm in the area employed as many as 5,000 production workers in 1955. A further important point is that the national pattern-setters in industrial relations such as the steel, automobile, and electrical industries are either not represented at all or have local plants in this same size class. Perhaps the biggest concentration of manufacturing employment is at the Pittsburg (California) plant of the Columbia-Geneva Division of U. S. Steel. The plant had about 4,500 production workers in 1956. Both General Motors and Ford operate assembly plants in the Bay Area, but neither of these national giants accounted for as many as 3,000 production workers in their plants in 1956. The same could be said of Bethlehem Steel, General Electric, Westinghouse, Food Machinery and Chemical Corporation, and Standard Oil of California. A large food-packing company, such as the California Packing Corporation, will exceed this figure at its seasonal peaks in employment but only for temporary employees.

For our purposes the significance of the relatively small size of the individual firms of the region is that it reduces the possibility that a single firm might set a health and welfare pattern that would dominate the local scene. Not only was no company headquartered in the area likely to fill the role of pacemaker but the national patterns set in the mass production industries have had their impact blunted by the small numbers of employees involved locally.

Shifting attention to employers in nonmanufacturing industries reveals some larger employers but they are not among the usual pattern-setters in labor-management relations. Among the largest companies are the utilities—the Pacific Telephone and Telegraph Company being generally accepted as the largest private employer with well over 10,000 employees—the Southern Pacific Railroad, United Air Lines, and the Bank of America. Neither the telephone company nor the Pacific Gas and Electric Company are highly organized and there would be general agreement that these industries are followers rather than leaders in this type of industrial relations policy. These remarks apply with equal force to the Bank of America.

Most likely candidate for a pattern-setter's role in the group would be the Southern Pacific Company but several factors have operated to prevent this. As in the United States as a whole, the railroads have tended to lie outside the mainstream of industrial relations matters in recent years. In addition, the western railroads have a long tradition of special arrangements typical of frontier industry in the field of health care. In the case of the Southern Pacific this has taken the form of an elaborate health system for employees providing comprehensive care and including the operation of a hospital owned by the health plan in San Francisco. The specialized character of this type of plan and its origins in a different era have apparently insulated it from the current controversy over the form and content of health and welfare plans.

The last group of employers to be reviewed are the various levels of government: city, state, and federal. Each of these governmental jurisdictions employs more workers in the Bay Area than any single private employer with the federal government well out in front. As the western headquarters for a wide variety of military and civil functions, San Francisco is a center of federal employment of impressive size. In 1956 about one of every twelve nonagricultural workers in the Census metropolitan area was on the payroll of the federal government. All levels of government accounted for almost 20 per cent of total employment or over 175,000 persons.[3] To date neither the national nor the state governments, however, have had any significant influence on health plans as employers, although the California State Employees Association was the first group enrolled under CPS in 1939 and is today one of the largest groups.

As in a few other cities, it is the municipal government that has served as a base for a significant innovation in medical economics.[4] Although the initiative for the municipal plan in question, the Health Service System (HSS) of the Municipal Employees of San Francisco, stemmed from a number of sources, including employee organizations, it will be discussed in the following paragraphs as a health plan based on a single employer unit.

The Health Service System was organized in 1937 through an amendment to the San Francisco City Charter. The amendment made it mandatory for all city employees to participate in a health system that guaranteed to the employee a free choice of doctor. It began operation in 1938 after certain tests of legality were successfully met. From that time until 1947 HSS offered a comprehensive health plan covering hospitalization and medical care, including first-visit doctor's care, for city employees and their dependents. In essence, during this period HSS was a self-insured health plan offering a choice of cash indemnity benefits or

---

[3] California Department of Industrial Relations, *Estimated Number of Wage and Salary Workers in Nonagricultural Establishments, By Industry, San Francisco–Oakland Metropolitan Area, 1953–56*, March, 1957 (mimeo).

[4] Substantial credit for the existence of the Health Insurance Plan of Greater New York, which, with the Kaiser Plan, is one of the major comprehensive health plans of the nation, goes to the municipal administration of New York City and former Mayor Fiorello H. LaGuardia. See *Available Health Plans and Group Insurance*, Hearings Before the Committee on Interstate and Foreign Commerce, House of Representatives, 83rd Congress, 2d session, 1954, Part 6, p. 1585.

service medical benefits from what amounted to a closed panel of doctors. The size of the panel varied with the fluctuating fortunes of the system. This unusual situation grew up because the administration of HSS formulated a schedule of fees for services, usually after consultation with the San Francisco Medical Society, which it then submitted for acceptance to the individual doctors practicing in the city. If the schedule was satisfactory to the representatives of the society, they recommended that members agree to render their services for the stipulated fees without extra charges to the patient.[5]

At times the Health Service System has enrolled on its "panel" a majority of the community's physicians; at other times the number agreeing to HSS contacts has dropped below 10 per cent of the practicing physicians. On occasions when the medical society and the HSS administration have been in conflict (usually but not always over financial matters), the society has recommended with considerable success that its members withdraw from coöperation with HSS pending the result of "negotiations."

Regardless of the number of doctors who have agreed to accept the fees as promulgated by HSS in full payment for their services, members could always go to any doctor of their choice, pay the bill directly, and then be reimbursed to the extent of the scheduled fees. As a result of these characteristics the system is best described as a combination of an indemnity type of self-insurance and a panel-type service plan.

The Health Service System has pioneered in one aspect of medical economics that has had a very substantial impact both locally and nationally. In 1947, after a particularly bitter dispute with the medical society, HSS and the Kaiser Foundation Health Plan arranged to offer the members a choice between the original "free-choice" plan described above and coverage under the Kaiser program. After a lengthy legal battle the provision of alternative health plans was authorized with the result that since that time HSS members have been offered their choice of four "plans." The pre-1947 system with its combination of "free-choice" and a panel whose size was dependent on current relations with the medical society was retained as Plan I, the Kaiser Foundation Health

---

[5] Originally without extra charges to all members of the system without income limitations, later to those members with incomes below a ceiling.

Plan became Plan II, and two other small group-practice plans made up the array of alternatives. In 1957 HSS had about 19,000 primary members, including the retired members who had retained their coverage. Total membership was about 34,000, including dependents. About 20,000 were in Plan I, about 12,000 in the Kaiser Plan, and about 1,800 in Plans III and IV combined.[6] Provision of "dual choice" in the sense of offering members of a welfare fund a choice between the Kaiser Plan and one or more other coverages has since become common in the Bay Area and has spread to other parts of the country from this beginning. This innovation is described at length in chapter ix.

There are two aspects in which the Health Service System has had some influence on broader health and welfare developments. The first is the introduction of the dual choice concept. The second is the technique of fee determination in which the medical society and HSS discuss the fee schedule to be placed in effect, followed at least in some instances by a recommendation by the society that its members enter into individual agreements with HSS to furnish service for the indicated fees. As will be noted later, various unions have attempted to achieve this same relationship with the organized medical profession without any substantial success. There is no evidence that any of the several union groups which have attempted to organize a panel of physicians similar to that of HSS have been able to do so on a scale remotely comparable.

With the exception of the Health Service System in the limited aspects noted above, no other single health plan experiment has had a widespread impact on health plans in general. In considering explanations for the failure of HSS to have set a health and welfare pattern, a number of possible reasons can be advanced: (1) HSS antedated the post-World War II health and welfare movement by a decade and was not a product of collective bargaining; (2) there has been a tradition of special fringe benefit arrangements for civil servants that have not spread in the past to private industry (though this situation is rapidly being reversed); and (3) partly as a result of the experience with HSS,

---

[6] Information furnished by the secretary of the Health Service System, Mr. Frank Collins.

the medical profession has been less anxious to agree to this type of arrangement than it was twenty years ago.

In reviewing the role of single employers in the Bay Area, the conclusion emerges that the industrial characteristics of the area are such as to inhibit the development of a dominant type of health and welfare plan. Private employers are either small in size or in industries characterized by pattern-following rather than pattern-setting in industrial relations. Governmental agencies have either participated in the health plan movement only to a very limited extent or have had their influence curtailed by external factors.

A further important factor that has contributed to the failure of employers to take a more active part in pressing for solutions to certain types of health insurance problems is what appears to be a reluctance on their part to risk open conflict with the medical profession. Sharing the profession's antipathy toward governmental intervention in the organizational structure of business and industry, employers have hesitated to align themselves with groups whose attempts to change medical organization or policies have been denounced as variants of socialism. There is little question that most employers believe themselves to be ideological allies of the doctors on general economic questions and feel it inappropriate to become involved in movements that threaten existing medical arrangements. Staff executives of employer associations in contrast to the employers themselves are likely, in this as well as other matters, to be less inhibited by considerations of this kind but, in general, they seem to share this view.

Union Structure

The characteristics of the employers noted in the previous section provide an excellent clue to the main features of the union movement in the Bay Area. Employment in the area is concentrated in nonmanufacturing and relatively small manufacturing firms. In 1956 the industrial category with the largest proportion of total employment in the metropolitan area was Wholesale and Retail Trade (23 per cent), followed by Manufacturing (21 per cent), Government (19 per cent), and the Service industries (13 per cent).[7]

---

[7] California Department of Industrial Relations, *op. cit.*

The pattern of union membership does not follow the pattern of employment since some of the industries with relatively low total employment, such as construction, are highly organized, while the opposite is true in others, such as government. From the industrial pattern, however, it is possible to predict the type of unionism dominant in the region. In general the local labor movement is dominated by the older unions formerly affiliated with the American Federation of Labor and organized around an occupational rather than an industrial base. In the metropolitan area as a whole, former AFL unions accounted for 85 per cent of total union membership in 1955, 9 per cent were in former CIO unions, and the remaining 6 per cent in independent unions.[8] While membership figures of particular international unions are not available separately for the Bay Area, the pattern of union membership by industry division permits the identification of key union groups in approximate fashion.

Table 6.1 summarizes the industrial distribution of union members in the area and identifies the principal union groups involved in each of the seven largest industrial classifications as well as available data permit.

The list of principal union groups illustrates that the major unions in terms of membership are usually the well-established, former AFL unions. Most of these unions, such as the construction unions and the unions of culinary workers, have a tradition of local or regional autonomy in determining major bargaining patterns. As a result the important local concentrations of union membership have been for the most part independent decision-making units in the field of health and welfare. With a few notable exceptions they have been able to make the type of arrangement they believed best in order to meet the needs of their members in the local medical market. Coupled with the variety of alternative programs available, this has meant that a diversity and flexibility of policy has been achieved that would have been impossible if the local patterns reflected decisions made at the level of national employers or national union headquarters. Many national groups have a relatively limited amount of freedom in health plan choices because some degree of uniformity is necessary in plans

---

[8] California Department of Industrial Relations, *Union Labor in California, 1955,* San Francisco, 1956, p. 9.

TABLE 6.1

UNION MEMBERSHIP IN THE SAN FRANCISCO BAY AREA
BY INDUSTRY, JULY, 1955

Industry	Membership	Principal union groups
Construction	87,700	Construction unions; Metal Trades unions; Teamsters
Wholesale and retail trade	79,800	International Longshoremen's and Warehousemen's Union (Ind.); Teamsters; Meat Cutters and Butcher Workmen; Retail Clerks; Hotel and Restaurant Employees and Bartenders; Building Service Employees
Transportation and warehousing ..	74,900	Teamsters; Street and Electric Railways Employees; Railroad unions (AFL and Ind.); Maritime unions (AFL and Ind.); ILWU (Ind.); Aviation Worker unions; Machinists
Metals and machinery	56,400	Metal Trade unions; United Automobile Workers (CIO); United Steelworkers (CIO)
Miscellaneous services .... (includes finance, insurance, real estate, personal, and business and professional services among others)	42,200	Machinists; Teamsters; Building Service Employees; Entertainment unions
Eating and drinking places	40,000	Building Service Employees; Hotel and Restaurant Employees and Bartenders
Food and kindred products	36,700	Teamsters; Meat Cutters and Butcher Workmen; United Packinghouse Workers (CIO); Bakery and Confectionery Workers
All other industries	107,000	
Total membership	524,700	

SOURCE: California Department of Industrial Relations, *Union Labor in California, 1955,* pp. 12, 23–60.

NOTE: The approximate character of this information should be stressed. In addition to limitations of the data cited in the original source, further selection and adjustments have been made. All union groups AFL unless otherwise noted.

meant to cover workers in different parts of the country, in urban and rural communities, and in firms with a heterogeneous work force in terms of occupation, sex, and age. The relatively independent Bay Area union groups have been able to exploit the variety of local arrangements in the health field and, more important, have been able to participate in the development of new techniques and institutional arrangements.

One major exception to the general rule of local autonomy should be noted. The largest single group of organized workers, the Teamsters, has adopted a health and welfare system which very substantially limits the ability of local groups to devise their own patterns of health plans. Teamster health and welfare arrangements are channeled through an organizational innovation known as the Teamsters' Security Fund (TSF). Created by the Western Conference of Teamsters, the regional subdivision of the parent union operating in the eleven western states,[9] the fund functions so as to introduce major elements of uniformity into the union's health program.

Within the Western Conference there are actually five regional branches of the Teamsters' Security Fund, one of which includes the two Joint Councils of Teamsters with jurisdiction over northern California. In essence, the fund is a device for centralizing the administration of the numerous separate welfare funds which exist in this complex union. TSF collects employer contributions for all funds, helps negotiate for insurance coverage, pays premiums, determines eligibility of members for benefits, and pays all claims. Within the boundaries of each of the regional branches of TSF an employee can move from any one of the individual funds to another without loss of benefits or eligibility.[10]

Various developments have made the public familiar with the need for effective internal financial controls over the operation of welfare funds in general and the Teamsters' funds in particular.

---

[9] California, Oregon, Washington, Idaho, Montana, Wyoming, Utah, Nevada, Arizona, New Mexico, and Colorado.

[10] In Northern California the TSF office handled thirty-two separate welfare trusts in 1956. The mobility provision noted in the text is more important to the individual Teamster in connection with the Teamster pension plan than with the health plans. Leaving a pension plan usually means the loss of important rights and benefits based on past service but this is much less true of health plans. In general, the Teamster pension plan permits the worker to move to any job anywhere in the jurisdiction of the entire Western Conference without penalty.

Irrespective of this problem, however, the Teamsters' Security Fund illustrates a sound and desirable principle of administration with a potential for efficiency and economy. Methods of securing the many benefits of pooling administration of welfare plans have been worked out by other union and employer groups as well as the Teamsters and the trend toward larger administrative units will probably continue.

It is a fact, however, that one of the results of centralization in the Teamsters' case has been a pressure for uniformity in health programs. The Teamster program relies exclusively on commercial insurance of a cash indemnity type with a fairly uniform set of benefits and a minimum of flexibility for experimentation on a local basis. Since the money available in each of the separate trusts will not support completely uniform benefits at satisfactory levels, flexibility is introduced to the extent of varying the degree of coverage of the standard list of benefits. For example, one contract may pay $12 per day of hospital benefits while a more affluent plan may pay $14 a day. Whatever the explanation or explanations, with a few exceptions such as the Bakery Wagon Drivers, the Bay Area Teamsters have been relatively inactive in the controversy over cost inflation, abuse of benefits, health centers, experience rating, and other problems.

Although in a few other smaller unions such as the Upholsterers Union, the national union office has intervened directly in local bargaining to influence the type of health plan adopted, most of the rest of the Bay Area labor movement has been able to decide this issue on a local basis.

While the two Joint Councils of Teamsters in northern California are blanketed into the Northern California Teamsters' Security Fund operation, for example, other area councils have been better able to pursue an independent course of action.[11]

---

[11] Labor movement nomenclature includes a bewildering collection of names for a certain grouping of unions which lies between the local and the national union levels in the organizational structure. In this study the term "area councils" is used to refer to several types of organizations: (1) groupings of the various locals of the same national union in a geographical area, e.g., the Joint Board of Culinary Workers, (2) groupings of the various locals of different national unions which work primarily in the same industry in a geographical area, e.g., the Building Trades Council, and (3) groupings of the various locals of the national unions affiliated with the same national federation in a geographical area, e.g., the East Bay Labor Council (AFL-CIO). Many of the first two types of councils are often important segments of the third type.

In the Bay Area the most important councils in terms of numbers of members are the Joint Board of Culinary Workers, the Metal Trades Council, the Building Trades Council, the Teamsters Joint Council, and the San Francisco Labor Council. The first four of these groups made up about half of the total membership in the fifth group, the San Francisco Labor Council, in 1952.[12]

Although all of these groups have been active in the health and welfare movement, the two most prominent have been the Joint Board of Culinary Workers and the San Francisco Labor Council.

The Joint Board of Culinary Workers includes seven locals of the Hotel and Restaurant Employees and Bartenders Union, most of the locals being organized around a particular occupational base such as the cooks, waiters, waitresses, and bartenders. Functioning as a bargaining agent and as an administering and coördinating center, the Joint Board represents a total of about 22,000 members and negotiates with four principal employer associations.[13] In addition many hundreds of small individual employers (mainly in the restaurant industry) sign the master agreements which come out of these negotiations. Locals making up this Joint Board have been important storm centers in health and welfare matters. Each of the four employer associations with which the Joint Board deals has its own health plan trust fund and, as noted in chapter vii, the record of events for this group provides an example of almost every possible combination of approaches to the health and welfare problem.

The San Francisco Labor Council has functioned as the official spokesman for the labor movement in the area of its jurisdiction for decades. While the council included only unions affiliated with the American Federation of Labor until the AFL-CIO merger was consummated at the local level, the structure of the city's labor movement made this qualification of minor importance. Since it

---

[12] E. R. Weinerman, *Labor Plans for Health*, San Francisco Labor Council, June, 1952, p. 14. Many of the locals making up the Building Trades Council were not affiliated with the labor council at this time.

[13] The associations are the Golden Gate Restaurant Association, the Hotel Employers Association (more descriptively known as "the large hotels association"), the San Francisco Hotel Owners Association (known as the "small hotels association"), and the San Francisco Club Institute. Other small groups of employers such as those in the growing motel or motor hotel field exist, in a less formal fashion, but the health and welfare funds are divided into four funds based primarily on the association structure.

has been estimated that more than 90 per cent of the organized workers in San Francisco are members of former AFL unions and since the overwhelming majority of these workers belong to locals represented on the council, it has been a key element in city-wide labor affairs.

Like other central labor councils of this type, the San Francisco body performs lobbying and public relations functions as one major activity. Its other principal concern is one of coördinating the activities of the local labor movement in bargaining and in the application of the economic sanctions used by unions in labor-management disputes, such as the strike, picketing, and the boycott. In the American labor movement the fundamental channel of authority runs from the national union to the local union with the area councils outside the chain of command and typically acting only in an advisory and coördinating capacity. Within these important limitations the council plays a substantial part in the activities of at least some of its member unions. A rather involved sequence of actions is called for when any of the approximately 160 locals affiliated with the council in 1955 embarks on contract negotiations. The role of the council is to assure that the affiliated locals that will be affected by a strike of one of their number are aware of the situation, are familiar with the issues at stake and with the efforts at settlement which have been made. The reasons for the strike call must be generally acceptable to them in order that their support may be assured. This support usually involves the observance of picket lines and possible financial aid.

Member unions of the council differ in their individual bargaining strength and their consequent need for council "sanction" with its resulting assistance in a strike. Where the full gamut of the council's prestrike procedures is followed, a form of "mediation" may occur. Employer representatives may appear with their union counterparts before the Executive Committee of the council in an effort to resolve the issues. In general, powerful local unions and locals of national unions that are insistent on the primacy of their authority use the full range of procedures infrequently. There are many situations, however, in which locals require the negotiating services of the staff of the council, the coöperation of other unions, and the general public support which the council may be able to muster to achieve their goals. In these cases the council plays an important role and there are instances when a failure to win official support for a strike has meant the abandonment of strongly backed union positions in bargaining.

The various functions served by the San Francisco Labor Council have been sufficient to enable it to act as a base for an interesting proposal in the health and welfare area. In 1952 it sponsored a study of the health plans negotiated by its members by a local physician active in health plan affairs.[14] The study recommended the establishment of a labor health center sponsored and administered by the council as the best means of providing a full range of medical services most efficiently and economically. Although the council pressed for the implementation of this plan for several months, no tangible results were achieved. The project has not been entirely abandoned and it forms an interesting example of the interplay between organizations which is the subject of this study. In addition to this incident, the council has served as a continuing point of contact in negotiations with the San Francisco Medical Society.

Mention should also be made of the health and welfare aspects of the collective-bargaining policy of the International Longshoremen's and Warehousemen's Union. The ILWU, an independent union, negotiates a coastwide collective-bargaining contract from its San Francisco headquarters. The union deals with two major employer associations in the Bay Area, the Pacific Maritime Association for longshoremen and the Distributors Association of Northern California for warehousemen, as well as with individual employers. The Longshoremen's Union has evinced much interest in and brought pressure for a well-articulated, comprehensive fringe benefit program. As a matter of policy the union strongly favors comprehensive medical care of the type exemplified by the Kaiser Plan (with "consumer representation" in policy-making as a further goal), but participates in the dual-choice program. In addition to a full complement of the usual health and welfare benefits, the ILWU has pioneered in providing dental care for children of longshoremen through the welfare fund as well as a number of other special programs.

---

[14] Published as *Labor Plans for Health*. For the details of this episode see chapter vii below.

In the later chapters a thorough analysis of the activities of the union movement in health and welfare will be made. Attention will be focused on those groups that have been most active in influencing developments. This section has attempted to identify some of these groups and to place them in the context of the general industrial relations environment of the Bay Area as a whole.

Role of the Employer Association

Partly as a result of the employer characteristics described earlier and partly as a result of widespread union organization, the San Francisco Bay Area has long been noted for a high degree of organization for industrial relations among employers. It has been estimated that approximately 65 employer associations organized in more or less formal fashion are functioning in San Francisco. In addition to the large numbers of individual employers who are members of these groups, many others who are nonmembers of their industry associations accept the master collective-bargaining agreement negotiated by the associations as their own basic labor agreement. The California Department of Industrial Relations has estimated that in July, 1955, about three-fourths of all employees covered by union contracts in the San Francisco–Oakland Metropolitan Area were working under contracts signed by more than one employer. This figure is roughly comparable to a 1951 estimate of about one-third for the United States as a whole and about 55 per cent for the Los Angeles area.[15]

In spite of the highly developed system of associations which has evolved over the years, for the most part the initiative in health and welfare matters has been left in the hands of the unions. Although explanations for this differ, the analysis that follows includes the more important reasons in the opinion of the writer. Some of these apply with equal force to employers generally while others are more applicable to associations as such.

[15] California Department of Industrial Relations, *op. cit.*, pp. 20–21. This same publication reports that 51 per cent of all wage and salary earners in the Metropolitan Area were union members as compared with 33 per cent in the United States and 37 per cent in the Los Angeles–Long Beach Metropolitan Area (pp. 10–11). This source is an example of the excellent material produced by the Division of Labor Statistics and Research of the Department. The estimate of 65 associations was made by William H. Smith, Director of Research and Analysis, Federated Employers of San Francisco.

1. Many employers regard their health and welfare expenditures as payments in lieu of direct wages. As such they argue that the disposition of these funds should be principally the responsibility of the representatives of the workers. Many union leaders are in full accord with this point of view. Reinforcing the employer position on this point is the feeling on the part of some of their number that it would be wise to avoid the problems and possible consequences of an active participation in the financial arrangements involved. This belief has been influential in spite of the efforts of lawyers and association staff members to convince their principals of the importance of their fiduciary responsibilities under the law. While this attitude exists among individual employers in their role as separate bargainers as well as among association members, as individual bargainers they are more likely to bargain health plans on a benefit basis rather than as money payments into a trust fund. Employers whose obligations are spelled out in the form of benefits are much more likely to interest themselves in the internal administration of a health plan than are those who are simply contributing a fixed sum of money to a trust fund.

2. Some of the larger associations negotiate a number of separate contracts with different unions which have widely different and strongly held opinions on health and welfare issues. An example would be the Pacific Maritime Association which deals primarily with the maritime unions (such as the Sailors Union of the Pacific) and with the International Longshoremen's and Warehousemen's Union. It would be difficult for either an employer association or an individual employer in this position to adopt a firm policy which it then insisted on applying to all its contracts. As a result, associations in this position tend to adapt themselves to the desires of the unions with which they deal. It should be pointed out, however, that on occasion an association that felt a strong desire to influence the choice of health plans has been able to win acceptance for its plan by arguing that the diversity of union proposals would make administration difficult and expensive. Because the association is a very convenient base for group coverage, this permits some bargaining advantage to accrue to an association that wants to use it.

3. In some industries the opposite situation prevails. Employers

in separate branches of an industry in which a trade or occupation is represented by a single union may form themselves into a number of employer associations each of which deals with the same union or unions. An excellent example of this is found in the construction industry which has an extremely complex bargaining structure for both the employers and the nineteen building trades unions in the area. Under these conditions there is a tendency for collective-bargaining settlements to be shaped so that they can be applied on a union-wide basis. In general, the unions are the largest and most stable decision-making units in the industry. In addition, they define the scope of the job market for their members who may move from employer to employer without being limited by employer association boundary lines and without losing insurance coverage.

In these circumstances bargaining leadership does not pass entirely by default to the unions since in the construction industry, for example, it is common for the larger general contractors, organized as the Associated General Contractors, to set the collective-bargaining pattern in their negotiations with the various unions. It is true, however, that the settlements are negotiated with the knowledge that they must be applied in a large number of diverse situations in which the unions involved provide the principal common element.

4. Since an association by definition involves a number of separate employers there may be important differences of opinion as to the health plan policy to be adopted by the association. In these cases there is a temptation for the association staff to let the union take the initiative rather than attempt to resolve the internal disputes in order to develop a strong association stand that might very well have to be compromised or abandoned in the bargaining process anyway.

5. During the greater part of the period since World War II, employers, both in and out of the associations, have been on the defensive as far as collective-bargaining demands are concerned. They have been reacting to union demands rather than initiating action on their own. In addition, most of the associations have only recently, if at all, been developing competence in the complex problems of employee benefit plans. In the past, association staffs

have been built up to deal with unions in a bargaining rather than in a service relationship. This latter type of activity is more directly related to the traditional personnel management function than to the collective-bargaining activity that has been the historic concern of the associations. The assumption of this "administrative" role in addition to their more accustomed "negotiatory" character has required the development of a new expertise and a broader concept of association activity which has been slow to evolve.

As usual there are exceptions to the generalization that the employer associations have been relatively passive in health plan development. Most important among the exceptions has been the policy adopted by a few major associations of negotiating health plans that specify the employers' obligation in terms of benefits to be provided rather than in terms of money contributions to a trust fund. This approach has been common in the case of large national employers such as the automobile and steel companies but has been less characteristic of multiemployer groups. In the Bay Area two of the large associations that have adopted this system are the California Metal Trades Association and the San Francisco Retailers' Council. Where it has been used, this approach tends to place the initiative in dealing with the problems raised by health insurance coverage in the hands of the employers to a greater extent than when a welfare fund with a joint labor-management board of trustees is organized. Unions in this situation are still active in pressing for the solution of difficulties that arise but this is usually also accompanied by an increase in interest and activity on the part of the employers.

Conclusion

One of the chief purposes of this brief review of the industrial relations structure has been to explain why the activities of the unions in the Bay Area will be the center of attention in the remainder of this study. Where appropriate, employer or other group activity on behalf of the medical consumer will be analyzed but on the whole the unions have been the dynamic element in the area of negotiated health plans and as such will receive the greatest emphasis. This chapter has attempted to justify this decision on the grounds of the dearth of large employers in the region, the general lack of aggressiveness in health and welfare matters displayed by most employers and employer associations alike, and the local autonomy of most of the union movement.

Chapter VII | Tactics and Strategy in Health Plan Affairs

The policy process tends to reflect the goals of the highly organized because organizations provide leaders with the negotiable rewards and deprivations that make control over other leaders possible.[1]

When the period of rapid growth in negotiated health plans began in 1949, there were very few unions or employers in the Bay Area with more than a rudimentary knowledge of the issues that would be raised by this new development. In spite of their experience with group insurance in general, it is also probably true that neither the insuring organizations, the medical profession nor any of the other interested parties were aware of the new problems, or at least the accentuated form of old problems, that would develop.

Throughout the Bay Area, as in the nation as a whole, some employers and some union groups had been part of the growth of group-health insurance business prior to 1949. Some employers had made group-health plans available to their employees, usually either on the basis of joint contributions or as completely employee-financed programs. Some local unions had formed health plan groups and made coverage available to their members on a voluntary basis at the member's own expense. In a few instances, health benefits had been negotiated in collective bargaining and made part of the contract settlement. The Kaiser Plan, for ex-

---

[1] R. A. Dahl and C. E. Lindblom, *Politics, Economics and Welfare* (New York: Harper, 1953), p. 340.

ample, enrolled its first "negotiated group" in 1946, shortly after it was opened to the public. Relative to the demand for persons with specialized knowledge that sprang up with the surge of growth in the years immediately following 1949, however, the number of union or employer officials with any experience with the problems of administration in this field was minute. In addition, experience with the small-scale, voluntary, noncontractual, largely worker-financed plans of this period provided few guideposts useful in handling the new programs. Setting up a plan in the early days involved little more than establishing contact with one of the insuring organizations, choosing one of the limited number of plan options available, arranging for a method of payment (often through payroll deduction handled by the employer), and doing some educational and promotional work among the prospective members. Among other requirements, the new collectively bargained plans created the necessity for complex financial and legal machinery for the collection and handling of funds, introduced a collective-bargaining contract of fixed term into the financial arrangements, and added the problem of dealing with the frequently passive, sometimes reluctant, and occasionally combative member who would never have participated in a voluntary plan.

Not only were administrative arrangements simpler, but, under the voluntary plans, the dissatisfied member could withdraw and use the money formerly paid in premiums to purchase health care in other ways. This would include the possibility of joining an alternative health plan sponsored by some other group such as a credit union or coöperative. When the health plan became an integral part of the union contract, the individual could still make his own arrangements (and many of them did). Except in very unusual circumstances, however, he could not recapture the cash equivalent of the insurance premium paid on his behalf by his employer. Since the union or the employer had committed the individual to an insurance program usually as an alternative to an increase in direct wages, some responsibility for the successful operation of the plan had to be assumed. The massive growth of health insurance coverage would have created problems of itself, but the new system changed the conditions of operation so drastically as to create a new situation.

Some of the administrative complexities resulting from the use of the collective-bargaining instrument to provide health insurance will be discussed in chapter ix. In this chapter the pattern of developments in the area of relationships between the unions and employers and the worker-members of the plans and between the unions and the medical profession will be analyzed. In essence, the activities to be discussed involve an attempt to establish a collective-bargaining system in which the contracting parties would be the unions and some unit of organized medicine.

Although the chronology of human affairs seldom permits an unambiguous division of events into time intervals, it will be useful to break the period 1949–1958 into subperiods. For convenience of discussion, subperiods have been designated as follows: Bargaining for Fee Schedules, The Labor Health Center Episode, The Closed-panel Approach, and Back to Fee Schedules. Obviously, with so many organizations and so many alternative strategies available, at any one time several of these approaches were being tried by various groups and sometimes more than one by the same group. As far as possible, however, these divisions are arranged chronologically and their titles are intended to indicate the main emphasis of the time period in question. The several phases of activity illustrated by this classification will be discussed in turn.

Bargaining for Fee Schedules

Since the activities of unions in medical affairs have been described as introducing some of the attributes of collective bargaining into medical economics, a very brief sketch of the development and characteristics of collective bargaining as a system for structuring the relationships existing between organized groups will be helpful.

The term, collective bargaining, is relatively new and its origin is usually traced to the English economist, Beatrice Potter (Mrs. Sydney Webb), who used it in a book published in 1891.[2] Although the basic process is older than the phrase used to describe it, the modern version of collective bargaining is largely a devel-

---

[2] An excellent historical review of the evolution of collective bargaining in the United States can be found in Neil W. Chamberlain, *Collective Bargaining* (New York: McGraw-Hill, 1951), chaps. 1 and 2.

opment of the twentieth century. Currently, collective bargaining involves permanent organizations of workers and employers, formal negotiations the results of which are embodied in written contracts, and procedures for the interpretation and administration of the contracts during their lifetime. The progressive elaboration of the machinery of collective bargaining is a product of a century and a half of evolution. Tracing the steps in this evolution provides a useful analogy for the development of organized relationships in the field of medical care.

The conditions under which employees worked were originally established solely by the employer and were seldom formalized into a standard pattern applying to all employees and publicized in advance. Wages, the price paid for labor, were set unilaterally and often varied from worker to worker in an unsystematic fashion. Larger employers sometimes adopted a schedule of wage rates for various categories of jobs and made these a basis for their wage policy. These rates could be applied as the employer saw fit and changed at any time.

The formation of unions in the early nineteenth century did not necessarily lead immediately to direct negotiations as to the schedule of wage rates to be established. Although such negotiations occurred, some unions, particularly craft unions, adopted a policy similar to that of the employers. The union would formulate its own "price list" and announce that its members had agreed to work only for employers who paid such rates. When an employer wage schedule and a union price list came into conflict, the relative strength of the parties, often tested by a strike, determined which was to prevail. Something very similar to this unilateral determination of a price list by unions has persisted for some occupations, e.g., barbers, to the present time.

As union organization became more permanent, conflict between the announced wage policies of employers and unions of their employees came to be the subject of negotiation and compromise as well as strikes. Unilateral decision-making became bilateral and an agreed-on schedule of wages was the result. As this process of "collective bargaining" developed, the scope of the matters considered in the negotiations broadened, the resulting agreement was reduced to writing, and the practice of specifying the time period during which the agreement would be honored came into use. As agreements broadened in this way and were regarded as binding the parties for a definite time interval, the problem of interpreting and administering the provisions of the agreement as they applied to individual workers in day-to-day operations emerged. Out of this need came the development of the concept of a "grievance" and a procedure for resolving such problems. The grievance procedure is a formal or informal method of settling a complaint about the implementation of a decision made by the employer in the operation of his business under the collective-bargaining contract.[3]

When the unions entered the medical care area, their members found themselves dealing with a large number of individual physicians each of whom set the prices for his services at his own discretion and reserved the right to vary them from patient to patient and to change them at will. Since the great majority of the welfare plans became customers of commercial insurance companies, something vaguely similar to an employer's "price list" did exist in the form of the indemnity schedules of the companies. There was, however, no direct link between the benefits listed in the schedules and the actual charges made by the suppliers of medical care. It is true that within any given surgical schedule the indemnity paid for, say, an appendectomy, might be expected to bear somewhat the same relationship to the benefit for a tonsillectomy as the actual fees charged for each of these operations bore to each other. However, the average level of the actual dollar indemnities paid for each operation is related to the premium to be charged for the policy and not to the actual charges of physicians. In other words, the insurance company might stand ready to write a policy paying an indemnity for an appendectomy of from $75 to $200 depending on the premium the buyer was willing to pay. The fee actually paid by the patient receiving the appendectomy would be a completely separate transaction between himself and the doctor. Especially in the early days of the

---

[3] Strictly speaking, grievance procedures can exist without a formal contract or without union organization. Many companies and governmental agencies which do not deal with unions have a variety of grievance procedures and in medical matters unions have been able on occasion to develop complaint machinery but have had little success in negotiating contracts. Although some of these latter systems may be effective, the complaint machinery developed under collective bargaining is typically so much more formal and effective in protecting the worker's interest as to constitute a class by itself.

health insurance boom, there were undoubtedly large numbers of persons who assumed that the amounts listed in the insurance schedule were intended to pay the fee levied by the surgeon in full. This caused a good deal of difficulty for the insurance companies and the medical profession as well as the union administrators. There is considerable evidence, however, that a substantial number of the union and employer negotiators were fully aware of the nature of the indemnity payment-fee relationship and that their complaints stemmed from a different problem.

The labor and management representatives who negotiated the first major wave of bargained health plans in 1949 had to be concerned with two related questions: How much money could be devoted to the purchase of health insurance, and what set of benefits should be purchased with the funds available? In answering the first question, no one was more expert than the parties to negotiations themselves. In answering the second, a large amount of information was soon made available by the insuring organizations and their sales representatives, a large and growing body of brokers and consultants, and the staff personnel of the local labor and trades councils, the national unions, and the two major federations. In the Bay Area, at least some of the unions and the employers asked the local medical societies to participate in discussions to define the role this new collective-bargaining instrument would play in the health affairs of their members. The metalworking industry and the metal trades unions appear to have been the first major group to deal with the medical societies on these issues. Representatives of both the California Metal Trades Association and some of the unions approached the San Francisco Medical Society in 1949 for assistance in setting up their health plans. The society provided an agency for such consultation in the form of a "Union Labor Committee" which was later augmented by a Fee Schedule Committee. This group entered into what was to become a series of discussions with various labor and management groups extending over several years.

Although these meetings served a number of purposes, the major goal of the unions involved was the establishment of some kind of a recognized link between the indemnity schedules of the insurance companies and the probable pattern and level of fees that their members could expect to be charged by the physicians in the locality. As a minimum, the unions hoped to get help in deciding on the level and type of benefits that it would be desirable to specify in their insurance contracts. Preferably, they would have liked to arrive at a fee schedule which would be the equivalent of a price list and which the society would bind its members to accept as full payment for their services. For its part, the society's Union Labor Committee (and its successors) was careful to stress its advisory role and to deny any power, or even any inclination, to enter into an agreement concerning the fees of members of the society.

As negotiated health plans spread throughout industry, the number of labor groups participating in meetings with the society increased. In addition to officials from various local unions and trades councils, representatives of the San Francisco Labor Council were drawn into the discussions at an early stage. As a larger proportion of its member unions became involved in the welfare plan issue, the council, largely through its secretary-treasurer, George Johns, attempted to assume a more active role in the discussions.

At the outset, the labor representatives apparently accepted, at least in some measure, the advisory role in which the society's committee cast itself.[4] As the unions acquired more knowledge of the field and as some of the early plans began to show signs of suffering from cost pressures, the labor representatives began to press more vigorously for a definite fee schedule to which the society would commit its members.

In response to these pressures, the Fee Schedule Committee did formulate a fee schedule "for the guidance" of the union negotiators.[5] In attempting to use this schedule, some of the unions found that the premiums required to pay for coverage of the scope recommended and at the level of fees recommended by the society could not be financed from the money available for welfare plan use. At least one major international union did adopt the surgical

---

[4] "They [the Metal Trades Council] . . . wish to have a minimum fee schedule that would provide ample indemnification for their workers. They ask our guidance in the matter of such a fee schedule." *Bulletin,* San Francisco Medical Society, May, 1950, p. 18.

[5] The motivation for compiling such a schedule is suggested by a statement from the annual report of the society's president to the effect that this was preferable to "having lists of procedures and fees thrust upon us by others as in the past. . . ." *Ibid.,* January, 1951, p. 24.

portion of the fee schedule and incorporate it into their insurance plan. This led to an incident indicative of the situation that had developed out of the meetings. In the booklets explaining the plan's coverage furnished to the individuals enrolled in the plan, a statement appeared to the effect that the San Francisco Medical Society had approved the fee schedule. A protest was entered by the society and the next printing was altered to say that the schedule had the approval, not of the society, but of the Fee Schedule Committee.

In explaining this incident to the membership of the society, the leadership pointed out that, ". . . It has since been made clear to a responsible official of the Labor Council that it is neither the intent nor the function of either the committee or of the Board of Directors of the San Francisco Medical Society to place the stamp of approval of the San Francisco Medical Society on any fee schedule. . . ." [6]

As the question of an officially sanctioned fee schedule emerged as the basic issue, the Board of Directors of the society culminated more than a year and a half of meetings with a "statement of principles" in regard to lay-controlled group-health insurance programs (as distinct from medically sponsored plans such as the California Physicians Service). The first three of the five principles touch directly on the subject matter of this section and deserve to be quoted in full:

"1. That all members of the Society may participate. There shall be a free choice of physician, which means no panel, selected either by an insurer, a lay group or the Society.

"2. That there must be no set or frozen fee schedule. The individual doctor's right to establish with his patient the fee to be paid must be respected.

"3. There can be no 'third party' placed in the middle of the all important and confidential doctor-patient relationship." [7]

In the language of industrial relations, this declaration amounted to denying recognition of the unions as bargaining agents for their members in the area of medical care and a refusal to bargain over fees.

The official reaction of one of the participating labor groups

---

[6] *Ibid.*, May, 1951, p. 18.
[7] *Ibid.*

to these pronouncements can be found in the *Official Bulletin* of the San Francisco Labor Council. By this time, labor was referring to its meetings with the society's committees as "negotiating sessions." A few quotations from the *Bulletin* will point up the difference between the council's and the society's view of the proceedings.

. . . Certainly it is not labor's desire to challenge the doctor's right to set his own fee; rather, that is what labor has asked the doctor to do. . . . The committee of the County Medical Society, however, has drawn up a fee schedule which is not a fee schedule at all but merely a guess as to what the fee may be unless the County Medical Society is willing to support and stand behind such a schedule. . . .

In the process of the many talks between the Medical Society committee and labor, it had been labor's understanding that the Medical Society would urge its members to cooperate in maintaining the fee schedule when it had been approved. Why else would labor sit down and talk with the Medical Society committee? Why else, indeed, would the Medical Society committee participate in such negotiating sessions? . . .[8]

By the middle of 1951 almost two years of discussions between various union groups and representatives of the San Francisco Medical Society had been completed. A fee schedule had been developed but the society had refused to give it any official sanction. Meanwhile cost pressures on existing plans were making themselves felt and at least some of the pressure was attributed to rising surgical fees.[9]

The unions had not only failed to "negotiate" an officially sponsored fee schedule but had found that the society would not accept the principle of negotiation and claimed to be unable to provide a medical bargaining representative with power to reach a binding agreement.

By this time the San Francisco Labor Council had begun to lay

[8] San Francisco Labor Council, *Official Bulletin*, December 5, 1951.

[9] The president of the society recognized the problem in a discussion of "Physician Responsibility in Medical Welfare Plans" in the society's *Bulletin* of November, 1951. He reported that a plan recently set up had adopted the "relatively liberal" fee schedule of the Union Labor Committee only to find that fees two or three times the published schedule had been levied by "a few physicians, with some possible padding of charges by a few others. . . ." (pp. 17 and 42). An official of the Painter's Union was quoted as early as August, 1949, as reporting that "the much-publicized employer-paid plan which the Painters negotiated a few months ago was proving to be a headache and a disillusionment in many respects. . . ." *Labor Review*, Bay Cities Metal Trades Council, August 17, 1949.

the groundwork for the next round of developments. The first move in a campaign that was to culminate in an attempt to establish a labor health center was made in July, 1951. If the traditional bargaining process could not give labor a voice in setting the terms on which medical care would be made available, something might be accomplished by organizing a system of producing and distributing medical care in which the nonmedical aspects of health care would be directly under labor control.

The Labor Health Center Episode

Although the local subdivisions of the national unions continued to work on their health and welfare problems, including relations with the medical profession, the center of the stage during 1952 was held by the San Francisco Labor Council with its dramatic proposal for the establishment of a labor health center. The first activity of the council seems to have come about as a by-product of a trip to Washington, D. C. in April, 1951, by a committee of the council in connection with the wage stabilization program operating during the Korean emergency. The committee took advantage of this opportunity to visit the newly established Health Center of the Hotel Trades Council and the Hotel Association in New York City and was apparently impressed by this type of arrangement.

What appears to have been the beginning of a campaign to build support for a San Francisco Health Center was launched in the labor council's *Official Bulletin* of July 18, 1951. This issue was devoted entirely to what was announced to be the first of several articles on medical care costs. Entitled "The High Cost of Medical Care," this first article announced in its opening sentence that "the cost of medical treatment and hospitalization is and long has been too high for the workingman's pocket-book. . . ." and went on to discuss the California Physicians Service. Quoting medical spokesmen to the effect that CPS received its original impetus in 1939 from the need to counter Governor Olson's proposal for a state system of compulsory medical insurance, the article concluded that: "It seems highly questionable whether CPS is the answer to the urgent needs of the people, whether something designed primarily as a political weapon can meet the challenge of present-day conditions, whether a medical hierarchy so devoted to the status quo and so fearful of change . . . can develop a program capable of growth and adaptation to fit the changing times and changing needs."

The second article appeared in the *Bulletin* of November 7, 1951, and dealt with hospital charges. A table of ward bed daily rates for sixteen San Francisco hospitals was reproduced showing that, on the average, rates had increased just under 80 per cent between July, 1946, and October, 1951. The theme of the discussion was that, "the cost of medical care has constantly outstripped the efforts of organized labor to provide health and welfare plans which will protect their members. . . ."

Immediately after this article came the next contribution in the *Bulletin* of November 14, 1951. This issue was devoted to "The Labor Health Center" and described three health centers established and run by labor groups. These were the Labor Health Institute, sponsored by Local 688 of the Teamsters Union in St. Louis (established in 1945), the New York Hotel Trades Council and Hotel Association Health Center (1950), and the Medical Service Plan of Philadelphia (1951), sponsored by the then-AFL Central Labor Union (the organizational equivalent of the San Francisco Labor Council).[10] The bulletin claimed that each center enjoyed "The enthusiastic backing of the medical profession in the various communities."

Estimating that negotiated health plans were generating an annual income of almost five million dollars in San Francisco, the writer suggested that: "Maybe that kind of money would buy more medical care for our people than it does. Perhaps a medical center would provide more and better service than our present health plans can offer. Undoubtedly the medical center merits a good deal of thoughtful investigation on the part of the San Francisco labor movement."

The series of articles concluded three weeks later with an essay on "Organized Medicine's Failure." This was the review of the relations with the San Francisco Medical Society from which the quotations in the preceding section of this chapter were taken.

In summary, the four articles could be viewed (1) as arguing

---

[10] Each of these programs is described in U. S. Department of Health, Education, and Welfare, *Management and Union Health and Medical Programs,* Public Health Service Pub. 329, Washington, 1954.

that CPS, the medical profession's approach to the health insurance issue, was inadequate; (2) as establishing the fact of rising costs in the hospital study; (3) as suggesting the health center alternative; and (4) as castigating the medical society for a lack of coöperation in dealing with the earlier attempt to cope with the problem, the fee schedule approach.

The next major step in the campaign was a resolution passed by the San Francisco Labor Council in March, 1952, providing for a survey of medical care for AFL workers and their families. The resolution called for "an analysis of existing health and welfare programs, a report of the necessary features to be included in a comprehensive labor health program, and a plan for achieving this goal. . . ." Dr. E. Richard Weinerman was retained by the council to conduct the survey.[11]

The Weinerman survey produced an impressive mass of evidence as to the status of the medical care programs of most of the AFL unions in the city of San Francisco. On the basis of his findings the author made two major criticisms of the existing situation. First, he criticized the type of medical care available under the typical health insurance contract as neglecting to provide for either preventive or catastrophic coverage. Second, he criticized the financial arrangements for the type of care that was included, as being inefficient and uneconomical. Dr. Weinerman estimated that "some 50 cents of each premium dollar is diverted into channels other than actual 'health value' for members." This estimate included not only the costs of inefficient administration, insurance company profits, and additions to reserves, but all forms of abuse as well. For these reasons, Dr. Weinerman advanced as the "primary conclusion" of his survey that adequate health services could "best be achieved through the organization of medical group practice in modern health centers under the auspices or with the representation of the union membership and the contributing employers. . . ."

As a step toward implementing the proposals of the report, Dr. Weinerman and the council entered into discussions with the

[11] This information is from the report of the survey: E. R. Weinerman, *Labor Plans for Health*, San Francisco Labor Council, 1952. Dr. Weinerman has been in private practice for several years in the East Bay and has in the past been associated with both the Kaiser Foundation Health Plan and the School of Public Health of the University of California.

Rockefeller Foundation for financial aid in launching the health center. This aid was seen as important as a means of paying for the costs of organization and planning, of providing equipment and physical facilities, of recruiting staff, and of providing working capital during the transition period when the participating unions would be converting to the health center approach. Discussions were also held with employer groups as to the attitude to be taken by employers in this question.

As the proposal took definite form, it called for the establishment of one or more physical facilities or "centers" where a staff of physicians employed by the organization would furnish diagnostic services and outpatient medical care, arrangements for hospitalization in the community's existing hospitals financed through hospital insurance with the possibility of health center hospitals held in reserve, and arrangements for in-hospital surgery and medical care to be provided by the center's staff of physicians. Nonmedical administration would be under the control of the council and the participating unions. Unions would decide voluntarily whether to affiliate with the center and those electing to do so would be expected to offer their members a choice between the center health program and a more orthodox medical insurance coverage. Throughout its promotion of the idea of a center, the labor council was at great pains to insist "that the voluntary nature of the program be clearly understood. . . . the determination to make use of or not to make use of the health center program must of course be a matter of voluntary choice on the part of the union member, the local union, and/or the trades council. . . . In establishing its health center program, the San Francisco Labor Council merely adds an additional possibility to the present range of welfare plan choices which are available to the labor movement." [12]

Meanwhile, the San Francisco Medical Society reacted vigorously to the publication of the Weinerman report and the subsequent official approval by the unions affiliated with the council of its proposal. New committees were appointed to consider the problem, four special meetings of the Board of Directors and six extra meetings of the Executive Council were held, two general membership meetings that taxed the capacity of the society's

[12] San Francisco Labor Council, *Official Bulletin*, July 30, 1952.

auditorium were devoted to this topic, mail communications and special surveys of membership attitudes were undertaken, and meetings were held with labor council committees, with employer groups, and with insurance company representatives. Liaison groups from the California Medical Association and the national headquarters of the American Medical Association in Chicago were also brought into the deliberations.

Out of this flurry of activity a pattern of strategy emerged including the following items:

1. The principle of health centers, established and controlled completely by labor groups, was rejected as unacceptable to the profession.

2. An analysis of the Weinerman report was made, an "answer" prepared, and a tentative offer of a substitute experimental medical system operating under medical society control was advanced. Nothing came of this proposal.

3. The society reëntered the fee schedule arena and established a new committee to draw up a plan that would involve "adoption of a fee schedule to apply to income brackets below a certain income and subject to periodic revision. It must further be under the direct control of the membership of the San Francisco Medical Society. . . ."

The wording quoted above appeared in a questionnaire submitted to the membership of the society. The proposal to adopt such a schedule received 779 favorable votes and 76 unfavorable. This was interpreted as making it "obvious that the membership was ready to take a bold step forward in medical economic progress by proposing Society formulation and supervision of prepaid health and welfare insurance, with a Society fee schedule to cover such plans." [13]

The reader will remember that less than a year and a half prior to the favorable vote on the proposal for a society-sponsored fee schedule, labor groups had been informed that it was "neither the intent nor the function" of the society to place their stamp of approval on any fee schedule. In addition, the principle had been

[13] The preceding quotations are from Samuel R. Sherman, M.D., "Union Labor Health and Welfare Insurance Plans," *California Medicine,* Vol. 79, No. 3, September, 1953, pp. 266–67. The questionnaire had been submitted in October, 1952. Dr. Sherman had been active in the contacts between the society and labor and became president of the society in 1954.

enunciated that there must be no set or frozen fee schedule and that the right of the individual doctor to establish with his patient the fee to be paid must be respected.

Although the seventeen months between the date of these statements and the acceptance of the new "principle" of a society-sanctioned fee schedule saw a number of other developments—all of which pressed the profession in the same direction—there is little doubt but that the prospect of a labor-sponsored health center was the most important single factor in bringing about the new policy. The society appears to have hoped that the official fee schedule approach might serve to divert the labor groups from establishing their center. In the event that such a center came into existence, the fee schedule system would at least increase the attractiveness of the alternative insurance programs that the unions had committed themselves to make available to individual members. The health center appeared to have generated progress toward labor's original goal of a definite fee schedule which the society could be counted on to "support and stand behind."

Unfortunately for its status as a bargaining weapon, the proposal soon encountered some insuperable difficulties. For one thing, after lengthy negotiations, the application for funds from the Rockefeller Foundation was denied. The refusal was couched in terms of the plan's failure to conform to the stated objectives of the foundation program. The labor council representatives felt that the refusal resulted, at least in part, from a reluctance to support a plan that appeared to be controversial and that lacked the backing of either the contributing employers or the local medical profession. Whatever the reasons for the denial of funds, it is unlikely that this would have been fatal to the proposal if it had enjoyed enthusiastic support from the council's member unions and if other factors had not been operative as well.[14]

It will be remembered that a body like the San Francisco Labor Council fills the role of a lobbyist in the political field and a local coördinator of economic action, e.g., strikes and picketing. It is not a party to collective-bargaining contracts in its own right and has only the relatively meager funds generated by the per capita

---

[14] The Philadelphia AFL Medical Service Plan, for example, was financed initially by loans from various sources such as "builders, hospital equipment concerns and others." U. S. Department of Health, Education, and Welfare, *op. cit.*, p. 89.

payments of member unions at its disposal. It must tailor its activities to fit the policies of the national unions and trades councils to which its member local unions belong. All this means that there are relatively narrow limits to the powers that can be exercised independently by the council. It is primarily dependent on methods of persuasion rather than authority.

In addition to these considerations, a perusal of the labor and public press reports of the day and the information gleaned from interviews and discussions with a substantial number of representatives of all the parties involved, suggests that the reasons for the failure of the center to materialize can be summed up as follows:

1. *National union policy.*—Some of the national unions whose locals and trades councils furnish substantial parts of the membership of the council have standardized health insurance programs and seem relatively uninterested in promoting local variations. An example is the Teamster Security Fund's administrative arrangements which are uniform for the eleven western states. In 1952 the Teamsters were one of the power centers of the council and a lack of enthusiasm on their part would have been an important drawback.

2. *The problem of institutional identification.*—Some of the national unions involved as well as their locals and regional subdivisions regard their health plans as important "union-building" devices. There apparently was some feeling that participation in a council-sponsored, multiunion health center would weaken member identification with the individual union program.

3. *The problem of geographical coverage.*—As noted in an earlier chapter, the geography of the Bay Area and its numerous political subdivisions have restricted the San Francisco Labor Council's jurisdiction to a small area and resulted in a widely dispersed geographical residential pattern. A single health center or a small number of health centers would be easily accessible to only a minority of the membership of many locals. This was a problem particularly for those locals or trades councils with a jurisdiction covering a large geographical area such as all of northern California.

4. *The availability of the Kaiser Foundation Health Plan.*—Much of the appeal of the health center proposal stemmed from

two of its characteristics—the provision of comprehensive care with service or full coverage benefits and the direct participation of the unions affiliated with the center in the nonmedical aspects of policy making. The first of these items, comprehensive service benefits, was already available from the Kaiser Foundation Health Plan. The Kaiser Plan was a going concern with modern physical facilities, fairly widely dispersed in the Bay Area and with a large professional staff. Faced with the obviously formidable obstacles to establishing their own operation, some union leaders have been willing to compromise the advantages of full union control and work with the Kaiser organization.

A further suggested explanation for the failure of the proposed center to win broader support, is that many workers feel that such centers resemble charity clinics. Some observers believe that the health plans have enabled many low-income workers to pay for their medical care as private patients for the first time. They are thought to be reluctant to support any plan that might appear to deprive them of this cherished status.

As the threat of the labor health center faded, a good deal of the urgency and spirit of compromise behind the activities of the San Francisco Medical Society seems to have dissipated fairly rapidly. The committee charged with the preparation of an official society fee schedule did not complete its work until some eight months after its formation. This schedule apparently was not released to the public but it was described by the secretary of the labor council as equivalent to a "$400 maximum fee surgical schedule." [15]

If this is an accurate characterization, the fee schedule was probably about one-third higher than the indemnity schedule then provided in the typical union contract. (This of course does not mean that all fees actually charged would necessarily have been equal to the schedule and one-third higher than the corresponding allowance.) This estimate is consistent with a statement by a medical society consultant who described the schedule as "not realistic" and substantially higher than the Alameda-Contra Costa Medical Association's median fee list. This latter list certainly would not be described as a low schedule for its time. In spite of the level of fees, the schedule was intended to apply only to

[15] San Francisco Labor Council, *Official Bulletin,* November 18, 1953.

families with annual incomes of less than $5,000. In addition, the schedule came equipped with the ubiquitous "statement of principles," which included declarations that the schedule was intended "solely as a guide," and that ". . . No member of the Society is obligated or compelled to work by this schedule . . . ," and that ". . . The principle of co-insurance should be invoked in this fee schedule whenever possible. . . ." [16]

It would be hard to find any evidence in this program of the aforementioned "bold step forward . . . by proposing Society formulation and supervision of prepaid health and welfare insurance, with a Society fee schedule to cover such plans. . . ." Instead we have a relatively high schedule intended for guidance only, limited to the lower-income groups, with fees that member-doctors are not only free to ignore but to which unspecified additional amounts were to be added as a matter of policy.

It is difficult to avoid the conclusion that as the menace of the labor health center receded, the society welcomed the opportunity to revert to its position at the time of the original breakdown in negotiations over fee schedules two years earlier.

This is not to conclude that the health center episode had no beneficial results from labor's point of view. It showed a potential for independent action, demonstrated some of the results that might be expected to flow from such action, strengthened the forces within the medical profession locally and in the state that were in favor of a policy of positive coöperation, and assisted individual unions in their own dealings with the professional groups. Even if the idea is never revived by the labor council or by a large national union, the comment of the local representative of an important union group seems appropriate—"It served its purpose."

The "Closed-panel" Approach

"Here is something to remember in dealing with unions. Negotiating with employers, their strategy revolves around two principles —demand more than you expect to get, and break the front of management by getting a favorable contract with one company, by one means or another, and thus establish a precedent. . . . unions now are seeking our [physicians'] services which are the

---

[16] *Ibid.*

chief commodity of any health and welfare plan. They are using the same tactics. . . ." [17]

Throughout the period when the attempts to negotiate a fee schedule were being tried and also while the labor council was trying to organize its health center, a number of national unions and at least one trades council were borrowing a weapon from their collective-bargaining arsenal for use in their dealings with medicine. If the medical society, the organized representative of the profession, would not agree to negotiate a price list and would not even support its own firm price list perhaps the unions could take the initiative. Several union groups attempted to bypass organized medicine to deal with the doctors as individuals. The technique was simple. The union groups would announce a price list for medical services (usually the schedule of indemnity allowances in their insurance contracts) and circularize the doctors in the area with invitations to sign an agreement as individuals or small groups to accept these fees as full payment for their services. Medical ethics are usually interpreted as preventing the union from publicizing the names of the doctors agreeing to such an arrangement. The customary method of circumventing this block is to notify the members of the health plan that the names of coöperating physicians may be secured by telephoning the union. The member could then patronize one of these physicians with the assurance that there would be no out-of-pocket costs for services covered by the insurance contract. Under these arrangements the union, in effect, has enrolled a group or "panel" of doctors to provide service benefits under a fee-for-service method of payment.

In order to be sure of securing the advantages of this arrangement a patient must select a doctor from those who have agreed to work under the schedule. A patient who selects a doctor not on the panel of coöperating doctors, however, loses only the advance assurance that the charge will be no greater than the specified fee. The amount of the indemnity allowance will be paid to the doctor of his choice and this sum may or may not cover the fee actually charged. Occasionally arrangements of this type are referred to as "closed panels," although this is not an accurate designation. Any

---

[17] Letter to the editor of the *Bulletin,* San Francisco Medical Society, from a former president of the society, Dr. William F. Bender, January, 1954, p. 16.

doctor usually can be included in the panel at will by agreeing to certain conditions. Further, since any nonpanel doctor can receive the full indemnity payment for the plan, the only part of the system that can be said to be "closed" to noncoöperating doctors is the referral list.

It is true that inclusion in the referral list may have an important bearing on the ability of a given doctor to share in the medical business of a health plan. The essence of a closed-panel system, however, is the refusal to pay indemnities to nonpanel doctors. The Kaiser Foundation Health Plan, which bears the brunt of the local attacks on closed panels, is "closed" in two senses. In addition to nonpayment of benefits to outside physicians, doctors as a whole cannot elect to be included in the medical staff at their option. Permitting universal affiliation with its panel providing certain minimum conditions are met, however, does not of itself protect a plan from the closed-panel charge as long as noncoöperating doctors cannot receive payments from the funds of the plan. By these standards, the California Physicians Service was a closed panel (although a very large one) until after World War II. There is little doubt that the need to eliminate this feature was behind the postwar reorganization that, among other things, permitted nonparticipating doctors to collect fees from CPS.

None of the unions attempting the panel approach to the problem of establishing a firm price structure for medical services has been successful to any significant degree. The Painters Fund is reported to have been one of the most successful in assembling a panel; in 1956 it had enrolled about forty-three doctors. Since the plan covers almost ten thousand primary subscribers plus their dependents and these members work for employers scattered over seven counties, the panel could have little practical effect. The panel approach has been most popular with the unions affiliated with the Building Trades Council, but in May, 1957, the San Francisco Labor Council also attempted to exploit this device. Like its predecessors, this attempt enjoyed little success but the method employed illustrates the technique. The council, through its secretary, George Johns, prepared a fee schedule covering home, hospital and office calls, and surgery. The schedule had a $300 maximum fee for surgery indicating that the fees specified fell somewhere between those listed in the CPS schedule for fami-

lies with annual incomes of $4,200 and those for families with
incomes of $6,000. Along with an explanatory letter, the sched-
ule was sent by registered mail to the doctors in San Francisco. Each doctor was then asked to sign and return a statement
agreeing "to limit their charges in conformance with the above
maximums in cases involving union members and dependents
covered by health and welfare plans."

Labor groups believe that enough physicians in practice in the
Bay Area would accept this system to make it work if it were not
for the opposition of organized medicine to the panel approach.
Although the medical societies have not publicly threatened official action against members agreeing to such arrangements, there
is no question but that the practice is frowned on within the societies.[18] As long as panels assembled in this way are relatively
small and remain "open" (i.e., pay indemnities to all physicians
serving the patient-members of the plan), the profession could
live with the system. The danger to the profession lies in the possibility that the panels might grow to a size that would permit the
sponsoring groups to deny nonmember-doctors access to membership except on terms specified by the sponsors.

To make such a denial effective, the sponsoring group has to
be able to overcome the resistance of some of its employee members to transferring their medical business from their present
physicians to doctors who are panel members. Only if the number
of plan members who would object to such a shift can be reduced to politically manageable proportions can the panel organizers be successful in converting their panel from an open
to a closed status, thereby acquiring real bargaining leverage
against the medical profession. An example of the situation that
may result when a health plan has achieved this position is provided by the United Mine Workers Welfare and Retirement Fund.
At times the Miner's Fund has experimented with requiring surgery
to be performed, as far as practicable, only by physicians certified
by the appropriate specialty board. It has also experimented with

[18] The San Francisco Medical Society's official reaction to the labor council's
attempt to set up a panel was a "letter" to its members signed by the president
of the society published in the *Bulletin* of June, 1957. The letter noted that there
had been no consultation between the society and the council on the schedule and
concluded: "The Society's Executive Committee feels that the proposed schedule
is *not* reasonable, adequate or realistic." (p. 22).

requiring attending physicians to consult with a specialist before permitting hospitalization in nonemergency cases.[19] Objections were entered to both of these procedures by various medical societies since the first denied many physicians payment for surgery they might be qualified to perform and the second tended to convince the patient that he might as well have gone directly to the consulting specialist.

More recently, the fund is reported to have specified the doctors in particular communities to whom it would pay indemnities while excluding others (i.e., setting up a closed panel). It has also encouraged the organization of group clinics and sponsored the entry of new doctors into a community. Organized medicine is reported to have retaliated by refusing to admit certain doctors allied with the fund to the county medical societies and, as of 1958, legal action was being initiated.[20]

The circumstances under which the Mine Workers Fund operates illustrate the potentialities of organized consumer activity in an exaggerated form compared to those of smaller funds located in metropolitan areas. These same potentialities, however, are inherent in substantial degree in any instance where the organized groups represent a large fraction of the medical business of a community (as in San Francisco). The medical profession seems to be well aware of this fact.

It is interesting that some union groups are reluctant to become involved in the recruitment and maintenance of a panel of physicians. They feel that union-maintained panel lists imply an endorsement or sponsorship of particular physicians that they may not wish to undertake. This attitude reflects a feeling that they are unlikely to be able to build up a panel of sufficient size and balance among specialties and geographical areas to be effective. Even if a satisfactory panel could be recruited, they believe it would be wiser to avoid entanglement in these arrangements unless the union is able to exert more control over quality of medical care and costs than the panel device promises to give them under present conditions.

---

[19] Warren F. Draper, M.D., "The Quest of the UMWA Welfare and Retirement Fund for the Best Medical Care Obtainable for its Beneficiaries," paper presented at the Annual Meeting of the American Association for the Surgery of Trauma, November 1, 1957.

[20] *Wall Street Journal,* Pacific Coast Edition, March 12, 1958.

An interesting example of a union that has successfully organized a panel that meets the objection of lack of control is provided by the health plan of New York Local 338 of the Retail, Wholesale, and Department Store Union. This local has developed a panel of about 55 physicians who provide a comprehensive coverage to some 5,000 members and 15,000 dependents on a service benefit basis.[21] The doctors are reimbursed through a capitation (flat fee per patient) system and also engage in private practice. The plan has been in operation since 1940 and is reported to have aroused little opposition from the medical profession. The local employs a physician as medical director who is responsible for recruiting the panel and for all contacts with the member-doctors. The director and the panel doctors hold regular meetings at which problems of quality of care are discussed. The role of the medical director may be the crucial factor in explaining why the direct recruitment of panels by union officials has not been successful in San Francisco.

Failing in their attempt to bypass the medical societies and reach fee agreements with individual doctors, labor groups moved to exploit another version of the closed-panel approach. During what was probably the peak of labor's struggle with rising medical costs in 1953 and 1954, the Kaiser Foundation Health Plan completed major additions to its hospital facilities in the city of San Francisco and in the rapidly growing suburban area of the East Bay. This not only increased the membership capacity of the Kaiser Plan but also provided wide geographical dispersion of facilities for the first time.

As noted earlier, the Kaiser Plan offers comprehensive medical care with the "certainty of coverage" feature that permits the patient to know in advance the out-of-pocket cost (if any) associated with any item of medical service. In the context of the present discussion, the Kaiser Plan in the Bay Area could be regarded as

---

[21] Information in this section has been taken from the statement of Max Steinbock, *Hearings on the Extension of Voluntary Health Insurance*, School of Public Health, Columbia University, New York, 1955, pp. 74–77 and from a letter from Mr. Steinbock to the author.

This union has a number of interesting welfare arrangements in New York and it might be pointed out that the much-publicized Labor Health Institute of Teamsters Local 688 in St. Louis was originally organized while the St. Louis group in question was also affiliated with the Retail, Wholesale, and Department Store Union.

an already existing closed panel of some 300 physicians, operating in modern hospital and clinic facilities and fairly well located to serve the bulk of the membership of many union groups. Affiliation with the plan appeared to some unions to offer an alternative to continued operation under indemnity insurance programs. The availability of membership in the Kaiser Plan would either meet their cost problems directly, or indirectly through providing bargaining pressure with the medical societies.

Occupying a leading role in the new situation was the Joint Executive Board of Culinary Workers, Bartenders, and Hotel and Club Service Workers, the bargaining arm of six locals of the Hotel and Restaurant Employees and Bartenders International Union (usually referred to simply as the Culinary Workers for obvious reasons).[22] The locals making up the Joint Board became involved in health and welfare problems in 1951. Their health plan arrangements followed the collective-bargaining structure that already existed in the "industry." Each of the four employer associations with which they bargain became the base for a separate welfare trust fund arrangement.

With an occupational jurisdiction ranging from head waiter in a luxury hotel on Nob Hill to dishwasher in a small bar and grill at a less fashionable address, with a heterogeneous mixture of age groups and racial groups, and with a large percentage of women and transient workers, the Culinary Workers present a health plan problem of truly formidable proportions. As evidence of that fact, between 1951 and 1956 the Joint Board's health and welfare business had passed through the hands of four different commercial insurance companies and was in 1958 resting somewhat uneasily with a choice of coverage between the Kaiser Plan and CPS.[23]

All four of the Culinary Workers' welfare trust funds began operations early in 1951 but soon ran into financial difficulties. On the assumption that the first-year losses were the result of a need for "catching up" on a backlog of care, the insurance companies

---

[22] One of the health centers referred to in the review of the labor health center episode is sponsored by the New York branch of this international union.

[23] Two of the funds had dealt successively with the Connecticut General, Occidental, and Continental Casualty companies while the other two had been underwritten in turn by the Liberty Mutual, Occidental, and Continental Casualty companies. The changes resulted from consistently bad loss experience resulting in a recurrent need to propose higher premiums and/or reduced benefits.

continued the contracts into the second year. When loss ratios (benefits paid/premiums) continued to exceed 100 per cent, pressure mounted for an increase in premiums or a reduction in benefits. An increase in the employer-paid premium contributions was precluded because this amount was part of the collective-bargaining contract and had been fixed for the five-year term of the contract or until 1955. About halfway through the second year two of the funds replaced their original insurance carrier with another company. By the end of the second year the other two funds had also replaced the original underwriter and the benefits to be provided by the plans in the future had been reduced in an attempt to bring loss ratios under control. As the third year (1953) came to a close with continued substantial losses, it became obvious that drastic action would be needed to save the health plan.

The opening of the new Kaiser hospital and medical center in San Francisco suggested an alternative to the hard-pressed officials of the Joint Board. Two of the four funds, accounting for about 13,000 of the approximately 19,000 employees eligible for benefits, entered into negotiations with Kaiser representatives. The possible transfer of a block of 13,000 employees plus their dependents from the open medical market to a closed panel offered the labor groups an excellent opportunity to dramatize their health and welfare problems. The impact would be sharpened by the fact that the Culinary Workers could be said to have another block of almost 6,000 employees in reserve in their other two funds. There were also a large number of other union health plans ready to proclaim vigorously the difficulties that rising medical costs were causing.

With the two Culinary Worker funds scheduled to enter the Kaiser Plan on April 1, 1954, the San Francisco Labor Council, in conjunction with the AFL State Federation of Labor and eleven other central labor councils, took the lead in arranging a two-day Health and Welfare Plan Conference in San Francisco in March. In the March 3 issue of the *Official Bulletin*, the council secretary penned "An Open Letter to MY Doctor" which began with the statement that a group of "many thousand workers would join the Kaiser Plan in a few weeks." To make sure that the significance of this "precedent" was understood, the letter reviewed the failure of the fee discussions and concluded that "it seems the new trend is toward service plans." Already concerned with the expansion of the Kaiser facilities, the medical society reacted promptly. One week later, the *Bulletin* of March 10 carried an official reply from Dr. Samuel Sherman, president of the society and veteran of the earlier fee discussions. Once again the society showed its adaptability to changing conditions as Dr. Sherman noted that, "Since our last conference, some of the thinking of our medical members has become more elastic in regard to types of prepaid health insurance. . . ." The letter went on to suggest that the council "open the door and continue discussion . . ." toward a solution of their problems.

Continuing their offensive, the labor representatives in attendance at the conference climaxed two days of discussion, much of it outspokenly critical of the hospital, medical, and pharmaceutical groups, by adopting a series of committee reports. One of these concluded that "the Kaiser Foundation Plan is at this time the most attractive one to trade union groups. . . ." Other reports recommended action on labor-controlled health centers and an intensified effort to recruit panels of doctors.

The medical society's counter to the transfers to the Kaiser Plan, both actual and threatened, took two forms. Society influence was exerted to bring about the adoption by the Kaiser Plan of a policy of offering all members of negotiated plans the choice of enrolling in an open-panel type of insurance plan as an alternative to Kaiser coverage. This "free-choice" policy had the effect of reducing the ability of the union leaders to manipulate their health plan business so as to secure bargaining advantages since it tended to make the distribution of each member's business a matter of individual choice.[24] As a result of this development the two Culinary Workers' funds that entered the Kaiser Plan in April, 1954, offered only Kaiser coverage to their members for one year and then worked out a choice between Kaiser and the Continental Casualty Company. The other two funds continued their indemnity coverage on an exclusive basis until the end of 1954 and then adopted the choice system. The development of the choice program had both advantages and disadvantages to the union, the Kaiser Plan, and the medical profession in general. Among the more important ad-

---

[24] This system is discussed at some length in chapter ix in the section on the choice program.

vantages, the program protected the union leadership from the necessity of insisting that all members utilize the Kaiser facilities to benefit from the welfare plan, protected Kaiser from the charge of capturing involuntary membership and, for the medical profession, retained the medical business of about 8,000 of the 19,000 members eligible for welfare benefits.

A more positive result of the various types of pressures that the labor movement had been able to bring to bear on the doctors over the years was the launching of a new series of attempts by the medical profession to compete with the certainty of coverage feature of Kaiser. In practice, this amounted to a return to the fee schedule approach in one form or another.

Back to Fee Schedules

While the events described in earlier sections were taking place, a different pattern of developments emerged in another sector of the Bay Area. In the East Bay attempts to "negotiate" with the Alameda-Contra Costa Medical Association (Alameda County Medical Society prior to the merger in 1950) had been made by a few unions and desultory talk of a health center, possibly sponsored by a major national union or organized as a form of consumer coöperative, had been heard. Also, since the Kaiser Plan was based in Oakland, Kaiser's role as an alternative to other health plans had been discussed. Reflecting the locus of power in employer, union, and medical organization, however, the developments in San Francisco had tended to dominate the more tentative stirrings of activity in the East Bay. Nevertheless, in chapter v it was noted that the Alameda County Medical Society had been the original financial sponsors of the northern California Blue Cross organization and also that they had furnished much of the leadership in a campaign of criticism of CPS that was responsible, in part, for the split between CPS and Blue Cross. In the new era of health plan–medical society relationships, the ACCMA was once more to play an important role.

The roots of the new development go back to the end of World War II when the Alameda society adopted a policy of moving aggressively to improve the public relations of the medical profession in the East Bay. During the war the booming population growth of the area had combined with the wartime shortages of medical personnel to create a situation marked by a good deal of public resentment. As the war ended the Kaiser (then Permanente) Health Plan shifted the base of its activities from the rapidly declining shipbuilding industry to the general public in the East Bay. In Sacramento, Governor Earl Warren was pressing a serious attempt to establish a state health insurance system. Assessing the situation, the Alameda society decided that a positive program was needed to rehabilitate the position of the medical profession. To direct the program the society brought in Rollen Waterson, the first full-time executive secretary to be employed by a county medical society in northern California. Waterson had been working in a similar capacity with the medical society in Lake County, Indiana, for several years. On his arrival in Oakland, he immediately launched a campaign, in his words, to "urbanize the country doctor."

It would be unfair to Waterson's very real abilities to describe his activities as those of "public relations" as this term is usually understood. Although he did perform public relations work in this sense in very effective fashion,[25] his influence within the medical profession over the years was exerted in other important matters.

The significance of the appointment of Waterson was that, for the first time, an important medical society had organized itself to deal continuously with the public generally and, more specifically, with the representatives of the variety of organizations with whom the medical profession came into contact. Prior to the creation of the post of full-time, lay executive secretary, the Alameda society (like most others) had carried on its business with the aid of the part-time services of a member physician and part-time clerical assistance.[26] In addition to the part-time secretary the society's

---

[25] For example, during the campaign for state health insurance, the Alameda society countered the charge that many citizens could not afford medical care by inserting the following advertisement in East Bay newspapers: "Wanted . . . information concerning anyone in Alameda County who believes he cannot get needed care because he hasn't the means to pay his doctor." (*Bulletin*, Alameda County Medical Society, July 1951.) The *Bulletin* itself was established by Waterson and in its first issue ten new committees were proposed including among them, Public Relations, Speakers Bureau, Newspaper Relations, and Legislative Subcommittee.

[26] In less than ten years the society, by then the Alameda-Contra Costa Medical Association, occupied a new two-story building and employed about forty people. Almost half of this rather startling total made up the staff of the Blood Bank, an

executive arm included a president, usually a physician subject to the demands of an active practice, elected annually. Policy matters of substance were handled by a committee system of member-physicians. Except for the addition of a full-time lay secretary no major change in the executive arrangements occurred, but the existence of an energetic representative continuously engaged in conducting the day-to-day affairs of the organization represented an important break with the former system. As the interrelationships between medicine and the other elements of the community became more complex, the full-time secretary provided a point of contact through which the society's policies could be transmitted to the public and through which the public's point of view on medical issues could be transmitted to the profession. A good case can be made for the proposition that the device of a lay executive secretary, at least in the society, introduced a kind of "mediator" into the relationships between members and organized segments of the public.[27]

Something of the same "mediation" function is performed by the lay administrative staff of the California Physicians Service. Exposed to continuous contact with the problems of medical economics as seen by the consumer and enjoying some measure of status and confidence within the medical profession, these personnel often serve as a channel of communication that facilitates growth of understanding on both sides.

Although Waterson's activities should be regarded as a consequence as well as a cause of the new approaches to medical economics that developed in the society and in the California Medical Association, there is no question but that his influence has been substantial.[28] Combined with the pressures generated by the

---

activity taken over administratively in the postwar period but having little to do with the society's activities. Most of the societies in the Bay Area had also hired full-time secretaries by this time and had shown similar patterns of staff growth relative to their size.

[27] Waterson has remarked that a majority of his efforts were directed to "working with the doctors" rather than with the public.

[28] In the first issue of the *Bulletin* of the Alameda society in June, 1946, Editor Waterson stated, "we believe that the future of the private practice of medicine can be preserved if, in addition to voluntary prepayment, county medical societies . . . will protect the public from those very few individual physicians who cannot, with enlightened selfishness, cooperate with their colleagues through their county medical societies, and who cannot deliver an ethical service, honestly priced."

In 1952 Waterson began serving as a consultant with the state medical associa-

expansion of the Kaiser Plan into new territory and the efforts of the labor movement to utilize the labor health center and possible transfer to Kaiser as bargaining threats, the result was a series of developments that went some distance in the direction of labor's original demands for a firm fee list, supported by the professional associations.

The first step was taken by the Alameda-Contra Costa Medical Association. During the winter of 1953–1954 the Kaiser Plan was bringing two newly constructed hospitals into service, one of them located in Contra Costa County. Having faced the competition of the Kaiser Plan in Oakland for years, the ACCMA was ready to move farther and faster to meet this situation than its San Francisco counterpart. The plan adopted was the promulgation of a "median fee list" (in official discussion, the designation "list" was consistently used rather than "schedule"). In essence, the ACCMA adopted the policy that the San Francisco Labor Council had unsuccessfully urged the San Francisco Medical Society to accept. It published a complete fee list and announced that, in the absence of a prior agreement to the contrary, the indicated fees would be regarded as the maximum to be charged except in unusual circumstances. In the event of a dispute over fees the committee considering the dispute was instructed as follows: "the committee shall determine whether there had been prior agreement; if there had been prior agreement the committee will support the doctor in this agreement; if there had not been prior agreement and if there are no circumstances warranting an additional charge to the patient, the ACCMA committee ruling on the complaint will defend the patient's right to pay no more than the usual fee determined by the annual fee survey." [29]

Statements like this would be meaningless if the fees listed had not been fairly representative of actual charges in the community. There is no way of testing this relationship but in chapter iv the average charges for appendectomies and tonsillectomies paid by members of the California Metal Trades health plan during 1954–

---

tion, working with a study committee that brought about the second major revamping of CPS since World War II. The report of the committee indicates that his contribution was a major one. See the Medical Services Commission Report to the House of Delegates of the CMA in May, 1954, *California Medicine*, June, 1954.

[29] From the referendum resolution passed by the society, August 7, 1953. This resolution is reproduced in full in the copies of the fee list.

1957 were shown to be similar to those noted in the 1954 ACCMA list. Comparison with the state-wide CPS $6,000 income-ceiling schedule suggests that this list was somewhat higher but probably not drastically so. In short, the list seems to have been fairly realistic in relation to the fees charged patients with average family incomes.

The adoption of this fee policy by the ACCMA attracted national attention although a somewhat similar plan had been instituted earlier by a Colorado medical society. Nevertheless, although the "median fee list" did represent a major break with the policy followed by the San Francisco society and in many ways met the demands of labor groups for a schedule that organized medicine was willing to "support and stand behind," it was not overwhelming in its impact. There appear to have been at least two important reasons for this:

1. Even if the list is accepted as not having been substantially higher than average fees for most services, it was substantially higher than the indemnity schedule in the average health plan in 1954. Of the negotiated indemnity plans in northern California at that time, 70 per cent reported surgical schedules with maximum payments of $300 or less and almost nine out of ten reported maximums of $350 or below.[30] The ACCMA list was certainly higher than a $300 schedule and probably higher than the typical $350 schedule. This meant that it was quite possible for a fee to vary within the limits set by the list and still to be substantially higher than the indemnity benefit, thereby requiring an out-of-pocket payment by the patient. Until the list and the indemnity schedules approached the same level, the list was not likely to be of major importance.

2. The list was designed for a specific purpose and considerable care was taken to control its use. In an attempt to regulate its application, the document containing the list was copyrighted. It was stated that the "major purpose" of the fee list was to give those interested in health insurance an indication of the approximate level at which indemnities should be set. Members were promised that individual patients asking for information about specific fees would be told to get that information from their per-

---

[30] California Department of Industrial Relations, *Labor-Management Negotiated Health and Welfare Plans*, 1955, p. 33.

sonal physicians. The resolution authorizing the fee survey stipulated that the fees would not be published in any periodical. Distribution of the list was primarily to insurance companies and
administrators or negotiators of health plans on the assumption
that the resulting indemnity schedules would then be related to
the median fees in the list. Neither the general public nor the
general membership of negotiated health plans had the list made
available to them. In other words, the list was to be used as an
internal administrative control and as a guide in negotiations. As
a control instrument, it appeared to assume that a conscientious
health plan administrator reviewing claims might notice an above-
list fee, ascertain that no prior agreement had been reached, challenge the fee to the doctor involved, and thereby reduce or eliminate an out-of-pocket charge for a patient. Generally, however,
individual patients did not know how the fees charged compared
with the fees on the list, even when prior discussion of fees took
place.

In spite of these limitations it is still true that the ACCMA
median fee list represented the acceptance of the principle of a
society-developed set of fees that were to be regarded as maxima
under certain circumstances. Although the fees were determined
unilaterally, this represented an important step toward meeting
the desires of health plans for explicit action of a positive character.

The 1953–1954 expansion of the Kaiser Plan was not limited to
Contra Costa County or the Bay Area but included new hospital
facilities in southern California as well. As a result the medical
professon developed an interest in state-wide countermeasures.
In 1954 a committee of the California Medical Association, assisted by Waterson, completed a study of the problem of state-
wide closed-panel competition.[31] The final report recommended
that as a long-range approach to the problem of prepayment
health plans, the CMA adopt a "Usual Fee Indemnity Plan" that
was, in essence, the same as the ACCMA median fee list system.
Since it was felt, however, that a substantial time period would
be necessary to implement the plan successfully it was deemed
necessary to adopt a "temporary stop-gap." This "temporary"
expedient was the creation of a new California Physicians Service

---

[31] This committee report can be found in *California Medicine*, June, 1954.

program that would provide full service benefits for families with incomes up to $6,000 a year in addition to the existing service program for families earning less than $4,200. The higher-income ceiling would require a higher premium from the subscriber and would pay higher fees to the physicians. This concession to the service principle in a report that stressed the long-run desirability of the indemnity approach was frankly acknowledged to be the result of competition from the Kaiser Plan.[32]

The administration of CPS has periodically pressed the CMA for upward revisions of the income ceiling. Ever since the early days of CPS, the state medical association has regularly expressed itself in favor of the eventual complete abandonment of the service benefit principle but, on examination, the most explicit statements of this long-term goal are typically coupled with the announcement of a "short-term" extension of the principle under the stress of immediate circumstances.

The service benefit element in California Physicians Service is its distinguishing feature and the element in the contract that makes it attractive to purchasers. The income ceiling is crucial to CPS since it determines the point at which the program changes from service to indemnity. The men who have the job of selling CPS coverage to groups, particularly to labor groups, face two problems. First, in an area marked by high average wages and in a culture in which families with multiple wage earners are fairly common, many union groups have very substantial proportions of their membership over even the $6,000 income ceiling. To these groups CPS has nothing distinctive to offer and must compete with Blue Cross and commercial insurance companies as a cash indemnity insurance plan. In this competition, CPS has certain cost handicaps stemming from its status as a physician-sponsored plan. Secondly, since most sizable negotiated plans are likely to cover a fairly wide range of occupations and of family income levels, CPS finds itself selling a contract that provides varying benefits as among individuals, each of whom pays the same premium. Trust fund administrators apparently find it particularly difficult to justify to their members why a uniform em-

---

[32] The report includes the statement that: "Raising this ceiling may make of CPS a more immediately useful weapon in the competitive battle with the closed panel plans."

ployer contribution provides full payment for an operation for one member but only partial payment for the same operation for another member. This, of course, is only a particular example of the general problem of varying fees according to the ability to pay and of determining the ability-to-pay status of a patient with health insurance.

Raising the income ceiling of CPS to a level at which a major part of a plan's membership is eligible for service benefit coverage is similar in its impact to establishing a maximum fee schedule binding on the physician-members of CPS. By insuring with CPS, the trustees of a negotiated plan, in effect, become parties to an agreement as to the maximum fees that will be charged that part of the membership with below-ceiling incomes. The fees specified in the agreement are not subject to direct negotiation between the parties to the contract, but the unilateral determination of these fees is nevertheless influenced by the actions of the health plan trustees. The raising of CPS ceilings in this case, for example, is testimony to the effectiveness of labor's threat to utilize closed panels of doctors to counter rising medical fees, whether the closed panel be recruited by individual agreement, gathered in labor health centers, or provided by the Permanente medical groups affiliated with the Kaiser Plan.

When the California Medical Association established the $6,000 ceiling program, an attempt was made to soften the impact through the device of permitting each county society to decide for itself whether the new program would be offered in its territory. Since competition from Kaiser was localized in the San Francisco and Los Angeles areas, the county societies outside the Kaiser orbit could continue to operate with only the earlier $4,200 ceiling contract. This proved to be an unnecessary precaution since the great majority of California counties asked for the installation of the higher-ceiling program. This suggests that outside the high-cost metropolitan areas, the fee schedule of the $6,000 contract may have looked rather attractive to local practitioners.

A further development in the reluctant flirtation of the medical profession with fee schedules took place in 1956 with the publication of the CMA's Relative Value Schedule. Based on a complete survey of fees in the state, this schedule provides a ranking of these fees by their "relative value." The purpose of the schedule is to enable any society desiring to set up a plan similar to the ACCMA median fee list or the proposed California Medical Association "Usual Fee Indemnity Plan" to do so with a minimum of difficulty. It eliminates the need for a local survey of "usual fees" and permits any society to establish a schedule simply by adopting an appropriate dollar multiplier to be applied to the Relative Value Schedule. (In 1958 the ACCMA replaced its own with the CMA schedule.) Although the schedule has had some influence, e.g., in San Joaquin County, it does not seem to have played a significant role to date. It is available, however, should local conditions create a need for the schedule approach and is thus further evidence of the pressures in this direction.

Related to this development but of more interest for our purposes is the attempt to persuade the California Medical Association to adopt a state-wide fee schedule that it "would support and stand behind" throughout California. The proposal amounts to adopting a specific fee schedule and guaranteeing that, subject to certain minimum conditions, these fees would be accepted as full payment for at least those patients below a fairly high income ceiling. In effect, this would amount to the extension of the advantages of the CPS system to all insurance underwriters. The commercial insurance industry has established a national committee to work toward this system in the several states and the California branch has met with the CMA to discuss this possibility. To date nothing has come of this proposal.[33]

In this area of the collectively bargained plans, an interesting variation of this approach has been tried by a prominent national firm of employee-benefit consultants that has as clients several large union-management trust funds. The consulting firm reportedly represents funds covering a substantial percentage of all the employees in negotiated health plans in California. Part of its strategy as a representative of its customers has been an attempt to assume the role of bargaining agent for the plans as a group in negotiating a fee schedule with the California Medical Association. Although meetings have been held, as of 1958 this approach has produced no results.

---

[33] The Tennessee Medical Association instituted a system of this type several years ago.

Finally, both northern and southern California have seen the creation of committees made up of a number of health plan administrators and intended to serve as coördinating bodies for the activities of the various separate union-management funds. The initial impetus for these groups came from the Institute of Industrial Relations of the University of California at Los Angeles. With financial support from the Rockefeller Foundation, a "Health Plan Consultants Committee" was organized in Los Angeles from representatives of a fairly large number of negotiated health plans. The purpose of the group is to consider a coördinated approach to the general problems of collectively bargained health plans, such as extension of coverage to needed forms of medical care, coverage of problem groups, etc., as well as financial problems. Particularly in the early years of its existence, however, much of the discussion centered on questions of fees and costs and this continues to be an active subject. A similar group, the Labor Health and Welfare Council, was organized in the East Bay in 1956 under the sponsorship of the Institute of Industrial Relations on the Berkeley campus of the University. Although these groups could hardly be regarded as bargaining agents for the health plans, fairly continuous contact with the medical societies has been maintained and this has contributed to a better understanding of the problems of fees and finances by all.

Summary and Conclusions

In briefly reviewing the tactics and strategy involved in the relationships between the representatives of organized labor and organized medicine since 1949, it seems possible to pick out a pattern of developments.

Once health and welfare plans were negotiated, union activity began with attempts to establish a collective-bargaining relationship with the medical societies in an effort to secure firm schedules of fees. Finding their bargaining strength unequal to this task, they adopted the tactic of making individual agreements with physicians on mutually acceptable terms. At the same time, a serious attempt was made to modify the organizational structure of the production of medical services by establishing a labor health center in which the organization and financing of medical care would be subject to union control. When this project failed to materialize, the Kaiser Plan expansion seemed to offer a workable alternative and this was skillfully utilized as a bargaining lever.

While the pressures produced by the combination of union action and Kaiser expansion ebbed and flowed, the medical profession was feeling its way toward a workable program. Although a number of purely local solutions appeared (see the next two chapters for examples), the most general reaction seemed to be a tendency to work toward some variation of the fee schedule approach. The Alameda-Contra Costa Medical Association led the way with its "median fee list" and most of the state accepted the new California Physicians Service $6,000 income-ceiling program. As the period ended, CPS was experimenting with a $7,200 income-ceiling program, the Relative Value Schedule had been developed by the state association for use as a base for schedules when conditions required their adoption, and the pressures for negotiated schedules were building up from the insurance industry as well as from labor groups and their representatives among the employee-benefit consultants.[34]

Obviously the results of the efforts of labor groups to acquire some degree of influence in the economics of medicine in the Bay Area could not be described as revolutionary. On the other hand, it appears justifiable to argue that the results have not been negligible. An imposing variety of pressure techniques has been experimented with and, in each case, they remain available to be exploited at an opportune time in the future. In addition to progress toward formal, published fee schedules and the raising of income ceilings, the most important change that has occurred has been the structuring of relationships between organized medicine and organized labor. Systems of communication have been developed on both sides, a subtle educational process has taken place, and a supply of personnel with a considerable amount of specialized knowledge has been developed.

The reader should remember that the events chronicled in this chapter took place during a period in which economic and political conditions favored conservatism. Employment was at record

---

[34] It might be noted that during this period the federal government inaugurated its Medicare program for furnishing medical care to the dependents of servicemen and California instituted a program for state financing of care for the aged, blind, and for needy children. Both of these use fee schedules.

levels, on the average, wages of workers and incomes of physicians were rising, and collective-bargaining gains were relatively easy to come by in many instances. On the political front, during most of the time interval, relatively conservative administrations were in power in both Sacramento and Washington. As a result of favorable economic conditions many unions were able to live with rising health and welfare costs. The members of these unions could pay additional charges relatively easily and prosperous doctors were able to take strong stands on principles of medical economics that might not have attracted solid support from the profession in more difficult times. On the political front it would be a rash prophet who would forecast that the eight years after 1958 would see no more active interest in national or state health insurance than did the eight years prior to 1958.

In short, starting as neophytes in medical economics, labor groups acquired a great deal of knowledge and made considerable progress toward establishing a bargaining position in that field during a period when external factors were not especially propitious. With the groundwork laid, the impact on the medical profession would soon be substantial even if changes continued at the rate attained during the years 1949–1958.

Chapter VIII | A Case Study in Medical Economics

Spokesmen for the medical profession have referred to the relationship existing between organized labor and the "closed-panel" group-practice medical organization in terms suggesting the existence of a natural (and somewhat unholy) alliance between the two. As an offshoot of its principal function of bargaining with management, labor has assumed a role as the representative of individual consumers of medical services in their relations with the suppliers of medical care. For its part, group practice of medicine represents an organizational innovation in the "methods of production" of medical care and often in the "system of distribution" as well. Facing, on the one hand, bargaining pressure from organized consumers and, on the other, competition from a new form of practice, the individual doctor sees the possibility of losing the freedom he enjoys as an independent entrepreneur. Singly, each of the opposing forces represents a substantial threat to the traditional fee-for-service system of solo medical practice. In combination, their potential as disturbers of the medical peace is multiplied. The explosive character of their association stems from the complementary nature of the two organizations. It is inevitable that the private practitioner of medicine should be disturbed by the prospect of the organized consumers and the organized suppliers joining forces, drying up the market for his services, and forcing him to change his way of medical life.

Combination may stem from many motives and may take many

different forms: it may represent a straightforward business arrangement between two self-sufficient organizations with no ideological or strategic considerations involved; it may be a marriage of convenience dictated by financial necessity or by the desire to create bargaining leverage in the market place; it may be the result of sincere conviction by union officials of the desirability of the type of medical practice represented by a particular independent closed-panel group. Most disturbing of all to the profession, the combination may come into being through the union becoming a sort of medical entrepreneur and taking the initiative in bringing a closed-panel group into existence. In the previous chapter we saw that Bay Area labor organizations had tried both the alliance and the direct sponsorship approach in their experiments with group-practice medicine.

An excellent opportunity to examine in detail the development of one type of an alliance between a local labor union and a closed-panel group-practice health plan and the resulting impact on the economics of medical care is to be found in the experiences of the hospital and the physicians of Pittsburg, California, Local 1440 of the United Steelworkers of America, and the Kaiser Foundation Health Plan.

From the researcher's point of view, a happy combination of circumstances makes this episode rewarding raw material. The community is a well-defined economic unit, the local doctors formed naturally into a cohesive body based on the already existing hospital medical staff organization, and the local union represented an aggregation of workers who, with their families, made up a major part of the population of the community. All parties concerned were frank and coöperative in furnishing information and the happenings were important and newsworthy enough to warrant thorough press coverage so that the gaps might be filled in.[1] This incident aptly illustrates the types of problems involved

[1] Information on which this account is based was secured through examination of back issues of the Pittsburg (California) *Post-Dispatch* and a series of interviews and discussions with a number of persons directly involved. Principal among the latter were the following: William Milano, financial secretary of Local 1440, USW, Thomas Neary of Local 1440's Insurance Committee, William Sheuber, executive secretary of the Alameda-Contra Costa Medical Association (assistant secretary in 1953), Dr. J. K. Barbieri, former president of the medical staff of the Pittsburg Community Hospital, and Avram Yedidia of the Kaiser Foundation Health Plan. Unless otherwise noted, conclusions and interpretations are those of the writer.

in adjusting to organized activity in the fields of health insurance, medical practice, and industrial relations. Since it shows the way one set of solutions was evolved and some of the results of the solutions, the affair will be analyzed in considerable detail.

The Background of the Pittsburg Incident

An industrial community with a population of 13,000 in 1950, Pittsburg is located in Contra Costa County on the Sacramento River about forty miles east and somewhat north of the city of San Francisco. Since World War II the suburbanization of the San Francisco–Oakland metropolitan area has resulted in a rapid growth in population in the thirty-mile wide area lying between the city of Oakland on the east side of San Francisco Bay and Pittsburg. By 1953 suburban development had spread far out into the hinterland along the traffic arteries leading into Oakland and settled areas around the bay to a point about two-thirds of the distance to Pittsburg. The town itself, however, was and still is separated by a narrow belt of agricultural land from the spreading suburbs. It has therefore retained its own identity, both economically and geographically. Since the suburban area east of Oakland is almost entirely residential, Pittsburg lies outside the usual commuting range of the dominant East Bay industrial centers. On the other hand, the town is not large enough to have become the central city of an economic area of its own. As a result, Pittsburg can be described as a fairly self-contained economic unit with a largely resident labor force augmented by a substantial minority drawn from the communities of Antioch, about four miles to the east, and Concord, lying about ten miles to the west and at the effective outer limit of the East Bay commuting range.

The economy of Pittsburg is dominated by the steel industry, represented in this instance by the Columbia-Geneva Steel Division of the United States Steel Corporation (USS). The company usually employs something over 4,000 workers and is the largest employer in the locality. Although part of the labor force is drawn from neighboring communities, a conservative estimate would place the proportion of the town's population made up of steelworkers and their families at close to 50 per cent.

As in the rest of the United States Steel Corporation, the vast majority of the workers at the Pittsburg mill have been organized

by the United Steelworkers of America (USW). Bargaining relationships were established prior to World War II with the Pittsburg group being represented currently by Local 1440 of the
Steelworkers. Since the war the national union has negotiated a
number of benefit programs, including a health and welfare plan.
Like many other union groups, however, the Pittsburg local became interested in health insurance long before the national program of the USW was established through collective bargaining.
Beginning in 1941 the local union arranged for group-health insurance coverage on an indemnity basis through a commercial insurance company. This program was voluntary, was financed entirely
by the workers concerned, and was local in scope with the union
furnishing the initiative for the plan. In order to handle health
insurance affairs the local formed an Insurance Committee.

In contract negotiations in 1949 the national union won from
the steel industry insurance for hospital expenses on a national
basis underwritten by the Blue Cross organization. This collectively bargained program was financed through joint contributions by the company and the individual employee with very high
member participation being the rule. As a party to the national
agreement, Local 1440 was included in this arrangement. In addition, Local 1440 elected to continue a supplementary program to
be carried with the commercial insurance company underwriting
its previous health insurance plan. The coverage of the national
plan was supplemented by surgical and limited medical benefits
on a purely voluntary basis at the worker's expense.

In later negotiations the national union expanded the coverage
afforded by the national plan, adding benefits and raising the level
of indemnification for benefits already included. As the basic national plan expanded into new areas of coverage, the local supplementary plan was adjusted to conform to the new situation.
Instead of concentrating on furnishing a type of coverage not included in the national program, emphasis was placed on the supplementation of benefit payments which were inadequate to meet
local medical care costs. By 1953 Local 1440's health insurance
"package" included a basic hospitalization and surgical coverage
jointly financed under a national collective-bargaining agreement
plus a local, voluntary program of indemnity insurance arranged
for by the local union and paid for entirely by the worker.

During the lengthy period over which the 1953 program evolved, the union officers and members experienced a pattern of developments familiar to many other unions active in health and welfare affairs. Members came to believe that their health insurance program was contributing to an inflation of medical care costs. They complained to the Insurance Committee and the union officials that their medical bills were not being met by the insurance benefits. More important, the union felt that its attempts to increase the adequacy of insurance coverage by increasing benefits through supplementary insurance were being offset by increases in charges by the hospitals and the medical profession. They believed that these increases might not have occurred or might not have been as large if the insurance program had not been in existence. To this rather common bill of complaints, the Pittsburg local added another. The union members and their families began to feel that medical care was not being made available by the profession at times convenient to the patient and that home calls were difficult to secure in what the patients believed were emergencies. There was a feeling that the two classes of complaints were linked in that the workers felt that the high incomes they were sure were being generated by the health plans encouraged a lack of concern for these problems on the part of some members of the medical profession.

The union had made an attempt to deal with the problem of inflation of costs by a direct approach to the doctors of the community. Prior to one of the expansions of coverage arranged by the union, the financial secretary of the local reported meeting with a committee of doctors to ask for an informal agreement that fees would not be raised after the new benefits were placed in effect. No decision was reached at the meeting and no further meetings could be arranged. Even though union officials felt that only a minority of doctors were at fault, considerable general resentment against the local representatives of the medical profession developed.

For their part the local doctors felt that increases in medical costs due to the general inflation characteristic of the time were being confused with the effects of the insurance programs. Although willing to admit that a small minority of doctors might take advantage of the financial opportunities opened up by health insurance, they felt that the complaints about bad service were exaggerated. The doctors felt that an atmosphere had developed in which unfortunate incidents that otherwise might have gone unnoticed were magnified and assigned an unwarranted interpretation.

This was where matters stood in Pittsburg in 1953 as a new hospital affiliated with the Kaiser Foundation Health Plan was nearing completion in the town of Walnut Creek.

The Kaiser Plan Expansion

Prior to the rapid suburban development referred to earlier, Walnut Creek had been a small village located at the junction of the major traffic routes in eastern Contra Costa County about halfway between Oakland and Pittsburg. With the rapid growth of the area in the postwar period, the central location of the community and its strategic position in the road network gave promise of making it the suburban trading center of the territory. When the medical organizations associated with the Kaiser Foundation embarked on a major expansion of facilities, Walnut Creek was chosen as the site for a new hospital. Until this time the single major medical facility of the foundation in northern California had been the Oakland hospital. The new hospital in Walnut Creek would enable Kaiser to serve the increasing number of health plan members who were moving to the suburbs and also to tap the potential membership in the growing towns. Since securing services under the Kaiser system is contingent on access to a Kaiser hospital or clinic, the location of facilities is an important factor in the growth of the plan. The Kaiser method of operation is to establish a hospital in a population center and provide a series of clinics to furnish outpatient care to members who cannot conveniently use the central facility. The location of the Oakland hospital had previously circumscribed the area within which Kaiser could provide complete service. A hospital in Walnut Creek would extend the area about fifteen miles eastward.

This move introduced the Kaiser Plan into the "medical market" of Pittsburg. The Walnut Creek center, an attractive, very modern, ranch-type hospital of about seventy beds,[2] would be less

---

[2] Later expanded to approximately 100 beds, partly as a result of developments outlined in this chapter.

than twenty miles from the center of Pittsburg. With hospitalization and ancillary services available in Walnut Creek, outpatient facilities in Pittsburg would make membership in the health plan practicable for local residents.

It is inevitable that any organization operating a group insurance program in eastern Contra Costa County would be interested in Columbia Steel as the largest single employer in the district. The Kaiser group was already engaged in an unusual program on the west side of San Francisco Bay with the Steelworkers local at the plant of Bethlehem Steel in South San Francisco. The opening of the Kaiser hospital in Walnut Creek raised the question of a similar arrangement for Pittsburg.

The first public indication of the undercurrents existing in the situation came when the local newspaper carried a story headed, "City Medics Ready Own Plan in Face of Kaiser 'Invasion,'" on June 22, 1953. The story reported that the doctors of the community had reacted to reports that Kaiser was "eyeing Pittsburg as a site for a clinic" by preparing a competitive health insurance plan to be sponsored by the medical profession of Pittsburg and adjacent communities. The "Doctors Plan," as the program came to be known instead of the more formal designation "East Contra Costa Medical Service Plan," proposed to supplement the existing national union program by converting it from an indemnity plan to a service plan with increased coverage.

Reports of the "invasion" were publicly confirmed shortly after this first story when the zoning authorities received a petition for a change in the status of a local property that would permit it to be used as a medical building by the Kaiser Foundation. This application, as well as at least one other involving a different location, was denied by the zoning authorities after considerable discussion centering around land-use patterns and parking problems.

These moves were the opening skirmishes in a community contest involving issues of medical economics which raged for the next three months and has shown sporadic signs of life at intervals since that time.

The issue centered around the supplementary insurance program that, in one form or another, Local 1440 had sponsored for

[margin notes:] Doctors' alternative health insurance plan

Use of petition to zoning authorities

many years. The basic insurance program developed through negotiations between USS and the USW was not in question since all parties recognized that a major alteration in the national program would be difficult to accomplish. The Kaiser proposal, modeled on the program already in existence at the Bethlehem Steel plant, was to make available to steelworkers who enrolled in their supplemental plan the full range of services offered to the regular Kaiser subscribers. Kaiser would be reimbursed by the underwriters for any services rendered that were included in the national Blue Cross–Blue Shield contract. Services not covered by the national contract that were part of the Kaiser program (e.g., outpatient care) would be furnished in return for a monthly premium to be paid by the enrolled member exactly as he had paid for his previous supplement.

It might be said of the Kaiser proposal that it permitted the maximum change in medical care arrangements with the minimum change in administrative procedures.

So far as administration was concerned, the company and the underwriting agencies all faced relatively minor problems, while the worker and the union were almost unaffected. The company continued to pay premiums for its national coverage to Blue Cross–Blue Shield. Changing the payroll deduction on the voluntary supplementary coverage from the commercial insurance company to the Kaiser Foundation was a small matter. A minor problem of amending contract language dealing with the type of bed accommodations involved in the national insurance program had to be worked out between company, union, and Blue Cross representatives.

To the Blue Cross and Blue Shield organizations, the new arrangement meant reimbursing the Kaiser Foundation for hospital and medical services in approximately the same manner in which they already reimbursed member hospitals and participating doctors in their regular program.

To the Kaiser organization the new plan involved substantial increases in administrative burden over their usual method of operation. Separate records for the steelworker members with the details of their treatment would have to be maintained since this would be necessary in billing Blue Cross–Blue Shield for reimbursement. This represented a disadvantage to a plan that claims as one of its virtues the elimination of record-keeping for each unit of medical service in processing claims for reimbursement.

The real impact of the Kaiser proposal promised to be felt by the individual medical practitioners and the hospital in the community. Like commercial indemnity insurance generally, the original supplement underwritten by the commercial insurance company concerned itself with the financing of medical care without affecting the manner in which it was organized or distributed. The Kaiser Plan is a method of medical organization as well as an insurance mechanism. To the degree that the individual steelworkers in Pittsburg elected to secure their medical care from the Kaiser hospital and staff of doctors, the demand for the services of the community hospital and the private practitioners of the Pittsburg area would be curtailed and their incomes reduced. In effect, the entrance of the Kaiser Plan into Pittsburg represented a massive addition to the supply of medical services in the area, an addition all the more threatening since it brought with it its own system of prepayment for medical care.

Reaction of the Medical Profession

At first glance the violent reaction of the Pittsburg area doctors to the Kaiser "invasion" may seem a little difficult to explain. After all, the basic Blue Cross–Blue Shield coverage was unaffected by the Kaiser proposal. Individual workers could still secure their medical services from the local hospital and the local doctors and be reimbursed for their charges to the extent of the hospital and surgical coverages of the national plan. At issue was the voluntary program of supplementation to be financed entirely by the worker himself. The explanation of the importance attached to the problem lies in the high valuation the steelworkers placed on relatively complete medical coverage and on the element known as "certainty of coverage." [3] This high valuation was attested to by the long history of independent activity by the local union in the health insurance field, by the consistently high member participation in the voluntary supplementary program, and by the con-

---

[3] As noted earlier, certainty of coverage means advance knowledge that the prescribed medical services will be furnished with no additional charges, or at the most, with relatively small, definitely fixed charges to be paid by the patient.

tinuous broadening of coverage advocated and eventually secured in both the national and the supplementary insurance program.

Certainty of coverage and comprehensive service were the major advantages of the Kaiser program as formulated for the union Insurance Committee. Assuming that, as in the past, a large majority of the workers elected to participate in the voluntary program, it was almost certain that they would not forego the certainty of coverage feature of the Kaiser proposal which required the securing of services from Kaiser facilities. It seemed logical to assume that the selection of the proposed Kaiser supplement by a steelworker would imply the loss of all, or at least a major part, of his family's medical business by private physicians.

Providing a plan of their own that would have the same or offsetting advantages as the Kaiser proposal, and that would protect their position was the problem facing the Pittsburg doctors.

It has been estimated that at this time there were perhaps thirty doctors in private practice in Pittsburg itself with about half again as many in adjacent areas close enough to be directly affected. This estimate is borne out by the fact that two early announcements of the "Doctors Plan" carried signatures of forty-one and forty-two doctors as sponsors.

These men were members of the East Contra Costa Branch of the Alameda-Contra Costa Medical Association, the third largest county medical society in the state of California and one with a nationally known program of medical public relations. The "Alameda Plan," as the program had come to be called, was felt to have been effective in raising the prestige of both the profession and the society with the public. The essentials of the program had spread to other county societies in the Bay Area and in the state; its success was one of the major factors in the decision of the much smaller Contra Costa society to amalgamate with the neighboring Alameda society in 1950.

Prominent among the objectives of the Alameda Plan was the elimination or at least the amelioration of exactly the kind of complaints that were characteristic of the Pittsburg situation. Among other features, the program included provision for twenty-four-hour emergency service, an explicit guarantee of medical service for all regardless of ability to pay, fee complaint committees, and, in general, as close as possible liaison with organized lay groups in the community. Elements of this plan had been in existence in Pittsburg prior to the amalgamation of the two county societies and other elements had been introduced since that time. In 1953, however, the accumulated dissatisfaction built up in previous years had not been eliminated nor had any effective contact between the doctors as a group and Local 1440 been established.

In retrospect, it is difficult to avoid the conclusion that the local doctors and the hospital were fighting a losing battle from the start. This did not prevent the waging of a campaign featured by considerable energy and ingenuity if not always the best possible strategy.

Allies in the doctors' cause were available in the executive staff of the ACCMA and the California Physicians Service, the society-sponsored health insurance plan.

Neither the county medical association nor CPS was used directly as the organizational vehicle for the Pittsburg doctors' counteroffensive. The approximately forty-five doctors immediately involved represented about 3 per cent of the membership of the ACCMA and the supplementation issue with which they were faced was an unusual problem not of general concern. In addition, the great bulk of the membership practiced in the original East Bay stronghold of the Kaiser Plan and were hardened veterans of the general competitive situation now being introduced in a special form in Pittsburg. In any event, the plan evolved as an alternative to the Kaiser proposal was an independent entity not sponsored by either the ACCMA or CPS. Staff members of the association were called upon to work on the public relations and promotional barrage which accompanied the campaign, and the CPS organization was enlisted to handle the administrative details of the Doctors Plan. Nevertheless, the plan remained a local phenomenon which at no time actively involved as many as 10 per cent of the ACCMA's membership.

Local leadership was assumed by the president of the medical staff of the community hospital. Active roles were also taken by the hospital administrator, the executive secretary of the association and his assistant, and physician-members of the hospital board of directors and the insurance committee of the hospital medical staff.

The formulation of a specific proposal to be presented to the

union was the first task and for this purpose an insurance consultant was engaged. As initially developed, the Doctors Plan
concentrated on providing certainty of coverage for medical and
surgical services specified in the national Blue Cross–Blue Shield
contract and, in general, refrained from offering additional benefits in an attempt to match the comprehensive character of Kaiser
coverage. In effect the doctors offered to accept as full payment
the fee schedules provided in the national insurance contracts
plus a pro rata share of the premium income which would be
generated by a supplementary insurance contract. Premium
charges for the Doctors Plan supplement were to be slightly *Doctors'*
higher than the Kaiser premiums. *Plan*

In view of the criticism leveled at the profession for conditions of
service existing previously, it is interesting to note that the last
two points in the public announcement of the Doctors Plan concerned the setting up of two joint doctor-union committees, one
to improve twenty-four-hour emergency service and one to "enforce the performance of the plan by the doctors, and prevent
over-use and abuse by patients."

Two weeks after the first public disclosure of the "essentials"
of the Doctors Plan, the Insurance Committee of Local 1440 announced the choice of the Kaiser proposal as the new supplementary coverage to the existing contract. With the announcement of
this choice, the doctors opened a campaign to reverse this decision that was to last for two months and to culminate in an unusual ballot box battle.

Before incidents in the controversy are outlined, the union position in the situation will be briefly sketched.

Attitude of the Union

Kaiser's supplementation of the Steelworkers' insurance program
at the Bethlehem Steel plant in the West Bay has already been
noted. In addition to their knowledge of this arrangement through
the union, the Pittsburg local officers had long been acquainted
with Kaiser's major operation in the East Bay and had been in
informal contact with representatives of the plan. To the officials
of the local and the members of the Insurance Committee, there
were several considerations involved in selecting their new insurance program. Of major importance were the features of the

Kaiser Plan which have already been discussed, certainty of coverage and relatively comprehensive medical care. In addition to these technical characteristics of the proposal, there were a number of what might be called "institutional" factors present in the situation, factors that were to some extent independent of the specific details of the competing medical plans.

Important among these were the real or fancied grievances which the union officers felt they and their members had in the areas of above-schedule charges and access to service. Feeling as they did, it was not surprising that the officers welcomed the opportunity to make their dissatisfaction felt through a clear-cut public action that would affect a substantial portion of the practice of many of the Pittsburg doctors.

Aside from possible personal feeling in the matter, the Kaiser Plan represented an alternative source of medical care that would provide continuous bargaining leverage so long as it operated in the community. Testifying to the effectiveness of this threat was the very existence of the Doctors Plan. Officials responsible for the long-term conduct of their members' health insurance problems would think twice before rejecting a weapon that had been shown to be so effective even before it was actually called into use. The first requirement of effective bargaining is the existence of an alternative to immediate agreement. Kaiser's move into Pittsburg would enable the union to abandon its role as a petitioner and to adopt its more accustomed role as a bargainer in relations with the doctors and the hospital in the community. With an eye toward the future, the officers of the union, men to whom bargaining is a profession, recognized their stake in helping the Kaiser organization secure a firm foothold in the local medical market.

Still another "institutional" factor figured in the decision. One of the most frustrating aspects of union officials' activities in health and welfare matters has been the absence of any formalized bargaining agency within the medical profession. Familiar with the tradition among laymen that the medical societies exert effective discipline among their membership in matters such as admission to practice and professional ethics, unions have been disappointed with the amorphous character of their relationship with organized medicine. They have been impatient with fine distinctions between fee "schedules" and "lists," between a society's "adopting" a fee schedule for its members and its "recommending" it to them. In short, the absence of machinery for making and enforcing binding agreements on the pricing of medical services for definite periods of time has been, in the unions' view, an irritating and somewhat suspect state of affairs. Officers of Local 1440 had been unsuccessful in their attempts to secure even an informal agreement to maintain a level of fee charges originally established unilaterally by the doctors in their individual capacities. Dealing with the Kaiser Foundation Health Plan offered the possibility of a negotiated contract, with fixed charges for a definite range of services, effective for a specified period of time, and with provision for continuous contact between the parties to discuss the administration of the agreement. This system introduced some of the familiar paraphernalia of collective bargaining into health and welfare matters.

Reviewing the complex of forces working toward the selection of the Kaiser supplement suggests that the hastily conceived Doctors Plan had little chance of winning the endorsement of the Insurance Committee. Union representatives discussed the plan with the doctors and the consultant during the period of development, but the task of overcoming the variety of advantages that the selection of Kaiser seemed to offer the leadership of the union was too great to overcome, at least in the limited time available.

The Doctors Appeal to the Membership

Faced with the decision of the Insurance Committee, the doctors adopted a strategy familiar enough in labor-management disputes but highly unusual in medical circles. In the name of the East Contra Costa Medical Services Plan, the Pittsburg doctors embarked on an aggressive public campaign addressed to the rank and file of Local 1440. In effect union members were asked to repudiate the decision of their official representatives on the Insurance Committee.

On reaching an impasse in collective-bargaining negotiations, a common management tactic is to deplore (before the largest possible audience) the fact that the union membership lacks an opportunity to express itself directly on the merits of the rejected proposals. It is usually suggested that the details of these proposals have been carefully concealed from the rank and file by the officers. Instances exist where this technique has been successful, but in most cases it is ineffective and on many occasions "the battle of the full-page ads" is tacitly recognized as part of the ritual of the bargaining process.

In the next several weeks the doctors and their advisers displayed a considerable knowledge of the rhetoric of labor-management conflict as their activities ran the gamut of newspaper statements, large advertisements, direct mail approaches, handbills, speeches, "open letters," and sound trucks. Sketching the major developments as they occurred will give something of the flavor of this remarkable episode.

One week after the announcement (July 7) of the Kaiser selection by the Insurance Committee, the administrator of the community hospital was reported in the press to have declared that the Doctors Plan benefits far exceeded those of the Kaiser Plan. In the traditional manner, he charged that the local union's choice had been dictated by orders from the San Francisco or Pittsburgh (Pennsylvania) offices of the national union. In the same speech the community was reminded that the hospital was subsidized by tax money and was currently operating at a deficit being met from past reserves. Loss of the hospital was pictured as a possible consequence of the introduction of the Kaiser Plan.

A few days later the hard-working strategy board of the Doctors Plan mailed to members of the union a return post card carrying the statement:

"I am not satisfied with the Health Plan offered me by my union committee. I prefer to subscribe to the Doctors Plan which gives me the choice of my own doctor and the hospital of my own choosing."

This attempt to provide a channel for an expression of latent dissatisfaction with the Committee's decision did not yield enough returned cards to warrant an announcement of the results.

Closing out the first week of the doctors' intensified campaign, a physician-member of the board of directors of the local hospital was reported in the press as having bitterly attacked the union decision at a meeting of the board. Following the classic pattern, the charge was made that the Insurance Committee "does not represent the rank and file. . . ." and that it had accepted the Kaiser

Plan without informing steelworkers of the Doctors Plan. Local 1440 was depicted as ruled by a "clique" of thirty or forty members and the speaker was quoted as stating that ". . . The steelworkers should be allowed to decide on a democratic basis what medical plan they want." As a final note the committee was warned of the "terrible responsibility" of recommending a break in the traditional doctor-patient relationship.[4]

According to the report, the speaker had few allies at the meeting; the majority of the board took the position that it was not their place to recommend policy to the union. This incident represented the first public challenge to Local 1440 to submit the matter to a membership referendum, a challenge that was later to be accepted.

As the second week of the stepped-up program of the varied group behind the Doctors Plan began, the financial secretary of the local in a speech before a service club luncheon denied the existence of a "hassle" with the doctors. Reviewing the local's long-standing interest in health insurance for its members, he reported contacting the physicians in Pittsburg, Antioch, and Concord in 1948, one year before the national program was installed, with regard to a possible hospital plan. Of the three cities, only the Pittsburg doctors failed to respond leaving the union "with no alternative but to continue dealing with outside agencies for a group-health plan." Regarding the present proposal of the doctors' group, he noted that it was "only a proposition that included benefits already negotiated for by the union . . ." and not a complete health plan.[5]

Unfortunately for the thesis that no "hassle" existed, the issue of the newspaper carrying the report of the secretary's speech also contained a large advertisement for the doctors' group. Leading off with: "Dear Columbia Steel Employee and Family: These Are The Facts!" it pointed up the lack of "free choice" of hospital and doctor inherent in the Kaiser system of operation.

Proponents of the Doctors Plan fired their last salvo of the first phase of the battle on July 27 in the form of a full-page advertisement in the newspaper. Signed by forty-two doctors, it reproduced a letter addressed to the Insurance Committee outlining the de-

---

[4] Pittsburg *Post-Dispatch,* July 20, 1953.
[5] *Ibid.,* July 22, 1953.

tails of the Doctors Plan substantially as previously announced. Featured in the most prominent position in the advertisement, however, was a new volley aimed at Local 1440. Referring to a newspaper report of a visit of a national union representative from Pittsburgh, Pennsylvania, and a regional officer from the Bay Area, the text implied that the proposed Kaiser contract was being "investigated" by the national union. The advertisement implied a reversal of the previous claim that the Kaiser sign-up was being dictated by absentee union leadership in Pittsburgh and San Francisco, and indicated a belief that obdurate local officers were preventing the backers of the Doctors Plan from meeting with "these Eastern CIO officials." Steelworkers and their families were asked to "insist that this meeting be arranged."

With the July issue of Local 1440's membership newsletter, devoted to answering criticisms made by the doctors' group against the local officers and the Kaiser proposal, the public record of this hectic two-week period is completed.

Important developments occurred during the month of August but the controversy was removed from the public eye by a negotiated cease-fire. Modification of the Doctors Plan by broadening coverage to provide services, such as home and office calls, not included in the national insurance contract was undertaken to meet the objection that this was not a complete health plan. For its part, Local 1440 accepted the challenge to hold a membership referendum on the question, and scheduled a secret-ballot vote for September 3.

Disagreement exists as to the exact terms of the truce. The doctors' group understood that the union officials were to remain neutral in the dispute until after the election; in return the doctors agreed to abandon their public campaign. According to their view, preëlection activity was to be confined to providing each eligible employee with the details of the two alternative proposals for insurance supplementation. Local 1440's officers interpreted the agreement as permitting them to include along with the packet distributed two days before the vote and containing copies of the provisions of the two plans, a statement from the Insurance Committee recommending the selection of the Kaiser Plan and criticizing the Doctors Plan in some detail. Inscribed in large letters at the bottom of the statement was the message: "Uphold the

Public Campaign Referendum

Position of Your Union. Vote Yes on the Kaiser Foundation Health Plan." This interpretation of "neutrality" was regarded by the doctors as a flagrant violation of the previous understanding. With only two days remaining before the balloting, the backers of the Doctors Plan flung themselves into renewed activity.

The next day's newspaper, the last issue before the beginning of the vote, carried another full-page advertisement for the Doctors Plan. Opening up with the statement: "Due to MISREPRESENTATION of our plan on the part of your Union Insurance Committee and Executive Board as indicated in their 'YELLOW SHEET!' " the advertisement went on to rebut the criticisms contained in the Insurance Committee's recommendation circulated with the description of the plans. In addition the revised version of the Doctors Plan was made public for the first time.

Sponsors of the plan had not been idle during the lull in the exchange of public statements. The number of participating physicians had been increased from the original 40 or so to 115, representing a wide variety of medical specialties and blanketing much of the East Bay. Coverage under the plan had been expanded to include home and office calls, outpatient X-ray services and eye examinations when prescribed and "injectible" drugs exclusive of cortisone and prescription drugs. These features were in addition to the guarantee of full coverage for hospital, surgical, and maternity benefits, and for doctors' visits in the hospital which had been a part of the earlier version. At a supplementary premium of less than five dollars for family coverage, the Doctors Plan offered insurance coverage at least equal to and probably better than the best open-panel health and welfare plan in existence in the area at that time.[6]

Expansion of coverage in revised Doctors' Plan

"Election day" was marked by developments that must be almost unique in the record of the public relations of the medical profession. As the working shifts changed in the steel plant, in-

---

[6] Remember that the cost of the basic national program, jointly financed by company and member, was the same for both supplements and was in addition to the figure cited in the text. Comparative premiums for the supplements are given below:

	Kaiser	Doctors Plan
Single member	$1.90	$1.85
Subscriber and 1 dependent	3.35	3.70
Family of 3 or more	4.40	4.85

coming workers were met in the company parking lot by a number of doctors, their wives, and members of the hospital auxiliary who were distributing campaign literature for the Doctors Plan. For part of the day a sound truck was stationed at one strategic location exhorting the workers to "Retain your family doctor," or warning them, "Don't be a captive patient." So intent were the backers on getting their message across that, at one point when it appeared they might be denied access to the parking lot, plans were made to drop the leaflets from an airplane. Representatives of the sheriff's office appeared on the scene, summoned by a telephone call warning of possible trouble, but no incidents occurred.[7]

During the day reports on the progress of the election were issued and Pittsburg experienced some of the traditional excitement of the election process. When the polls were closed, almost two-thirds of the eligible workers had voted. The Kaiser Plan won by a margin of 2,182 to 440.

The Aftermath

Defeat in the election marked the virtual end of the Doctors Plan. Although its sponsors announced that it would be available to other groups in the community, in fact it disappeared from the scene. This does not mean that the Columbia Steel employees were permanently conceded to the Kaiser organization by the local medical profession. Both the Kaiser Foundation Health Plan and the traditional fee-for-service independent physician system for providing medical care have confirmed detractors as well as supporters among the consumers of medical care. Battling a background of strong resentment against the medical profession, with the official representatives of the local union solidly arrayed against it, and with only a few weeks to prepare and publicize a program, the Doctors Plan still won the votes of 440 steelworkers. As expected, a large majority of the eligible workers elected to purchase the Kaiser supplement in accordance with the past pattern of high participation in the supplementary insurance program. Within about six months, however, an approach had been made to the medical profession outside union channels by a group of workers interested in exploring the possibility of developing a "free-choice" alternative to the Kaiser plan.

[7] Pittsburg *Post-Dispatch*, September 3, 1953, and personal interview.

Attempts by the secretary of the county medical association to interest commercial insurance companies in providing a supplement to compete with Kaiser were unsuccessful in the face of company indifference, union opposition, and the entrenched position of the Kaiser supplement. Nevertheless, as a result of interest shown at a meeting between a small group of employees and the association's secretary (held out-of-doors in the familiar parking lot when plans to secure other space failed), efforts to develop a competitive plan continued.

Approximately one year after their defeat at the polls, the doctors of Pittsburg announced a new supplementary plan to be available to the steelworkers on an individual voluntary basis. Built around the standard CPS contract of that period but with considerably wider coverage, the plan was designed to pay the doctors for services not included in the national contract and to make up the difference between the Blue Cross–Blue Shield schedule and the fee schedule of the regular $4,200 income-ceiling contract of CPS. As a further concession, the $4,200 income-ceiling schedule was to be accepted as full payment by the doctors regardless of the family income of the member. This plan closely approached the Doctors Plan in benefits but was offered at a premium of approximately $7.00 for family coverage in competition with the then-current $5.70 premium for the Kaiser Plan. Illustrating the flexibility of the CPS mechanism in "meeting the market" in special competitive situations, the plan was limited to the Columbia Steel employee group.

Two years after reëntering the contest, the California Physicians Service supplement had enrolled over 400 members while the Kaiser supplement had something over 3,000 subscribers. In assessing the significance of this comparison, account must be taken of a very substantial advantage enjoyed by Kaiser in that the worker can arrange a payroll deduction for his premiums. Acquisition of this status is the current goal of the CPS program. All parties agree that any voluntary program with the checkoff privilege possesses a valuable asset.

Unanimous agreement on the importance of the payroll deduction privilege points up a source of bargaining strength of Local 1440 against both plans. In the final analysis, control over the checkoff of premiums for either program is in the hands of the employer, the United States Steel Corporation. Like all American employers, USS finds itself the collection agent for a growing variety of programs. At considerable administrative expense, deductions must be made for federal income tax, old age and survivors insurance, state disability insurance, union dues, the Kaiser supplement, savings bonds purchases, and the contributory part of the company's private insurance plans such as the group life insurance and the basic health and welfare program. Suggestions that the company add to this growing list still another health insurance program were not enthusiastically received when they were advanced by the doctors' representatives. The company is reported to have held out hope that if 25 per cent of the employees enrolled in the CPS program, consideration would be given to installing a deduction system. This would require boosting membership in the plan from 400 plus to about 1,000, a gain which would be difficult to register even if there were a deduction system in effect and one which is admittedly almost impossible without it.

But there is a potential short cut to the coveted checkoff status. If Local 1440 were to adopt a policy of offering its membership a choice of the two types of medical plans on equal terms, the company would probably agree to broadening the checkoff to include the CPS supplement. Ample precedent exists for this choice arrangement between the Kaiser Plan and other types of coverage in the more than thirty "dual-choice" health and welfare plans in the area.

Unfortunately for the doctors' position, the union officers believe they have good reason for continuing the present arrangement. Some lingering resentment about the charges that played such a large part in the 1953 dispute still exists. More important, the officers feel that the ability to grant or withhold the Insurance Committee's endorsement and the associated checkoff privilege that in practice goes with it, affords them bargaining leverage against both the plan currently holding the contract and any other plan aspiring to the same status. Installation of a choice arrangement would deprive the officers of the only real sanction that can be employed against the insurance carrier and would transfer the control over the distribution of the medical business from the union to each of the members in their individual capacity. Although there might be advantages to the member in this situation in the short run, the union officers feel that in the long run the combination of specialized knowledge and bargaining pressures available to the Insurance Committee will produce better insurance coverage from whichever agency wins the contract. The fact that those union members who have any strong preference for a private physician over the Kaiser medical group can stay out of the union-approved program at no greater cost than the inconvenience of making a monthly remittance to CPS prevents any real pressure for a choice plan arising among the membership.

Also important is the feeling of the union officers that they have a voice in the administration of the Kaiser Plan that might be lacking in the CPS plan. Their position might be summed up in the statement of one of the officials: "We aren't about to secure a payroll deduction for a plan in which we have no control."

In the foregoing there has been no discussion of the impact of the new situation on the personal fortunes of individual doctors in the Pittsburg area. There is no doubt but that the size and the structure of the medical profession engaged in the private practice of medicine in Pittsburg and the neighboring communities is different from what it would have been if the Kaiser Foundation Health Plan were not providing the bulk of the medical care for the approximately 9,600 persons represented by the steelworkers and their families enrolled in the supplemental program. Assuming that those families subscribing to the Kaiser Plan utilize its services, $150,000 would be a rough estimate of the gross annual income diverted from the physicians in the locality as of 1957. An estimate of the gross annual income lost to the community hospital would be much higher, probably in the neighborhood of $300,000. Reductions in individual doctor's incomes of from one-quarter to one-third were reported after the new supplemental insurance program went into effect.

Effects; Reductions in doctors' incomes

In discussions of the Pittsburg affair, references are often made to "some doctors" who were forced to leave the community because of the reduction in their practice. An attempt to verify this statement led to the tentative conclusion that the departure of one doctor was almost certainly due to the effect of the new medical arrangement and that it was possibly an important factor in the departure of another. A third physician went on active military service at that time, facilitating adaptation to the new level of demand. A comparison of the doctors listing Pittsburg addresses in the 1952 and the 1954 directories of the Alameda-Contra Costa Medical Association confirms this estimate.

Failure of the population of doctors in private practice to grow despite the continuing population growth has been the way in which the situation has resolved itself. A substantial though unknown increase in population has occurred but few new doctors had opened practice in Pittsburg through 1956.

The view has been expressed that by 1956 the incomes of the doctors involved had probably returned to their former level. If true, this would imply that the approximately 9,600 family members lost to Kaiser had been replaced or that per capita expenditures on medical care had risen substantially. It is questionable that the required 50 per cent increase in population in Pittsburg and environs has occurred or that increases in expenditures have made up the deficit. As a general statement, it seems a little optimistic to assume that the individual doctors had recovered their position completely by mid-1957.

Conclusions

Several of the generalizations made in the earlier chapters of this study are supported by this description of a specific episode in medical economics. The following conclusions seem warranted by the Pittsburg experience.

1. Organized consumer activity in the market for medical care calls forth the necessity for increasing organization on the part of the suppliers of medical care. Elaboration of the forms of the traditional medical organizations antedates the union's concern with health and welfare matters on a large scale, but the introduction of a skilled, aggressive bargaining agent into the situation has greatly accelerated the pace of development and increased the variety of directions it has taken. It cannot be denied that Local 1440 was in large measure responsible for (*a*) the creation of the Doctors Plan and the necessary machinery for implementing it, (*b*) the proposal for continuous doctor-union committee activity in the areas of planning local emergency medical service and in the policing of doctors' observance of the medical plan and the members' usage of it, (*c*) the development of a special California

Physicians Service program solely for the Pittsburg market, and (*d*) continuous informal contact with the county medical association and the local hospital administrator in efforts to consolidate and improve the position of the current alternative insurance plan.

Adjustments in previous methods of operation have not been limited to the private practitioners of medicine. Although Local 1440 did not pioneer the supplementation program as developed by the Kaiser Plan, its experience affords an example of both the advantages and disadvantages of this arrangement to Kaiser. While it permits a local group-practice plan to participate in a health program operating on a national scale and is very useful in special circumstances, the supplementation arrangement required the development of a new type of coverage with extensive additions to administrative burden. Proliferation of the types of contracts offered is at variance with the principles under which the Kaiser Plan presently operates and its administrators are not enthusiastic about the possible spread of this program.

Like the medical society and the local doctors, the Kaiser Plan has found it necessary to increase the staff time devoted to non-medical services because of the necessity for meetings and discussions with the representatives of their organized members.

2. Through its pressure for certainty of coverage, organized consumer activity has substantially modified the pricing structure and the pricing process of the medical profession. Traditionally, physicians have regarded as one of their most jealously guarded prerogatives the setting of fees for their own services. Charges to different patients for the same procedure have varied within the practice of a single physician; charges to the same individual for the same procedure have varied when performed by different physicians. Certainty of coverage requires that the agency arranging for payment have advance knowledge of the limits of liability for charges for medical service. This creates pressure for uniformity of fees within the practice of each physician and, if free choice of physician is to be preserved, for uniformity among physicians. Absolute uniformity need not be the rule, but the system of differentials among the physician-members must be the subject of general agreement and not the result of individual action in fee-setting.

In Pittsburg the successive plans proposed by the doctors furnish a small-scale example of the stages through which the solution to problems of this nature has passed. In its final form the Doctors Plan was a type of service plan paying participating doctors on a unit value system. In plans of this type the total amount of money available is determined by the premiums charged and, since the total number of units of medical service to be rendered in return for this sum is variable, the amount to be paid to the doctor for each unit cannot be determined in advance. As a result, the Pittsburg doctors by binding themselves to make no additional charges were eliminating uncertainty about the size of the patient's bill at the cost of introducing uncertainty about the dollar value of their services. Their incomes would depend in part on the results of spreading the premium income from the plan among the participating doctors in accordance with a predetermined formula. Plans of this type not only deny the individual doctor the right of setting his own fees but, under some circumstances, make the fee unpredictable in advance. As the Doctors Plan finally evolved, there is some doubt that the financial results would have been satisfactory from the doctors' point of view.

The California Physicians Service supplement which replaced the now-defunct Doctors Plan tries to avoid this situation by specifying a fixed fee schedule in advance, setting premiums expected to cover this schedule under normal utilization and to build up a reserve for unusual circumstances. Since in the event of adverse experiences, CPS cannot pay out money it does not have but must reduce doctors' fees, the basic difference in the two systems is the size of the safety factor which may be built into the premium structure and on which the integrity of the fee schedule depends.

Abandonment of the $4,200 family income limitation that normally qualifies the use of the particular fee schedule adopted in the Pittsburg CPS program is another example of the way in which the fee-setting process responds to the pressure of events. The same wearing away of the income-ceiling principle of CPS operation is observable in other localities in the state and has been discussed in chapter vii.

3. One of the most significant points emphasized by the Pittsburg episode is that the impact of the organization of the medical

consumer does not result in a once-for-all change in the economics of medical care. The "Pittsburg story" did not end in September, 1953, with the plant election. Indications are that the summer of that year marked the beginning of a bargaining process that will be almost continuous in the future. Accommodation to an environment of constant change rather than an adjustment to a permanent new order is the problem faced by the various organizations involved. As the costs of providing medical care and hospitalization rise, as rates of utilization by members change, as new items of coverage are included in both the national and the supplemental contracts, the union, the hospital and medical profession, and the Kaiser Plan will all have to adjust to new alignments of forces. The medical group's attempts to achieve the privilege of payroll deduction and the union's reluctance to give up bargaining leverage against both plans are evidence that present relationships are not static.

In addition to modifying the *method* of payment for part of the doctors' practice, Local 1440 has demonstrated that, as long as alternative health plans are available, the *total amount* paid for medical services will reflect the results of a form of collective bargaining. Not only will the union have influenced the way in which the total sum spent for care is distributed among the private practitioners and between the private practitioners and the Kaiser Plan, but, within limits, the union will have influenced the size of the total as well. As the medical groups attempt to maintain their relative position in successive renegotiations of their plan contracts in an economy in which costs and prices are rising, this problem will become increasingly important. Originally the steelworker health and welfare program undoubtedly raised the total expenditures for medical care in the area substantially over what would have prevailed in its absence. In the future the financial results, whatever they may be, will depend on the outcome of a bargaining process between representatives of the interested parties, a process much different from the traditional method of setting fees.

Chapter IX | Some Problems and Some Solutions

In the preceding chapters it has been shown that when a number of aggressive, independent decision-making units are confronted with a particular group of problems, the result will be a varied and ingenious set of approaches to a solution. In chapter vii attempts of the union groups in the Bay Area to develop a method of influencing the pricing process for medical services were reviewed. It was concluded that the impact of this activity on the methods of pricing and the level of prices had been significant, although to date no formal machinery of bargaining has been organized. In the preceding chapter the sequence of events that led a union representing a major part of the working population of an entire community to ally itself with a closed-panel health plan was described. The impact of this situation on the medical profession in the locality was analyzed. In this chapter some further illustrations of the diversity of medical arrangements generated in the decade during which the labor movement has been active in medical matters will be explored.

The four developments analyzed in the following sections were selected because they represent examples of different types of issues that have arisen. The first one discussed is the choice program of the Kaiser Foundation Health Plan. This unusual approach to a particular problem appears to have been originated by Kaiser and has been in operation since 1948 in one form or another. It has attracted national attention and in recent years other group-practice, prepayment health plans (e.g., the Health Insurance Plan of Greater New York) have adopted it. One of the interesting characteristics of the choice program is that it allows a specialized prepayment plan limited to a local area to participate in the health insurance program of national companies and national unions. This device adds a useful element of flexibility to these plans and perhaps points a way to greater diversity of practice in other plans that might be introduced later.

The second issue discussed in this chapter, experience rating, demonstrates that flexibility has drawbacks as well as advantages. Most of the section is concerned with experience rating as a general problem but the role that the negotiated plans have played in promoting the spread of the practice will also be examined.

The third development examined in this chapter is the interesting experimentation that has been carried on through a medically sponsored health insurance organization, the San Joaquin Foundation for Medical Care. The two quite different programs operated by this organization illustrate the way a county medical society can provide a vehicle for experiments that would be difficult to organize on a wider scale.

The last section of this chapter outlines the way in which some of the administrative problems of superimposing a group insurance program on an existing set of institutions organized for collective bargaining has been handled.

The Choice Program of the Kaiser Plan

A good claim can be made for the proposition that the "free-choice" or "dual-choice" program of the Kaiser Foundation Health Plan is the most important single innovation to come out of the Bay Area health plan experience. In its most general form, the choice program is based on the principle that the members of group-health insurance plans should enjoy a choice among various types of health insurance coverage. As it has developed, the choice program serves as a method of limiting the possibility that any one type of health insurance organization might secure a monopoly of the medical business of a particular group of health plan members. Considered from a more positive point of view, the choice program is a method of assuring individual health plan members of an opportunity to choose from among competing systems of medical organization at periodic intervals.

The meaning and importance of the choice program offer an excellent example of the way in which administrative devices have changed their content and purpose as the health insurance movement evolved. In its original form, the choice principle was enunciated in order to permit the Kaiser Plan to gain access to a part of the medical business of a particular health plan. As negotiated health plans grew in importance, the choice program increased greatly in significance as it was called on to serve a number of other purposes, for example, to limit the ability of the trustees of a welfare fund to use the power of decision in the choice of an insurance carrier as a bargaining weapon in trust fund-carrier negotiations.

The principle of individual member choice was first put forth by the Kaiser Plan in connection with a proposal to the Health Service System, the medical service plan of the employees of the city and county of San Francisco. The HSS was established in 1937 as a compulsory, employee-financed health program through the device of a charter amendment that included a guarantee of free choice of doctor to the employee. It originally operated with a fee schedule and an open panel of physicians who agreed to accept the fee as full payment for services rendered to members. The fee schedule was arrived at after discussion with the San Francisco Medical Society. In most years, the society has endorsed the HSS program.

During most of its life, HSS has been successful in maintaining a high average number of doctors on its panel in contrast to the abortive attempts of the union groups to establish this kind of relationship (see chapter vii). It has already been noted that the attitude of organized medicine toward programs of this type seems to be related to the identity of the sponsor, the number of members and their income level, and the date of establishment. All of these factors were originally more favorable to HSS than they are today, either to the unions or to HSS.

When the society has not been able to reach an agreement as to a schedule of fees, when the dollar value of the schedule of fees has been too low, when the payment of fees has been long delayed, or when issues of "ethical" relationships with the manage-

ment of HSS have arisen, the society has sometimes renounced its
policy of coöperation. This action has typically coincided with a
wave of resignations of physicians from the panel. In 1948 a combination of financial and ethical difficulties resulted in the occurrence of one of these breakdowns in joint relationship. At that
time the Kaiser Plan proposed that the members of HSS be given
an opportunity to exercise their "free choice of doctor" by choosing the Kaiser Plan as an alternative to the existing open-panel
system. The issue was fought through the employee benefit administrative agencies of the city and finally in the courts, with the
final result being the development of four alternative health plan
choices for the members of HSS.[1] Although Kaiser at this time did
not operate a hospital in San Francisco, it gained approximately
1,000 subscribers (3,000 persons, including dependents), or something like 8 per cent of the eligible members in the first enrollment. The HSS members are given a chance to change their regis-
tration every six months and, as of 1957, the Kaiser Plan included
about one-third of the 35,000 subscribers and dependents in the
system.[2]

Even though the choice concept continued to be applied in
particular situations, it did not again become a major issue until
the growth of collectively bargained health plans on a large scale.

It is the related elements of centralized decision-making and
universal membership that make the question of individual member choice a vital one. The reader will note that these features are
common to both HSS and negotiated health plans. They are not
involved in the more prosaic applications of the choice principle
in which competing voluntary group insurance programs are offered to workers who pay their own premiums and who have
available the additional alternative of not subscribing to any plan.
(Employees of the University of California, for example, are offered a choice of Blue Cross, Kaiser, or, as members of the California State Employees Association, California Physicians Service
on a voluntary, employee-financed basis.)

Even the latter type of choice program raises some interesting
questions involving the economics of insurance. With the develop-

---

[1] The open-panel system was continued and the Kaiser Plan and two small
"closed-panel" groups were added.

[2] Information as to HSS was secured from Mr. Frank Collins, secretary to the
Board of Directors of HSS, June, 1957.

ment of group insurance, it was possible to eliminate some tests of insurability by relying on the assumption that if a large proportion (say 75 per cent) of a group of employed persons were enrolled, the insured group would have characteristics similar to those of the population as a whole. Even in their more innocuous voluntary form, choice programs require the relaxation of the 75 per cent rule with the possibility that the proportion of eligible workers electing a particular coverage may fall as low as 2 to 3 per cent. When the possibility that the benefits or the premiums of the various choices may differ is introduced, the problem of "adverse selection" arises in potentially acute form.[3]

For these reasons and others, the Kaiser Plan originally found the other insurers reluctant to participate in the offering of alternative coverages on a choice basis. At one time Kaiser contemplated the establishment of an indemnity health insurance company of its own in order to be able to offer fund trustees a "free choice" alternative coverage. Although as of 1958, California Physicians Service, Blue Cross, and some of the commercial insurance companies were participating in the choice program, representatives of each type of insurer expressed themselves to the writer as being unenthusiastic about the situation. Competitive pressures kept the system functioning.

As negotiated health plans grew in size and number and some labor groups developed the strategy of using the Kaiser Plan as a foil in their duels with the medical societies, the choice system began to take on a new aspect. In the early years the Kaiser Plan had stressed the choice arrangement in order to permit it to participate in programs to which it otherwise could not have gained access. The characteristics of the Kaiser Plan are unusual enough compared to the traditional system of medical practice so that most employers and union leaders would be reluctant to adopt it as the sole alternative available to all of their employees and members. By arguing the virtues of free choice, Kaiser was able to secure the business of those members who desired the Kaiser type of coverage. Of particular importance before the expansion

---

[3] Adverse selection occurs when the poorer insurance risks systematically tend to choose a particular alternative. An important form of adverse selection occurs when the poorer risks elect to be covered while the better risks remain uninsured. Risks are "poorer" or "better" if they are more or less likely to incur a loss than the average member of the group as a whole.

of facilities in 1953, the choice program meant that Kaiser did not have to limit its enrollment to groups whose members lived in areas with access to a Kaiser facility.

The growth of negotiated plans changed the role of the choice program and accentuated its usefulness to the Kaiser Plan in the following ways:

1. With all members of a negotiated plan automatically blanketed into a program, unions and employers became even more reluctant to specify Kaiser as the single available health plan. If a minority of a voluntary group wanted another form of medical service, they could remain outside the plan and make their own arrangements. In a negotiated group this alternative still existed but those members not using the specified plan would be losing the value of the premiums contributed on their behalf.

2. Although figures are not available, the advent of negotiated plans almost certainly increased the average size of the health plan groups which were customers for coverage. Voluntary groups limited to a single plant or a single employer became part of a national or regional plan or part of a plan based on an employer association or on union jurisdiction. Free choice provided a mechanism whereby some part of the business of any plan in the Bay Area could be retained for Kaiser. It has, for example, permitted Kaiser to share in the business of the General Motors, Ford, and Chrysler national plans.[4]

3. The problem of the "captive member" was solved. Rather than lose the value of the premiums contributed by their employers, some members of the negotiated plans who were either lukewarm toward the Kaiser system or even actively opposed to it tended to use at least some of the Kaiser services. Plan officials believe that their continued success depends on the nature of the word-of-mouth information being transmitted by members. The existence of any sizable number of reluctant members would almost certainly increase the likelihood of unsatisfactory reports being circulated.

4. The potential development of a "captive" membership group worsened the Kaiser Plan's already difficult relations with the

---

[4] The reader will remember from chapter viii that Kaiser has also been able to participate in the national health plans of United States Steel and Bethlehem Steel through a supplemental program developed with the United Steelworkers.

medical profession. Kaiser spokesmen had been arguing for years that a patient's choice of the plan was a valid interpretation of the profession's phrase "free choice of doctor." If they permitted welfare fund trustees to blanket unwilling members into the plan, they would be forced to abandon this position. Reversing the original situation, the choice program thus acted to ensure the rest of the medical profession access to some part of the medical business that might otherwise have gone entirely to Kaiser.

5. Like the private practitioners, Kaiser Plan officials were interested in limiting the bargaining power of the labor and management groups with which they deal. Acceptance of the choice philosophy by the trustees of a fund substantially reduces their power to allocate the medical business of the group among competing types of insurers (but not among companies of the same type). The choice program has the effect of decentralizing the decision as to the form of medical organization to the individual member.

As a result of these considerations, by 1954 the Kaiser Plan had adopted a policy of urging that each welfare fund contracting with Kaiser offer its members a choice of coverage that would permit them to secure medical care on an open-panel basis if they so desired. This policy was applied not only to negotiated plans entering Kaiser for the first time but also to funds already under contract as these contracts came up for their annual renewals.

The Mechanics of the Choice Program

The mechanics by which individual members are given a choice of health plans vary according to the specific conditions under which each welfare fund operates. In one approach to the financial problem the parties to the collective-bargaining contract agree that the welfare fund will purchase one of the group contracts available from Kaiser at the appropriate monthly premium rate for that type of coverage.[5] This rate determines the monthly premium per employee for the alternative insurance coverage. The scope and scale of benefits to be provided for this premium are

---

[5] Kaiser operates with different monthly rates for a single subscriber, subscribers with one dependent, and subscribers with two or more dependents. Welfare funds are quoted a single "composite" rate per enrolled employee. One example of the system discussed in the text is the health plan of the warehouse locals of the International Longshoremen's and Warehousemen's Union and the Distributors Association of Northern California.

determined by negotiations with the insurance carriers interested in the business.

Under this system an increase in the premium rate for Kaiser Plan coverage automatically generates a larger premium for the insurance coverage and may permit an increase in the benefits available under the alternative plan. Conversely, adverse claim experience under the insurance plan may necessitate a reduction in the indemnity benefits provided since the available premium is limited to that charged by Kaiser. It is tempting to speculate on the possible consequences of this arrangement for the two insuring organizations involved. At first glance, it would appear that either of these possible situations would be likely to be detrimental to the interests of the Kaiser Plan. If benefits offered by the competitive insurance plan are increased, the relative attractiveness of the competitive plan increases and Kaiser may suffer a loss of members as a result. These lost members are as likely to be those with low utilization of medical services (and hence low cost to the Kaiser Plan) as they are to be members with high utilization. On the other hand, if the loss experience of the alternative insurance plan requires a reduction in benefits, this may mean that the group as a whole or at least that portion choosing the insurance plan has had higher-than-average utilization rates. The resulting shift to the Kaiser Plan will tend to raise the average utilization rates of the Kaiser members.

This kind of reasoning oversimplifies the problem since it gives a high degree of importance to economic calculation as a determinant of the choice of each member. In connection with this study more than 200 subscribers to one of the choice plans of the Joint Board of Culinary Workers were interviewed at length in an attempt to determine the reasons for their choices. The answers suggested that the specific characteristics of the medical benefits offered were considerably less important in determining the choice made than were more subjective factors.[6] The Kaiser Plan and the

---

[6] Of 106 Kaiser subscribers interviewed, 50 reported that they chose the Kaiser Plan at least partly as a result of the advice or the reported experience of other persons. Of the 107 interviewees who were enrolled in the alternative insurance program, 76 gave the freedom of choice of doctor as the reason or as one of the major reasons for their choice. The survey was of the Joint Board of Culinary Workers–Hotel Employers Association fund. Special acknowledgment is made of the coöperation of Anthony Anselmo, executive secretary of the board, and the officers of the various affiliated locals.

open-panel alternatives are so dissimilar in their fundamental approach to the problem of medical care organization that it would probably take drastic changes in benefit structures to induce the members to reëvaluate their basic position. In this particular plan almost one-quarter of the members shifted from one plan to another at the first opportunity to make such a choice but the shifts almost exactly offset each other. Many of the persons changing plans at this time had received no medical care at all under their original choice up to the time of the shift.[7] Most administrators who have experience with the choice program agree that valid generalizations are very difficult to make and that each group seems to have its own peculiar characteristics.

A more common method of handling the financial aspects of the choice program involves writing into the collective-bargaining contract a dollar-and-cents contribution per employee to be paid into the welfare fund to finance health insurance. This permits the fund trustees to arrange for alternative forms of coverage without requiring the cost of the two coverages to bear any specific relation to one another.

The four funds of the Culinary Workers illustrate some of the possibilities inherent in this approach. In 1954, the Joint Board of Culinary Workers and the several employer associations agreed on a fixed monthly health fund contribution per employee. This amount was not sufficient to permit the fund managers to purchase standard Kaiser coverage and to offer the members the option of an indemnity plan of broad scope. The trustees met this problem by limiting the benefits of the alternative insurance plan to the employee only (excluding dependents) and thereby reducing the required premium. As a result, the fund allocates its money unequally between Kaiser and the alternative plan and has some flexibility in meeting financial problems as they arise. The Kaiser composite premium rate depends on the ratio of single members and members with dependents choosing Kaiser and on the changes

---

[7] Further evidence of the importance of subjective and noneconomic factors is provided by the behavior of Culinary Worker subscribers with dependents. In this plan dependents (who account for something like two-thirds of all medical costs in the typical family) were covered automatically at no cost to the subscriber in the Kaiser Plan but were covered in the insurance plan only if the subscriber himself paid an additional premium. In spite of this, 41 per cent of the 115 interviewees with eligible dependents chose the alternative insurance plan.

in premiums for the Kaiser Plan as a whole. The indemnity insurance premium rate reflects the level of costs incurred by those choosing this alternative.[8] This system may permit the accumulation of reserves to meet future increases in premiums during the life of the collective-bargaining contract or to increase coverage. In the system described earlier in which the alternative plan premium is geared to the cost of Kaiser coverage, an increase in Kaiser rates provides a larger premium for the alternative as well. The employer has an open-ended obligation to the union. In contrast, under the arrangement now under discussion an increase in the premium of either plan places the whole welfare fund under financial pressure since employer contributions are fixed.

Particularly in choice plans, negotiation of a fixed employer contribution is more common than negotiating an agreement to provide a particular set of medical benefits. It fixes the cost of the program to the employer for the term of the collective-bargaining contract and relieves him of the necessity of concerning himself directly with many of the economic problems of welfare fund administration. This system also permits the trustees of the welfare fund to manipulate the details of cost and coverage of the alternative plans to meet the changing needs of the insured group.

The Choice Program in Practice

Students of medical organization and medical economics have viewed the development of the choice program of the Kaiser Plan as providing an excellent opportunity for the study of consumer preferences as between competing methods of organizing the provision of medical services. On the surface, the choice program seems to offer a unique opportunity for studying the behavior of consumers when they are given a choice between (1) a comprehensive, group-practice, service plan with the accompanying drawbacks of a limitation of choice of physicians and hospitals,

---

[8] The success of this arrangement depends on a substantial number of employees with dependents choosing the insurance plan and a substantial number of single subscribers choosing the Kaiser Plan. As noted earlier, 41 per cent of the sample of employees from one Culinary Workers plan did not choose Kaiser even though they had dependents who would have been automatically included. Similarly, 40 per cent of those members of the sample without dependents did choose the Kaiser Plan. If all members with dependents chose Kaiser and all single members chose CPS, the Kaiser composite rate would be higher and the over-all cost substantially increased.

and (2) the more orthodox insurance programs providing relatively limited coverage on an indemnity benefit basis but offering an almost completely free choice of physicians and hospitals. (The situation is complicated somewhat, but not seriously, by the existence of CPS as an alternative in a few plans, since for families below the income ceilings, CPS is a service program rather than an indemnity program.)

Although the choice plans do provide some information as to this basic question, there are a number of important qualifications that limit the usefulness of conclusions drawn from this experience.

1. The Kaiser Plan is only one example of a comprehensive, group-practice, service program. It has important differences from other programs of this type and has its own strengths and weaknesses. Even valid generalizations from Kaiser experience need not be applicable to other situations involving other plans.

2. The alternatives to Kaiser coverage offered by welfare funds to their members include programs underwritten by CPS, by Blue Cross, and by a number of commercial insurance companies. These organizations stand ready to provide any one of a very large number of variations of health benefit "packages." In other words, while Kaiser's coverage options are standardized and few in number, the alternative plans differ substantially among themselves in the scope and scale of benefits provided. Comparisons of trends in choice over time are particularly difficult to interpret since the alternative plans change their benefit structure frequently, often in different directions. These changes reflect variations in the money available to the funds, the desires of the trustees, the medical experience of the plan's members, and other factors. In other words, the choice is not between two standard forms of alternative methods of medical organization, but between a particular comprehensive service system, the Kaiser Plan, and a wide variety of very specific alternatives, many of which change over time even within the same insured group.

3. Many individual members of plans that offer a formal choice actually cannot take advantage of this apparent freedom. One of the reasons the choice program was developed was to permit Kaiser to share in the business of welfare funds whose members were so dispersed geographically as to preclude Kaiser from com-

peting for the business of the fund as a whole. Even with the expansion of Kaiser facilities, many funds include members who do not have access to a facility or who have access only at considerable inconvenience. As an example, officials of one fund pointed out that a substantial drop in the previously high proportion of its membership electing Kaiser coverage occurred when it expanded its boundaries to include workers in an area where no Kaiser facility was available.

4. The welfare funds that are participating in the choice program are not necessarily a cross section of the population as a whole, of the working population, or even of the population with health insurance. In the course of the research for this study, it became evident that some union leaders and more employers are unfavorably disposed toward the Kaiser Plan as a matter of principle just as some union leaders and fewer employers are favorably disposed for the same reason. It is significant that only a little more than 10 per cent of the many separate negotiated plans in the Bay Area participate in the choice program although the advantages of offering the members a choice would seem to be substantial and the administrative difficulties of minor importance. In addition, since negotiated plans are based on specialized occupational and industrial groups, they are almost certainly highly differentiated with respect to characteristics that are of major importance to the health experience of the group. Examples of such characteristics are age, race, sex, type of work, and even hours of work since working schedules influence the ease with which members can secure medical care. It is quite possible, if not probable, therefore, that the decision to participate in the choice program is subject to a systematic bias that makes the result of an analysis of the program inapplicable to the insured population as a whole.

Although the results must be interpreted with caution, some of the operations of the choice plans will be reviewed below.

In the summer of 1956 there were twenty-seven negotiated health plans offering their members a choice between the Kaiser Plan and an open-panel alternative. Data as to the pattern of choice were available for twenty-three of these plans and are summarized in table 9.1.[9]

---

[9] These data were collected either from the organization administering the plan or from officials of the union or company involved. They were secured by a variety

TABLE 9.1

SELECTED DATA ON PLANS PARTICIPATING IN KAISER CHOICE PROGRAM, 1956

Total choice plans in effect	27
Plans included in tabulation	23
Total eligible for coverage	43,290
Total subscribers choosing Kaiser	28,190
Percentage choosing Kaiser	65
Range of percentages choosing Kaiser in individual plans	20–98
Average of percentages choosing Kaiser in individual plans	48
Range in size of individual plans	150–12,000
Total members in four plans of Joint Board of Culinary Workers	17,360
Total subscribers choosing Kaiser	9,580
Percentage choosing Kaiser	55
Total members in three plans of ILWU	17,350
Total subscribers choosing Kaiser	14,730
Percentage choosing Kaiser	85

SOURCE: See text.

The 23 funds for which data were available had a total of more than 43,000 subscribers enrolled in one or the other alternative in August, 1956. Of this total almost two-thirds had chosen the Kaiser Plan for their medical service, but this over-all proportion is distorted by the fact that 98 per cent of the membership of the largest single fund chose the Kaiser Plan. If the separate funds are considered as single units, slightly less than half of the membership, on the average, chose Kaiser.

Membership in the choice program is highly concentrated. The two largest plans are almost equal in size with about 12,000 members each. These two are the larger of the Culinary Workers' funds —the San Francisco Restaurant and Tavern Welfare Fund—and the joint plan of the International Longshoremen's and Warehousemen's Union and the Pacific Maritime Association. If the four funds of the Culinary Workers and the two ILWU funds are

---

of means: questionnaire, personal visit, or by telephone. The figures for most of the plans, particularly the larger ones, are quite accurate. In a few instances where it was apparent that the respondent's knowledge was approximate and resistance to more than a moderate degree of insistence was shown, the figures were included if the estimate was offered in an appropriate tone of confidence. Information on two of the four plans not included did not meet even this elastic standard. In one other plan, the only one of even moderate size in the excluded group, the choice option was suspended since the plant had been moved out of the Kaiser service area. Company officials for the fourth excluded plan insisted that their plan was not negotiated although it was so reported by Kaiser. Three of the four excluded plans were quite small.

considered as units, then each of these unions accounts for a total of more than 17,000 subscribers.

Both of these union groups are above average in the proportion of their members selecting the Kaiser alternative—55 per cent for the Culinary Workers and 85 per cent for the ILWU. As a result, the ILWU represents by far the largest single block of Kaiser members and the two unions together account for about 86 per cent of all choice plan members enrolled in the Kaiser Plan. Since the great bulk of negotiated plan membership is included in the figures in table 9.1, it can be concluded that at least three-quarters of all the negotiated plan business of Kaiser was provided by these two unions in 1956. For the Bay Area Kaiser operation as a whole, the ILWU and the Culinary Workers accounted for about one-fifth of total membership in 1956.[10]

Partly as a result of this strong representation, both unions have been able to establish a fairly formal medical "grievance procedure." The ILWU, for example, instructs the aggrieved member to bring his problem to the attention of the doctor immediately. If the issue is not settled satisfactorily, appeal to the health plan representative (a Kaiser employee) is the next step recommended. The next level of appeal is the welfare officer or secretary of the local union. Regular meetings attended by ranking representatives of the welfare fund and the Kaiser Plan provide the final stage of the process.[11] In addition to the grievance procedure, the ILWU was instrumental in bringing about the establishment of a Kaiser coverage that eliminates the need for per-visit surcharges paid by the patient in return for a higher premium. Some of the other implications of the concentration of negotiated plan membership in these two unions are explored in the next section.

As far as the pattern of choice is concerned, most observers

[10] According to the Kaiser Foundation monthly bulletin, *Plan for Health,* June, 1957, the average number of subscribers during 1956 was 121,000. Inclusion of dependents raised the total membership to 310,000. The ILWU and the Culinary Workers provided about 20 per cent of the subscribers and probably, though not necessarily, about the same proportion of total membership.

[11] That the negotiated plans have introduced a new element into health plan operation is suggested by the succinct language with which an ILWU booklet explaining the plan closes the section on grievances, ". . . Every beef settled properly sets good precedent for future services." In contrast, the writer attended a meeting of members of a large voluntary Kaiser group most of whom had been members for years without having any knowledge of the existence of a "health plan representative" for their group.

agree that one possibly valid generalization may be made. There appears to be a not-very-surprising tendency for the choice between the two types of plans to be related to the previous experience of the group with health insurance. If at the time of choice the group has had no previous experience with the different forms of medical organization, it is likely that the split between the two alternatives will be approximately even. If the group has either an indemnity plan or a Kaiser contract in effect at the time the choice is made, roughly two-thirds of the members will remain with the original type of plan while the other one-third will choose the newly available alternative. Some supporting evidence for this hypothesis is found in the fact that in fifteen of the twenty-three choice plans listed in table 9.1 between 31 and 66 per cent of the members chose Kaiser. Most of the other eight plans tended to cluster at the extremes: in two of them more than 95 per cent selected Kaiser; in four others about one-fifth of the members chose Kaiser.

The principal support for this generalization stems from the well-publicized experience of the four Culinary funds. Prior to adopting the choice program two of the funds had been continuously enrolled in indemnity insurance plans. These two groups divided 65 and 52 per cent in favor of the already established indemnity system. The other two funds had originally been covered by an indemnity contract but for one full year prior to the choice they had been exclusively enrolled in the Kaiser Plan. These two groups divided 67 and 74 per cent in favor of the established Kaiser Plan. The influence of inertia is further shown by the fact that after the first opportunity to register a new choice one year later, the three funds in which the choice had been predominantly in favor of one plan or the other had moved in the direction of a more equal division of members while the other remained constant at a 52–48 per cent division. After two more annual choice opportunities, the situation still appeared to be stabilized with the division for all four funds well within the 60–40 per cent interval.

Before drawing positive conclusions from what appears to be a rather consistent pattern of behavior, the reader is reminded that: (1) the Culinary funds give dependent coverage without extra cost under Kaiser but not under the alternative plans; (2)

the first year's choice was made between Kaiser and a commercial insurance plan while the second, third, and fourth choices were exercised between Kaiser and California Physicians Service; (3) the figures cited are net shifts—the gross shifts from one plan to another at choice dates have involved as many as one-fourth of the total membership; and (4) the data do not apply to an unchanging population that can be viewed as acquiring more medical sophistication as time goes on since a substantial number of new employees and newly eligible but formerly transient employees are being continually added to the plan.[12]

A review of the ILWU funds, the other major block of choice plan members, reveals an interesting variation in the experience with free choice. The ILWU is outspokenly in favor of the comprehensive, full-service benefit plan as the most effective method of organizing medical care. Although the ILWU strongly objects to the lack of "consumer representation" at Kaiser, in the absence of a union-controlled program it has supported the Kaiser concept. The big ILWU–PMA plan for longshoremen was organized as an exclusively Kaiser program at its inception in 1949. With the adoption of the choice principle as official Kaiser policy, an indemnity insurance alternative was offered for the first time in 1954. Something like 2 or 3 per cent of the membership took advantage of the new option; the rest retained their Kaiser membership. In the succeeding annual choices there has been no trend toward more equal division. On the other hand, the two warehousemen's locals of the ILWU negotiated their first welfare program with the Distributors Association of Northern California in 1953. This has been a choice plan from the beginning. As our hypothesis would have led us to expect, the warehousemen divided almost evenly between the two alternatives in spite of the international union's preference for service plans. In three succeeding

---

[12] The importance of this last point is emphasized by the results of a check of the status of the 213 members of the Culinary Worker funds who were interviewed in June, 1955. As of January 1, 1956, the date of the first annual choice after the program was instituted, the membership of 35 of the 213 interviewees had been terminated and 13 more had no current application pending for either option. One reason for the lack of applications may have been that although the workers were not currently employed, they had not been unemployed long enough to have been terminated. It should be stressed that at least some of these workers undoubtedly simply shifted from one of the Culinary Worker funds to another by changing employers without leaving the industry or becoming unemployed.

annual choices there has been a slight trend toward increased selection of Kaiser.

The complexity of the problem of analyzing a worker's motivation in choosing alternative health plans is further illustrated by a rather unexpected example of free choice in action. As previously remarked, some of the locals of the unions that negotiated health plans had already formed voluntary employee-financed groups enrolled either in Kaiser or in another plan. About 15,000 members of these voluntary groups have retained their membership in Kaiser groups at their own expense even though their newly negotiated health plan provided them with coverage in an indemnity insurance program. This carries the principle of "free choice" one step further since with this dual coverage these individual members can secure medical care from any doctor of their choice or from Kaiser. There appear to be two major reasons for this behavior. First, there is considerable informal evidence that some persons use Kaiser for certain types of service and use indemnity insurance with its free choice of doctor for other types. For example, one view seems to be that for periodic checkups, minor surgery, laboratory work, and pediatric care, the ready availability of Kaiser service at nominal out-of-pocket costs is highly valued. For more serious problems, some patients may want to be free to go to a particular specialist or a doctor with whom he (or more likely, she) has established a particular relationship. On the other hand, Kaiser coverage may be useful when a medical "catastrophe" involving complex, expensive care and long periods of hospitalization occurs since the limits of the usual indemnity coverage are rapidly exceeded in cases of this kind.

The second reason for maintaining dual coverage is straightforward financial gain. A patient with coverage in two indemnity plans or in Kaiser and an indemnity plan can benefit from his insurance protection twice for the same illness or can collect a cash indemnity from the insurance company if he uses Kaiser's service benefits. Cash equivalents cannot be collected from a medical organization providing service benefits. If, however, the actual care is provided by the service organization, the patient has a valid claim to any cash indemnity due him from other sources. Almost all of the parties concerned (except the patient) frown on this practice but it is difficult to control. In practice, dual coverage also arises by accident when two members of a family both are covered by negotiated plans that automatically include dependents.

The earlier suggestion that some members of Kaiser may regard this type of health plan and other plans offering free choice of doctor and hospital as different kinds of insurance protection suitable for different uses appears to have general application and to be independent of dual coverage. Over any time period an unknown number of Kaiser members undoubtedly secure medical service they are entitled to receive from Kaiser from outside doctors, paying for it out of their own pockets. In the course of this study several persons volunteered the information that they had gone "outside" Kaiser for services covered by their contract for a variety of reasons. It was noted in chapter v that the medical profession has tried to estimate the proportion of Kaiser members securing treatment from outside doctors without success. In the interviews of Culinary Workers enrolled in Kaiser an attempt was made to collect some information on the extent of this practice. Although the character of the results prevents the development of reliable quantitative data, it appeared that this situation occurred with some frequency. The reasons for going outside were varied, highly specific to the individual, sometimes confused, and sometimes based on a lack of knowledge. Persons who went outside often continued to use Kaiser services as well and at the next choice date, two-thirds of them remained in the Kaiser Plan. The one-third shifting allegiance to the alternative plan compares with about one-fourth of members of the plan as a whole who changed at that time (and the one-fourth who shifted in the other direction, from indemnity to Kaiser). About the only conclusion that can be drawn from this review is that the often-quoted statement that comprehensive service plans of the Kaiser type cover some 80 to 90 per cent of medical care costs[13] needs to be qualified by adding "for those patients who use all the necessary services to which they are entitled."

There is evidence that the members of other comprehensive health plans also go outside the physician panels of the plans for some of their medical care. Over a period of "many months" Dis-

---

[13] See, for example, E. R. Weinerman, *Labor Plans for Health,* San Francisco Labor Council, 1952, p. 30.

trict 65 of the Retail, Wholesale, and Department Store Union in New York City found that "approximately 30 per cent" of their members secured medical services from doctors not affiliated with their insurance carrier, the Health Insurance Plan of Greater New York.[14] These members were covered by the comprehensive insurance program of HIP entirely at their employer's expense yet went to additional personal expenditure to use an outside doctor for at least some services. More surprising, the union found that "about 25 per cent" of their membership had not even enrolled in HIP at all. The union concluded that "the type of program of which HIP is representative, while it has many wonderful qualities and has met the medical needs of a large number of our members, by itself it does not meet the needs of an organization like ours. . . ." The reader should not conclude that some 55 per cent of the members of this union objected to the type of medical service to which they were entitled and which were available to them. Some of the 30 per cent of the enrollees in HIP who went outside may nevertheless have used HIP for the bulk of their medical care. Other members of the nonuser group may have been covered by some other form of insurance program or may not have found an HIP facility accessible to them. This material does provide an indication of the importance of maximizing the freedom of choice among alternative programs through some administrative device.

A different approach from that of the Kaiser Plan to the problem of offering a choice among insurance systems to the members of a single plan has been organized in New York in recent years by Group Health Insurance Coöperative, Inc. This company originated in the consumer coöperative movement and in 1957 had 160,000 members in the metropolitan area. GHI maintains a panel of physicians who have agreed to accept the plan's fees as full payment for their services.[15] A member who does not or cannot use a doctor drawn from this panel is free to go to any physician of his choice and the plan will pay this physician a cash indemnity to-

---

[14] From the statement of Irving Baldinger, Director of the District 65 Medical Plan, *Hearings on the Extension of Voluntary Health Insurance* (New York: School of Public Health, Columbia University, 1955), pp. 69–70. District 65 has 24,000 members.

[15] Foundation on Employee Health, Medical Care and Welfare, *Study No. 1,* Parts B and C, June 1958, pp. 26, 41–43.

ward his fee. This interesting arrangement permits the patient to make a choice between a service and an indemnity system at will within the same plan. Any combination can be worked out to suit the patient's desires and needs. In effect this is similar to the California Physicians Service and other medically sponsored systems except that there are no income limitations for the service benefits and the plan is under lay sponsorship.

This review of the development and operation of the choice program of the Kaiser Plan and other organizations furnishes an excellent example of the way in which the diversity of organizational forms available and the interplay of various forces have acted to encourage experimentation to the benefit of the medical consumer. It is an illustration of the benefits inherent in a system that not only permits but encourages and almost compels the different parties involved in the medical care problem to reëxamine their basic positions and to adapt themselves to the evolving situation. The choice program represents a significant contribution to the improvement of the system of providing medical services in at least two major ways. First, it provides the consumer with an opportunity to choose the form of organization he considers best suited to his needs and to make other choices as he acquires more knowledge or as his needs change over his lifetime. Second, it exposes the different forms of organization to the pressures of competition with the resulting spur to improving service and tailoring special programs to meet special needs. In terms of consumer interest, the writer is aware of only one argument against the choice program—it permits the individual to make a decision that may be against his best interests as these interests are interpreted by someone else (e.g., his employer, his union officials, their consultants, or the medical profession). In the writer's opinion, because of the advantages for the beneficiaries for whom the welfare funds are established, choice programs should be made more widely available.[16]

Unfortunately, the decentralization of decision-making that permits and encourages experimentation of this sort has some drawbacks, one of which is discussed in the next section.

---

[16] Since the data on which this section is based were collected, at least two more funds of substantial size have decided to participate in the Kaiser program.

The Dilemma of Experience Rating

In the jargon of the insurance industry, experience rating refers to the practice of relating the premium for an insurance coverage to the loss experience of the specific group covered by the contract. Most people are familiar with some of the manifestations of experience rating in the form of attempts of the sellers of automobile insurance to isolate what is expected to be a low-risk group by occupation or other criteria (e.g., government employees, teachers, and members of automobile associations). Another familiar example is the practice of varying premiums according to the age of the drivers in the household or the number of years a driver has been insured without filing a claim.

The insurance principle involves spreading the cost of an unpredictable individual loss over a group of persons exposed to the same risk. Dividing the insured population as a whole into smaller units for rate-making purposes raises the question of the size and the composition of the group of persons to be included. If the group is defined as including an above-average number of "bad risks" with reference to the contingency insured against, the premium rate for this group will have to be higher than the average for the insured population as a whole to cover the losses that can be expected to occur. Conversely, a group whose members can be expected to suffer lower-than-average losses can be charged a below-average premium without a resulting loss to the insurer. In practice, high-cost health insurance groups are usually offered a combination of higher premiums and more restricted coverage but the net effect is the same.

It might appear that an insurance company practicing experience rating would be indifferent to the characteristics of the groups it insures since the premium rates are varied to compensate for the differential risks of loss. So far as this study is concerned, there are a number of flaws in this assumption. In health insurance the variation in rates of loss for groups with different characteristics is difficult to predict in advance. In the absence of exact knowledge, competitive pressures for underwriting volume may lead the rate makers to underestimate the possibilities of loss. A rate that experience shows to have been set too low may result in a loss that cannot be recovered. A group of insured persons whose losses turn out to be lower than was assumed at the time the premium was determined may often be successful in getting a "retroactive" rate adjustment or a rebate of premiums as a condition for continuing the contract with the insurance carrier. It is very difficult, however, for a carrier to reverse the situation and recover a loss suffered in a past period by charging higher premiums in the future. The carrier attempting this tactic finds that other companies stand ready to underwrite the coverage as entirely new business at its true future cost.[17]

A possibly extreme example of the situation that can arise in dealing with high-risk groups is provided by the experience of the welfare funds of the Joint Board of Culinary Workers and the employer associations. Each of the four funds was underwritten by three different insurance companies, each of whom lost money on the business. This was true even though the later underwriters had the records of the loss experience of the previous underwriters on which to base the premium rate to be charged.[18] At the time of contract renewal the insurance companies faced the question of whether to write off past losses, adjust premiums to cover future costs, and try again. Evenually, each of the four commercial companies involved withdrew and left the field to Kaiser and the California Physicians Service.

Difficulties would arise even if the cost of insuring any specific group could be made completely predictable in advance. The premium that would have to be charged certain groups would be so high as to be unworkable in many cases. If the group is one in which membership is universal, as is the case in the negotiated plans, the required premium may be higher than the group can or will pay. If the group is one in which health plan membership is voluntary for each member, the difficulties are compounded. The higher the premium charged a voluntary group,

---

[17] Usually the costs of the initial year of a contract with a specific carrier are higher than for subsequent renewals, so that changing carriers does involve some additional cost. Instances exist in which companies have quoted an artificially low initial rate in order to exploit this fact and "buy" future renewal.

[18] Anthony Anselmo, secretary of the joint board, reports that this loss record occurred not only in the face of the availability of actual claim experience for earlier years but also despite tighter administrative control over claims in the later years. A possible explanation that has been suggested is that the public controversies over the costs of the insurance plans have acted as a sort of advertising campaign for medical care. "It's like the 'Drink More Milk' campaign."

the more likely are the chances that adverse selection will occur. The members who feel that there is little likelihood of incurring substantial medical expenses remain out of the plan while those who believe that they are likely to incur such expenses enroll in the plan. This amounts to saying that the higher the premium, the more probable it is that the better-than-average risks in a group will, in effect, self-insure, leaving the poorer risks to participate in the insurance plan. This, of course, tends to raise the required premium still further. This is the sense in which it is sometimes remarked that continued increases in medical costs may "price voluntary health insurance out of the market." To hold a mass market, voluntary health insurance has to be inexpensive enough to persuade persons with relatively low chances of incurring large medical expenses to purchase the *protection* the insurance affords. At high premium rates the potential purchasers tend to be limited to those who feel that they are buying *medical service* they probably will need rather than buying *protection* against the possibility of loss.

The conclusion to be drawn is that groups so constituted as to include a relatively high proportion of persons likely to have high medical costs are difficult if not impossible to deal with in a system relying on commercial insurance companies practicing experience rating. There will always be groups for which the required premium rate will be so high as to make them unwilling or unable to participate in the health system. This will be true even if insured groups are limited to employed workers and their dependents, but it is particularly so if the concept of a group is expanded to include the unemployed, the disabled, families without breadwinners, the aged, the isolated worker, and other problem spots in the economy.

One method of dealing with this problem is to define the group to be used as the base of the insurance system so broadly as to spread the costs of the "problem" members thinly over the rest of the insured population. One obvious way to do this would be through compulsory health insurance in which the entire population of a state or the nation is considered as a single group. To date, this alternative has not been adopted in the United States. We have instead attempted a massive experiment in recruiting very large groups through the "Blue" organizations to serve as a base for a system of health insurance in which participation would be voluntary. Although private bodies such as employers or unions may bring about involuntary participation by some individuals as a condition of employment or membership, the apparatus of the state is not used to enroll any sizable proportion of the general population.

This experiment in voluntary insurance was pioneered by non-profit community organizations, usually allied in some way to the hospitals or the medical profession. The Blue Cross plans and the various versions of the Blue Shield-type of plan began operations with a concept of the "community" as a base for the group that would be used for premium rate-making purposes. Although for administrative purposes they enrolled a multitude of separate membership groups of all sizes in the pattern of commercial group insurance, the contract groups originally paid the same premium for the same coverage. This rate was developed from the financial results of the operation of the entire plan in that community, considered as a unit. In a sense, Blue Cross and Blue Shield rates for each separate geographical area could be regarded as representing a form of experience rating since there were a large number of such plans and their rates for the same coverage differed among different areas, in part because of differences in the medical experience of each plan's membership. The crucial point, however, is that, as originally organized, each plan had an exclusive geographical territory in which it operated without competition from other plans. The premium rates developed by each separate plan were "community rates" in a meaningful sense. As initially conceived, the Blue Cross and Blue Shield-type plans really did represent an attempt to devise a workable nongovernmental alternative to compulsory health insurance for the general population. This alternative had many of the advantages of the compulsory system but relied on persuasion rather than compulsion in recruiting membership.

With the entrance of the commercial insurance companies into the field of health insurance, the situation was radically changed. Their plans were competitive with the existing Blue plans in every community. The inevitable introduction of a system of experience rating in which the individual membership group served as the rate-making base rather than the "community" as a whole placed the community-wide plans under great pressure. As a general rule, in the new situation any individual membership group that had a lower loss ratio than the average for the insured population of the community as a whole could improve its position by insuring with a commercial carrier rather than one of the community-based plans. The low-loss groups in the latter organizations had been paying their own medical costs and contributing to the medical costs of the high-loss groups in the community at large. Through the operation of experience rating, they were offered the alternative of buying a contract in which their premium rates would reflect only their own medical costs.

Under the slogan of "Get the Most for Your Welfare Dollar," employers and union officials began investigating the merits of "competitive bidding" and the apparatus of experience rating. If the employer and union trustees of a welfare fund were laggard in discovering these advantages, they were aided and abetted by the employee benefit consultants,[19] the representatives of the insurance industry, and even legislative investigating bodies. This hardheaded, businesslike approach to health insurance saved some of the low-loss groups substantial sums of money. In the Bay Area, for example, two large negotiated plans are reported to have secured repayments from the medically sponsored service organizations amounting to several hundred thousand dollars as a condition for the renewal of their contracts.

Once experience rating is introduced into an area, the pressure on the plans attempting to retain the "community-rate" concept becomes irresistible. Unless they are to lose their low-loss groups to the commercial insurance carriers, they must meet the competition and experience rate these groups. And as a spokesman for California Physicians Service put it, ". . . Once you experience rate the good groups you have to experience rate the bad groups too." In the Bay Area both Blue Cross and CPS have had to adopt experience rating for at least a major part of their membership.[20]

---

[19] Many consultants and insurance brokers have been cool toward the nonprofit service plans because originally Blue Cross and Blue Shield organizations did not pay brokers' commissions. In the Bay Area, only the Kaiser Plan clings to this position at this time.

[20] In practice, carriers utilizing experience rating sometimes use it in a selective fashion. Most "bad groups" tend to be experience rated but only those "good groups" for which competition exists tend to be so rated. In connection with experience rating a Senate report noted that ". . . It has been pointed out that some

As of 1958 only the Kaiser Plan has retained the community-rate system and in that year it introduced an additional surcharge for members over 65 in order to meet some of the problems created by experience rating. Kaiser's reluctance to experience rate stems from a combination of loyalty to the community-rate principle and the fact that experience rating individual groups would force the keeping of detailed records on every service rendered. The administrative burden would dissipate one of the cost advantages of the plan.

Under any circumstances, experience rating would have made the nonprofit plan's adherence to a community-rate structure difficult, but two other factors made it decisive. The first was the rapid increase in over-all medical costs and the resulting increase in group insurance premiums. As premiums rose, the absolute differential between a community rate and a low-loss group rate came to represent important savings to a large plan. With the increase in premiums, even powerful unions in prosperous industries found their health plans under financial pressure, particularly if employer contributions were fixed by contract for a specific time. At any given negotiation there are limits to the possible gains that may be secured from the employer. Unions therefore found themselves buying the same "welfare package" in later negotiations at progressively increasing costs. Under these conditions it became important to seize any opportunity to effect a cost saving.

A second factor lending weight to the impact of experience rating was the growth of the negotiated health plans. Since almost all of these plans are at least partially employer financed, a more sophisticated insurance buyer used to dealing in commercial insurance incident to his business operations was brought into the picture. In addition, the unions themselves are better organized and staffed to realize the possibilities and to exploit them than were the more informal voluntary groups that preceded them.[21] If the unions adopted a policy of including coverage for their retired members in their health plans, if would help to solve part

insurance carriers do not treat all policyholders alike." Committee on Labor and Public Welfare, *Welfare and Pension Plans Investigation*, Senate Report No. 1734, 84th Congress, 2d session, p. 28. This report contains a wealth of factual and technical information on all aspects of the subject.

[21] Some unions, e.g., the United Automobile Workers, have officially supported the "community" approach to health insurance.

of this major problem but only a minority of unions cover retired members since, under experience rating, this raises premiums.

In the Bay Area there is no question but that unions and employers who have been introduced to health insurance as a result of collective bargaining have played a major role in making experience rating almost universal. It is not uncommon for negotiated plans to contract explicitly for a premium rate that exactly covers medical costs incurred plus a percentage allowance for a "loading" factor (administrative costs, profit, etc.) equal to the average "load" for the insurer's health business as a whole. The possibility of this kind of negotiation with the other carriers is an important reason why "good-risk" plans have been reluctant to offer their members a choice of Kaiser coverage at the Kaiser community rate.

It is questionable whether Kaiser can continue indefinitely to resist experience rating. As Blue Cross, CPS, and the commercial insurance carriers raise the premiums of the high-loss groups, the Kaiser community rate becomes more and more attractive to these groups. Insistence on the choice system affords Kaiser no protection against adverse selection since the insurance company alternatives become progressively less attractive in the high-loss groups as their cost rises and their benefits shrink. It is not accidental that the Culinary Workers' health plans have finally come to rest in the hands of the Kaiser Plan and CPS, after passing through four commercial insurance companies. Although less is known of the utilization of health services by members of the International Longshoremen's and Warehousemen's Union, the fact that, according to the welfare fund administrator, the average longshoreman is 55 years old suggests that they also may be a high-utilization group.[22]

In the title of this section the problem of experience rating is referred to as a "dilemma." This is a literal description since although its effects on the experiment in broad-scale voluntary health insurance are, in the writer's opinion, deplorable, it is ex-

---

[22] The ILWU's smaller warehouse group has an average age of 47. The ILWU is proud of the fact that the longshore welfare plan has covered retired workers but since 98 per cent of the men are Kaiser members, this was more to the credit of Kaiser than of the ILWU. In 1958 when Kaiser levied the over-65 surcharge, 19 per cent of the ILWU members were over 65. The fund has continued its coverage of these members although the composite premium was raised about $65.

tremely difficult to see how the situation could have been avoided once a compulsory health system was ruled out. Consider the following points:

1. Once the commercial insurance companies entered the field of health insurance, it was inevitable that they would compete against each other and against the nonprofit carriers for the good-risk groups. Had they entered into an agreement not to do so, it would have been impossible to enforce, would have been objected to by many of the insured groups, and probably would have been illegal. (The Senate report cited earlier did not object to experience rating but only to the fact that it was not uniform and universal.) To illustrate the difficulty of enforcement, note that requiring uniform premium rates for all contracts in a given area (a community rate) would not solve the problem unless all insurers were required to accept any group that applied for coverage at that rate.

2. Once experience rating was introduced, it was impossible for the nonprofit carriers to refuse to adopt it, but in doing so they abandoned their distinctive contribution to health insurance—the community rate. If Kaiser is able to hold out, it will be because the plan is a system of health care for which indemnity insurance is not a complete substitute at this time.

3. Once experience rating was introduced, it was inevitable that most trustees of welfare funds would take advantage of its operation wherever possible. In a real sense, it could be argued that it was their duty to the beneficiaries of the funds to do so. If the fund managers are to be criticized, criticism must be on the ground that their interpretation of the scope of the "group" to which they were responsible was too narrow. A very good case can be made that a welfare fund ought to regard its retired members as an integral part of the group entitled to protection. It might be argued that the social responsibilities of the welfare funds extend still further from the hard core of employed members, but it is not surprising that the financial costs of showing such responsibility are avoided by the great majority of plans.[23]

---

[23] In May, 1954, it was reported that only 7 of the 325 negotiated plans in Northern California provided retired members with as much as one year's health coverage at reduced benefits. California Department of Industrial Relations, *Health and Welfare Plans*, 1955, p. 64.

4. Even if some way had been found to protect the exclusive rights of the community-based nonprofit carriers in a given territory, eventually a variation of experience rating would probably have been introduced through the device of self-insurance. As they acquired experience with health insurance, large funds with below-average loss ratios probably would have left the community plans to underwrite their own members at lower cost.

Whether inevitable or not, the effect of experience rating has been to deal the promising concept of a virtually universal, voluntary, community-based health insurance system a mortal blow. It has become almost certain that substantial numbers of persons who might have been covered successfully by such a system will eventually be part of some form of governmentally sponsored health insurance. The rapid spread of negotiated plans contributed to the speed and the certainty with which experience rating has accomplished this result. Two of the Bay Area's large negotiated plans spearheaded the movement that brought about the use of experience rating by Blue Cross and CPS. There is reason to believe that the net effect of the inclusion of the negotiated plans in the Kaiser system has been an increase in cost for the plan as a whole. The collectively bargained health plans might have been the means of bringing health insurance to some of the problem groups in the population but so far, through encouraging experience rating, their net effect has been to worsen the situation of the marginal groups. This worsening has occurred because of the inability of the community plans to offset the losses incurred by high-cost groups against the gains formerly accruing from the low-cost groups prior to experience rating.

The ILWU and the San Joaquin Foundation for Medical Care

One of the most interesting outgrowths of the combination of collective bargaining and health insurance is the program worked out between the welfare fund of the International Longshoremen's and Warehousemen's Union and the Pacific Maritime Association and the San Joaquin Foundation for Medical Care.[24] The latter

---

[24] Information in this section was secured from publications of the society and the foundation and interviews with Dr. Donald Harrington, president of the foundation, Boyd Thompson, secretary of the society, and Mrs. Goldie Krantz, administrator for the ILWU–PMA welfare fund.

organization is a subsidiary corporation set up by the Medical Society of San Joaquin County in 1954.

San Joaquin County is outside the geographical boundaries of the Bay Area proper but well within its sphere of influence in medical and labor matters. It lies immediately east of Contra Costa and Alameda counties and its county seat, Stockton, is a city of some 80,000 population. Stockton, despite its location 100 miles from the ocean, is the third largest seaport in California. As a result the ILWU has about 700 longshoremen members working at the port. The medical society has approximately 200 active members and maintains its headquarters, staffed since 1952 by a full-time secretary in the Alameda pattern, in Stockton.

As in most of California, the labor movement in San Joaquin County is dominated by former AFL unions. In 1956 the secretary of the medical society estimated that there were about 36,000 union members in the area. During the hectic period of welfare fund activity in 1953, rumors circulated in Stockton that the Kaiser Foundation Health Plan had approached the local labor council with a health center proposal and that the labor groups in the area were also investigating the possibility of a labor-sponsored independent health center. The local Central Labor Council had been involved in the 1954 health and welfare conference in San Francisco referred to in chapter vii. The expansion of Kaiser into Pittsburg (described in chapter viii) in 1953 is also relevant to the background of the development of the San Joaquin Foundation since Stockton is only about forty miles east of Pittsburg.

The San Joaquin society reacted to the hectic events of the 1953–1954 period in a way that went a good deal beyond developments in either the San Francisco or the Alameda-Contra Costa medical societies.[25] Like the California Physicians Service at the state level, the foundation is a separate corporate organization, in this case sponsored and governed by the county society. It contracts annually for the services of member-doctors and as of May,

---

[25] The relationship between incidents in Pittsburg and the Bay Area proper and the foundation is pointed up by an editorial in the November, 1953, issue of the *Bulletin* of the San Joaquin society, ". . . To delay [the presentation of the Foundation proposal for membership approval] would be to invite disaster from three quarters: invasion of this area by outside closed panel systems, defections to closed panel medicine from within our own Society, and a demonstration to the public that we doctors are incapable of solving the economic ills of medicine." (p. 6).

1958, included about 86 per cent of the "active members" of the San Joaquin society.

The primary goal of the foundation is to provide "certainty of coverage" to the purchasers of health insurance within the framework of the solo practice of medicine on a fee-for-service basis. The achievement of this aim required that the usual indemnity insurance contract be converted into a service program. The mechanism with which the foundation accomplished this was an elaboration of the fee-schedule approach with some interesting variations.

The foundation began by adopting an approved set of health benefits, roughly similar to the usual surgical and medical coverage offered by indemnity companies and CPS. It then developed three fee schedules respectively applicable to families with incomes below $3,500, between $3,500 and $4,500, and above $4,500 without an upper limit.[26]

Up to this point, the foundation had followed the CPS pattern but now a significant innovation was introduced. Rather than underwrite the coverage itself, the foundation announced that it would guarantee to provide the benefits on a service basis to the purchasers of an approved contract underwritten by any insurance carrier, including CPS. Although the schedules contained an element of coinsurance or incidental fees (as does the Kaiser Plan), the foundation in effect made the CPS service benefit system available to all insurance carriers without an upper-income limit on eligibility. The premium rate at which the contract is sold to any group is determined by the insurance carriers in accordance with their usual practices, including experience rating.[27]

---

[26] The schedules were originally based on a survey of fees charged by the members of the society. The schedule applicable to the highest income group was set at the third quartile of the resulting range of fees (i.e., 75 per cent of the doctors usually charged fees equal to or less than the schedule). The middle-bracket schedule was set at approximately 75 per cent and the lower-bracket schedule at approximately 50 per cent of the highest schedule. When the California Medical Association Relative Value Schedule became available, the foundation adopted it with a multiplier of five for the top schedule and kept the other two schedules in about the same relationship as before. An indication of the absolute level of fees, in the county, is given by the fact that the third quartile schedule was reported as about equal to the ACCMA median fees. Incidentally, Rollen Waterson, former secretary of the ACCMA, worked with the San Joaquin society in setting up the foundation program.

[27] A glance at the concluding section in chapter vii above will remind the reader that the insurance industry and the unions have been pressing the California Medical Association to adopt a system similar to this on a state-wide basis.

An interesting variation in the usual administrative procedures of the commercial insurance companies has been introduced in the form of a claim review system. Any insurance program sponsored by the foundation must be administered in its office in Stockton by claims personnel who technically are employed by the insurance broker, agent, or insurance company representing the insured group. This permits claims to be subjected to a medical review by a physician-member of the foundation and provides a system of internal control under the administration of the foundation itself rather than through the medical review machinery of the insurers. This control system is probably more effective than the usual insurance company review.

This portion of the foundation program had enrolled twenty-three groups with a total of about 7,000 members by the spring of 1958. Because of the segregated income level approach, a single employer sometimes contributes two separate insured groups, usually one for the management personnel and one for the lower-paid production or clerical workers. Six of the twenty-three groups, including the warehousemen's local of the Longshoremen's Union in Stockton, were established as the result of collective-bargaining negotiations. Since the 7,000 members probably include something like 2,000 to 2,500 primary subscribers plus their dependents, it can be seen that the typical group is fairly small and that growth has been gradual over the four years of the foundation's existence.

Because some of the companies adopting the foundation's program have employees in other counties, doctors are enrolled who are resident in other counties and who belong to other county societies. In 1956, for example, 90 of the 144 physicians in neighboring Stanislaus County were members. In theory, this raises the possibility that the San Joaquin Foundation might expand substantially beyond the boundaries of the county, even to the (unlikely) extent of becoming a state-wide competitor of CPS. During the eventful 1953–1954 period described in chapter vii, Dr. Donald C. Harrington, president of the foundation, met with members of the medical society of at least one Bay Area county to discuss possible adoption of the foundation system. An interesting situation would arise if a major company (or union) with branches in San Joaquin County and in the Bay Area counties were to purchase a foundation-sponsored insurance contract from a commercial insurance company and request the Bay Area medical societies to permit enrollment of physicians in the adjoining Bay Area counties. If this proposal were accepted, it would place the foundation in the position of recruiting a panel of physicians pledged to providing medical care on what is essentially a service basis without income limitations. But, at present, there is no indication of a major expansion campaign. There is no question, however, that the existence of a no-income-ceiling program providing service benefits is one more competitive pressure keeping the service benefit portion of the state-wide CPS program very much alive.[28]

Although a number of unions have been enrolled in this branch of the foundation's program, the foundation's place in the longshoremen's section of the ILWU–PMA health program is of most interest to our study. The ILWU recognized that the separate corporate existence of an organization such as the foundation opened up the possibility of establishing health programs that even a coöperative county society would not have made available. During the first year of the foundation's existence, the ILWU entered into discussions with its officers to explore the possibility of developing a special program for its members. On July 1, 1955, the foundation and the ILWU inaugurated a health program that is certainly one of the most satisfactory in the United States from the union point of view.

One way of describing the San Joaquin Foundation–ILWU health plan is to point out that it resembles the CPS program as it existed at its beginnings in 1939. The plan provides each employee medical benefits including the following: (1) full coverage

[28] Some observers fail to appreciate the variety of pressures on the California Medical Association to continue to provide a workable service benefit system through CPS. This leads them to give an exaggerated importance to the fairly regular statements emanating from the Association's House of Delegates condemning fee schedules and the related service benefit system. As this study has pointed out, statements of principle have accompanied a progressive increase in the use of the fee schedule approach. For an example of such "viewing with alarm" see M. M. Davis, *Medical Care for Tomorrow* (New York: Harper, 1955), pp. 252–253. In this excellent book, Mr. Davis recognizes that a balance of competitive pressures has kept the service benefit programs in existence but deplores the "philosophy" expressed in official statements. In the writer's opinion, pressures for service benefits provided through guaranteed fee schedules are going to increase rather than decrease in the future and the official philosophy is likely to be irrelevant as a practical matter.

for any necessary surgery, major or minor, in or out of the hospital; (2) full coverage for seventy days of in-hospital medical care; (3) full coverage for home and office visits, including the first visit for illness; and (4) outpatient diagnostic X-ray and laboratory services up to $85 maximum for each illness every six months. Subject to the seventy day in-hospital limit and the $85 maximum for laboratory work, no employee would pay any additional fee, incidental or other, for medical services. Hospital coverage, including a form of "catastrophic" coverage, is provided under a separate contract with a commercial insurance carrier. Benefits can be secured from any one of the 170 physician-members.

In addition to these benefits for the employees, full maternity care, including prenatal, delivery, and postpartum care, are included along with twelve well-baby office visits per year at $1.00 per visit.

Dependents are provided with full surgical coverage, thirty-five days of in-hospital medical benefits, home and office visits at $2.00 and $1.00 fees respectively, beginning with the second visit for illness, and a maximum of $25 for laboratory work (raised to $50 in 1958). In effect, the longshoremen members of the ILWU in Stockton have a comprehensive, service benefit health plan with virtually free choice of doctors in the locality.

As originally negotiated in 1955, the ILWU–PMA welfare fund paid a $7.31 premium per employee to the foundation. (Hospital coverage cost an additional $5.69 per employee for a total of $13.00.) The foundation pays its physician-members on a fee-for-service basis using the CMA Relative Value Schedule as the base for a unit value system. In other words, the Relative Value Schedule determines the unit value of each item of service with the actual dollar value of the units being determined by dividing the total units of service rendered into the total funds available to the foundation for a given time period.

As originally designed, the ILWU–PMA program appears to have been something of a health insurance bargain. At the conclusion of the first year's operation the unit value system produced fees that were reported to be slightly below those specified in the San Joaquin Foundation's Schedule B (for families in the $3,500 to $4,500 income bracket). Since the average longshoreman has an annual income in excess of $4,500, the ILWU–PMA Fund was paying a premium below that which would have been charged a regular foundation subscriber in the top-income bracket, but was securing more comprehensive coverage. Futhermore, the program was paying physician-members fees below those in Schedule A (for families with incomes over $4,500 annually). When the contract came up for its annual renewal in 1957, the premium for medical coverage was boosted 20 per cent. As a result, by the renewal date in 1958 the fees paid doctors had been brought up to those in Schedule A, the foundation's top schedule,[29] and funds were available to raise the maximum laboratory allowance for dependents from $25 to $50 with no further increase in premiums. As of 1958, the combined premium for medical and hospital coverage being paid by the ILWU–PMA Fund was $16.61 per month compared with the initial premium of $13.00 in 1955. Even at this figure the ILWU members appear to have a better medical program than could have been secured under any of the other available foundation programs.

Part of the reason for this favorable position appears to be the willingness of the foundation and its physician-members to assume the risk of high utilization and to operate with a minimum of administrative overhead charged to the plan. This system virtually eliminates the need for the accumulation of reserves and minimizes the expense of handling the business aspects of the plan. If this plan were to be adopted on a large scale, it would be necessary to elaborate the administrative machinery under which the longshoremen's program is being handled and a substantial cost increase might result.

Although it is difficult to compare health insurance plans, it might be noted that the longshoremen in the Bay Area are offered coverage through the Kaiser Plan that is roughly comparable for substantially less cost.[30] As an important offsetting advantage,

[29] This schedule is the CMS Relative Value Schedule with a multiplier (or unit value) of five. According to the 1957 edition of the RVS, examples of fees are: routine office visit, $5.00; follow-up home visit, $7.50; appendectomy, $175; tonsillectomy, $75. (The surgical fees do not include separate listings of $35 and $25 for anesthesia.)

[30] The 1958 composite premium for the Bay Area longshoremen in Kaiser was $13.30 (including the surcharge for members over 65), compared to the $16.61 premium in Stockton. Incidentally, since the premium available for the ILWU warehousemen's insurance plan is tied to the Kaiser premium, the lower Kaiser charge explains why the warehousemen in Stockton have not been included in the longshoremen's type of plan.

the San Joaquin longshoremen enjoy something close to a free choice of doctor or hospital. (But note that the Kaiser Bay Area operation includes a larger total of doctors than does the foundation although the conditions under which choice is exercised are different.)

The San Joaquin Foundation's total program appears to be satisfactory to the medical profession in San Joaquin County. Although the growth of what might be called the commercial insurance version of the foundation's program has not been spectacular, the number of primary members enrolled in the sponsored plans more than tripled between 1956 and 1958. A good index of physician reaction is the high degree of participation in the program. Although there apparently has been a small drop in participation from about 90 per cent of the active members of the society in 1956 to 86 per cent in 1958, this is probably of little significance. (At least some of the nonmembers are in specialties that lie outside the foundation's program.) As far as the special ILWU–PMA program is concerned, the secretary of the society wrote the author in 1958 that ". . . The I.L.W.U. Committee, Foundation and Medical Society are in agreement that the I.L.W.U.–PMA program has been most satisfactory."

This experience raises the question as to the reasons for the success of this system in San Joaquin County and as to the possibility that it might be adopted in other areas. As a general statement, it can be said that organizational innovations of this type depend on the appearance of the appropriate personal leadership at a time when external circumstances are pressing for a change from established practices. This leadership existed in the county medical society; the combined effect of the Kaiser Plan expansion (actual and rumored) and the labor movement's exploration of the health center and physician-panel possibilities provided the impetus to change.

In addition to these general considerations, there are other fundamental factors explaining the apparently successful operation of the San Joaquin Foundation to date. Much of the explanation can be found in two circumstances. The first of these is the relatively small size of the society and the relatively homogeneous composition of the membership with regard to conditions of medical practice. Because of its small size, informal social controls over the quality and the cost of the medical care provided through the foundation are operative. The doctors know each other and the conditions of practice at first hand and the usual formal medical control systems are supplemented and made more effective by group pressures to maintain professional standards. In addition, the internal composition of the society with regard to specialization and type of practice is simple compared with the composition of a large society in a major medical center. In such centers the differentiation of practice, the high degree of specialization, the presence of teaching hospitals and medical schools and their staff all combine to make the society conscious of its role as a political-economic as well as a medical center. A move to reduce the diversity of fee systems, to impose more uniformity of fees and types of practice would be resisted much more strongly in the metropolitan medical centers.

The second circumstance working toward the success of the San Joaquin Foundation is the "umbrella effect" provided by the fact that collective-bargaining patterns are usually set in the metropolitan centers and the contributions to welfare funds reflect the level of medical costs in these areas. A fee schedule that would be opposed as inadequate by a large section of the profession in a major metropolitan area may look generous to doctors in the lower-cost small communities. For example, all of the members of the San Joaquin Foundation treating longshoremen are reported to be receiving as a matter of course fees that are well above the "usual fees" formerly charged by most of the doctors in the county.

If this analysis is correct it suggests that arrangements like those of the foundation are most likely to appear in other counties outside the major metropolitan medical centers—in California, this means outside of San Francisco and Los Angeles. Unions such as the Teamsters and the construction unions that have substantial numbers of members outside the major metropolitan areas may be able to develop special programs in these localities and, with this experience behind them, work back into the suburban and metropolitan counties. Proposals that have been put forth to "regionalize" the California Physicians Service may lead to similar results.

For this kind of a development to materialize it will be necessary for the unions involved to press for new institutional forms to replace the present system of coverage. The likelihood of such action is difficult to predict and again depends in part on personalities and external pressures. There is an apparent tendency to shift the locus of decision-making in collective bargaining to higher levels in the administrative hierarchy of the unions with decreased local autonomy. This could mean that experimentation may be less prevalent in the future, at least in those unions that are satisfied with their existing system. It could also mean, however, that the experimentation that does occur would be on a wider scale and more far-reaching in its effects.

In any event, the plan in San Joaquin County has thus far provided a successful experiment in furnishing certainty of coverage without income limitations in two entirely different organizational forms. Should the present structure of health insurance coverage be judged inadequate under the pressure of future developments, working models of possible new systems are available.

Some Structural Problems of Fund Administration

The discussion of the industrial relations structure in chapter vi stressed the relatively small size of manufacturing establishments in the Bay Area and the dominant position of multiemployer bargaining in most of its industries. In a 1948 paper on multiemployer bargaining in San Francisco,[31] Clark Kerr and Lloyd Fisher argued that the traditional concept of the employer association as a defensive organization concerned primarily with the negotiations of contracts needed to be expanded to include the "administrative" function of the associations in modern industrial relations. Kerr and Fisher had in mind the necessity for administration of the collective-bargaining contract during its term in the usual sense of securing uniform interpretation of its provisions. With the rapid and widespread development of the fringe benefit system, the problem of administration took on new dimensions and posed new problems for the unions and the associations. Some of the fringe benefits involved a form of group insurance and required at least formal employer participation in administration under the Taft-Hartley Act. The associations are the logical sources of such rep-

---

[31] Clark Kerr and Lloyd Fisher, "Multiple-Employer Bargaining: The San Francisco Experience," in Lester and Shister (eds.), *Insights into Labor Issues* (New York: Macmillan, 1948), pp. 30–32.

resentation and have frequently become the base for an insured group. "Administration" has expanded beyond its original meaning of the interpretation of a collective-bargaining contract to include the negotiation and administration of pension, health, and other types of subsidiary contractual arrangements.

In the relatively rare instances in which an employer association includes in its membership substantially all of the employers in an "industry" in the area (e.g., the Pacific Maritime Association), the new problems introduced by welfare fund contracts are comparatively easy to solve. The organizational machinery to handle the contracts is in existence and its range of activity is simply expanded to include the new programs. The new situation is likely to require no more than an addition to staff or the development of new skills by a member of the existing staff. More serious difficulties arise when the association includes only some (perhaps a minority) of the employers in the area. In addition, a union that deals with a number of associations may insist on a greater degree of uniformity and transferability of membership among employers with regard to welfare programs than with regard to wages and the other more traditional subjects of collective bargaining. In these circumstances new organizational arrangements have to be developed.

There appear to be two major alternatives available to a union and employer association bargaining unit to cope with the problems created by the existence of a large number of nonmember employers. One is by an extension of the "master-agreement" technique used in wage bargaining with embellishments to deal with the issues raised by fringe benefit programs. In wage bargaining, the unions have traditionally used the agreement with the employer associations as a pattern contract and "negotiated" it with little or no change in "bargaining" with employers who are nonmembers of the association. These employers typically fall into one of two main classifications: (1) They are similar to the member employers in the character of their business but are, in union parlance, "free riders" in the sense that they avoid the financial and other burdens of association membership. Usually these employers entertain no illusions about the freedom of action they retain by remaining out of the association. They often have explicitly agreed with the union to accept the master agreement negotiated with the association or, in the absence of such an agreement, follow this policy as a matter of course. (2) They may be local branches of large national firms which are reluctant to risk being party to a local settlement including a particular provision that would be embarrassing to company-wide policy. In practice, these employers may consistently accept the master agreement but they prefer to retain their freedom to reject a specific settlement. Sometimes firms in this position join the association and participate in its activities but reserve the right to modify or reject the final contract.

This situation can be handled by negotiating a welfare plan with the employer association that creates a welfare fund organization at least technically separate from the association. Membership in the fund is made independent of association membership and the master agreement then calls for each signatory to make his welfare contributions directly to the fund organization. Since the administrative costs of the fund are paid out of contributions, the members of the employer association are not subsidizing the cost of operations. The association often provides the employer representatives on the fund's board of trustees but, in practice, this is not a particularly onerous duty and would have had to be borne in any event if the association maintained its own program.[32]

For one reason or another, either the union, the association, or the nonmember employers may not favor this kind of system. When this is true, a different solution to the problem of the "independents" (nonmember employers) has been worked out. The union and employer association negotiate a collective-bargaining contract setting up a welfare program with the association membership serving as a base for the insured group. The union then extends the association contract to the independents in the classic master-agreement approach. Instead of blanketing them into an

---

[32] The agreement between the Golden Gate Restaurant Association and the Joint Board of Culinary Workers provides an example of this arrangement. The association includes about 220 of San Francisco's larger restaurants in its membership. The contract negotiated between the Culinary Workers and the Golden Gate Association becomes the master agreement for more than 2,100 other establishments (most of them small) in the city. All of the employers who are party to the welfare agreement send their contributions directly to the "San Francisco Restaurant and Tavern Welfare Fund," the agency which handles the welfare program.

all-inclusive fund organization, however, the union in effect becomes the vehicle for the formation of a completely separate organization made up of independent employers with its activities limited to administration of the welfare fund. The separation of the two funds often has only nominal consequences since all parties concerned usually have followed a policy of keeping the two programs as completely uniform as possible. The independents' plan has tended to become an appendage to the association plan even though two sets of trustees and two bank accounts exist. This arrangement does present a potential source of difficulty, however, since the two groups could conceivably have quite different experience with medical costs. Under experience rating this could result in one of the plans being forced either to modify its benefit structure in order to maintain premiums equal to the other plan or to accept a premium differential in order to maintain uniform benefits.

One example of the complications that develop when the policy of creating a single fund for the industry as a whole cannot be followed is furnished by the experience of the California Metal Trades Association and the metal trades unions with which it deals. The CMTA includes about 350 employers in its membership; the principal union with which it deals is the International Association of Machinists. When the CMTA entered health insurance in 1949 it adopted what is known as the "level-of-benefits" approach as opposed to the "fixed-contribution" approach.[33] This system has the characteristic of maintaining employer interest in the administration of the program since its cost is variable and depends in part on the efficiency with which the plan is handled. It has the disadvantage of unpredictability as to final cost.

The CMTA staff strongly believes in the virtues of the level-of-benefits approach as a matter of principle. In addition, as a practical matter, the fixed-contribution system would have been difficult to implement in the situation in which the CMTA operates. The current CMTA collective-bargaining contract specifies a set of medical and hospital benefits and calls for each employer to

---

[33] That is, the collective-bargaining contract specifies the health insurance benefits that will be provided the employees rather than the trust fund contribution that will be made. In the Bay Area most contracts are of the "fixed contribution" type.

furnish his employees these benefits as a minimum with supplementation permitted. This provision is carried over into the master agreement signed by the independent employers. Individual employers are not required to participate in the welfare program but, subject to the minimum benefit schedule in the contract, can provide health insurance in any way they desire, including self-insurance.

Under this system the CMTA administers a welfare trust fund that includes about 300 of the 350 member-employers. About 150 of the independent employers participate in a separate trust fund which was organized at the initiative of the Machinists Union. The larger employers among both the members and the independents tend to remain out of either trust fund and to make a wide variety of separate arrangements.[34] The CMTA fund is an insured plan underwritten by a commercial insurance company whereas the independents' trust fund currently has a contract with California Physicians Service. This variegated structure of health insurance coverage suggests that it is entirely possible, if not probable, that differences in benefits or premium costs among the various employers are likely to develop over the years. To date, this does not appear to have created major problems because of differential treatment of members of the same union locals or differential cost impacts for employers but it is a potential trouble spot.

Whether the health insurance arrangements are handled in the framework provided by an existing employer association or through a combination of an existing association and a special-purpose employer organization, the system is an interesting example of the broadening role of the multiemployer organizational unit. Originally formed to negotiate collective-bargaining contracts, the associations tended to develop a permanent staff to administer the contracts. From handling these labor relations matters on a joint basis, the associations are moving into areas that traditionally have been regarded as the province of personnel management. In addition to administering employee benefit programs,

---

[34] Although 300 of the 350 member-employers of the CMTA participate in the association trust fund it is estimated that the fund covers only about half of the employees of the CMTA members. The average employer in the independents' trust fund has 60 to 70 employees. Data on the CMTA from Robert Grunsky, executive director; on the independents' fund, from John Schievenza, IAM trustee.

some of the associations are attempting to expand their personnel activity into other fields as well. Since most of the members of the associations are too small to operate a full-fledged personnel department of their own, it appears that as union activity spreads beyond the traditional area of "wages and hours," there may be a trend to utilize the association machinery to provide some personnel services through a kind of "collective personnel department" just as it is now used to provide collective labor relations services.

Another "structural" problem that predominates in the industries in which employer associations are typically found is that of the "transient" or "casual" worker. Transient workers are those who work in an industry but who are not employed regularly enough to meet the eligibility requirements for coverage in the industry health plan(s).[35]

Although data are not available, it is the writer's impression that most plans in the Bay Area define eligibility standards so that persons not qualifying for full coverage for a particular time period have no coverage at all. Since contributions to the trust funds are often based on hours or days worked by *both* eligible and ineligible employees, substantial sums are often paid into the funds on behalf of workers who never become eligible for benefits.[36]

Some unions, however, have developed a separate coverage for transient workers that includes those employees who do not meet the eligibility requirements for full coverage but who do meet some specified lower standard. The scope of this coverage is usually limited either by including only the employee without his

---

[35] These requirements are usually stated in terms of the number of hours or days worked in a previous time period or in terms of employment status as of a certain date.

[36] That this source of income is substantial is shown by the fact that the Los Angeles Joint Board of Hotel and Restaurant Employees pays $18.00 per month for each *eligible* employee for the welfare coverages under their plan. Employers pay only $13.86 a month into the fund for an employee who works full forty-hour weeks; an employee who works only sixty hours a month is eligible for full coverage although only $4.80 (eight cents an hour) has been paid into the fund by his employer. This is financially feasible because ". . . The difference between what is paid in on that employee and the $18.00 is provided by contributions made on employees who never become eligible." John L. Cooper, "Supplemental Benefits Under the Los Angeles Joint Executive Board Health and Welfare Program," *Proceedings*, Health and Welfare Conference, Institute of Industrial Relations, University of California, 1957, p. 88. Mr. Cooper is president of the joint board.

dependents or by providing a narrower range of benefits. Depending on the standards of eligibility for transient coverage, this may permit a higher proportion of the workers "attached" to the industry to be granted some health insurance protection.

The foregoing section has once more demonstrated the ingenuity and flexibility by which some of the problems growing out of the attempt to create a noncompulsory system of health insurance can be solved. Although such a system may eventually be found to be cumbersome and inadequate in some important respects to the magnitude of the whole health insurance problem, it embodies the virtues as well as the faults of a private system. The virtues can be summed up in the word "flexibility"; the faults include complexity of administration and possibly inadequate scope of coverage.

Chapter X | *A Summing Up*

Perhaps the best way to pull together the threads of the discussion presented in the previous chapters is to advance a series of propositions. These propositions will be developed by reference to the material covered earlier. Further implications of this material will also be explored. A chapter detailing what appear to be the probable consequences of the experience with health insurance and collective bargaining will conclude the volume. Since collective bargaining for medical benefits is only a part of the health insurance movement, most of the propositions touch on general problems of the financing and the organization of medical services. These questions have been treated at length in a number of works devoted to the problems of providing medical care for the population as a whole.[1] Except in those areas where it is felt that the results of the present study seem to supplement or to elaborate on the usual treatment of the general issues, emphasis will be on those aspects that are related to the introduction of the medical care problem into labor-management relations.

Proposition 1. *The broadening of the scope of collective bargaining to include hospitalization and medical care benefits has*

---

[1] See, for example, Oscar N. Serbein, Jr., *Paying for Medical Care in the United States* (New York: Columbia University Press, 1953); M. M. Davis, *Medical Care for Tomorrow* (New York: Harper, 1955); and Odin W. Anderson (with J. J. Feldman), *Family Medical Costs and Voluntary Health Insurance: A Nationwide Survey* (New York: McGraw-Hill, 1956).

brought large numbers of workers under health insurance who would not otherwise have been included and has increased the depth and breadth of the protection provided by health insurance.

It is not difficult to defend the proposition that the quantitative effects of bringing "health and welfare" to the bargaining table have been substantial. Between 1946 and 1957 the number of workers covered by health insurance under collective-bargaining contracts grew from well under one million to more than twelve million with perhaps another twenty million dependents. Although some of this number undoubtedly had been previously covered in a voluntary health insurance program and some others would have joined even if negotiated plans had not been established, there is little question but that a large part of this group probably would not have been enrolled in other systems of coverage. It is possible that the larger employers in the United States at some time might have introduced health insurance into their personnel benefit systems without union pressure. Even if this had come to be generally accepted personnel practice, experience suggests that such plans would have been voluntary and would have been financed entirely by the employee or, at most, through a form of joint financing. Under these circumstances, a substantial proportion of the work force is likely to remain out of the plan. Even if most of the larger employers had established their own health plans, and even if these plans covered the great majority of their workers, large numbers of American workers are employed in areas of the economy in which there is no tradition of personnel benefits or the machinery to place them into effect. Perhaps the employers of the nation's construction workers, teamsters, and butchers would have been able to make health insurance programs available to their workers, but it is doubtful if this would have been true for groups such as culinary workers and building service workers. In short, collective bargaining brought many hundreds of thousands of workers and their dependents under health insurance in areas of the economy that would not otherwise have been covered at all and converted what at best would have been voluntary groups with partial membership into "100 per cent" groups. The indirect effects of converting health insurance into a "standard" employee benefit that has come to be taken almost for granted cannot be measured, but there is no doubt that the pattern-setting effect of the highly publicized negotiated health plans has been substantial, particularly in areas such as government employment. All in all, it seems conservative to say that a substantial portion of the customers of the health insurance movement have been recruited as a result of the operations of negotiated plans and that most of these were unlikely to have been recruited in any other way.

There are three ways in which the negotiated plans have affected the scope of health insurance coverage. First, the unions have many times introduced and always reinforced the pressures for including dependents in the insurance program. Since dependents account for about two-thirds of total family medical costs, this has been an expansion of major importance.

The second way in which negotiated plans have influenced the scope of health insurance has been the inclusion of more items of medical care. No other organized consumer group of any size has so consistently and vociferously demanded that health insurance include a broader spectrum of medical care.[2] At the present time, for example, the Health Plan Consultants Committee of Los Angeles, a group of administrators of union-management health plans, has been exploring the possibilities of including psychiatric care in health insurance contracts. Many items considered "uninsurable" by many carriers either because they are regarded as predictable in advance (e.g., physical examinations and maternity care) or because they are subject to abuse and are costly to administer (e.g., home and office visits), are now commonplace in health insurance contracts. Because union leaders function in a political environment in their unions, they are interested in benefits that produce observable, concrete evidence of advantages won for most members. If benefits are limited to major catastrophes and hence accrue only to a minority of the membership in any reasonable time period, the benefit program is not fulfilling its function in the internal politics of the union. Faced with the necessity of winning acceptance of a collective-bargaining settlement in which health insurance has been substituted for a wage increase, the union negotiator wants a program that will "pay off"

---

[2] Irving G. Pfeffer, Associate Professor of Insurance at UCLA, has put it this way, "The negotiated plans tend to be the laboratories where new types of coverage are developed." *Proceedings,* Health and Welfare Conference, Institute of Industrial Relations, California, 1957, p. 5.

for a substantial proportion of the membership in a year or two.

In addition to these practical considerations, most union leaders believe in comprehensive coverage as a matter of principle and continue to push for it on that ground. Arguments stressing the susceptibility of certain items of care to abuse are met with the reply that the answer lies in the development of a system of control of abuse rather than in the elimination of the item from insurance coverage. Arguments pointing out that the payment of frequent, small medical bills through the insurance company amounts to paying the company a substantial administrative fee for budgeting the patient's income rather than for the provision of insurance protection are equally ineffective. The American consumer is willing, even eager, to pay service charges to credit agencies in order to buy a tremendous variety of goods and services on the installment plan and is perfectly agreeable to buying medical care on the same basis.

The third way in which unions and employers have influenced the scope of health insurance has been to increase its "depth" as well as its breadth. In their quest for more complete protection, labor-management groups have led the way in raising benefit schedules. As compared with the more informal, voluntary groups in health insurance, the negotiated groups have had a more businesslike approach to their problems. Most of them have had a concept of the role they expect health insurance to play in meeting the medical bills of the group. In addition, they have sources of information on how well the insurance program is filling this role and an ability to do something about its shortcomings. In the typical voluntary group few of the individual members have any information as to how adequate the indemnities are in meeting medical expenses. They also have little knowledge of how to go about doing anything effective when shortcomings are brought to light. As a result, unions and employers (though not all members of either group by any means) represent the only major organizations systematically testing the protection afforded by health insurance against the actual need it is designed to meet.

This is an appropriate point at which to discuss briefly the attitude of the unions toward the latest innovation in health insurance, the "major medical" or "catastrophic" coverages. These coverages approach the problem of medical care costs in a manner different from the usual hospital, surgical, or medical indemnity contract. There are two principal variations of this coverage: (1) The major medical contract that includes a very broad range of medical services up to a relatively high dollar maximum with a substantial "deductible" and some "coinsurance" to be paid by the insured members.[3] (2) The catastrophic-coverage contract that is designed to "go on top" of the orthodox indemnity contract by extending coverage for longer periods of hospitalization and providing higher maximum benefits for surgery or other services.[4] The major medical contract is meant to be a substitute for the usual indemnity contract whereas the catastrophic contract assumes the existence of a basic plan and provides a supplement to it.

Because of its break with traditional practice, the major medical variation has attracted the most attention. The number of persons enrolled in this form of insurance has been growing rapidly, although it is still small in total. With some exceptions, unions have either ignored this development or have been actively hostile to it.[5] Employers, on the other hand, have been much more favorably disposed to it and have been among its active proponents.

Union hostility toward the major medical contract has stemmed from a number of sources. The protection is regarded as illusory in the sense that most workers would find that the insurance would pay none or a relatively small portion of their medical bills.[6] The system is also regarded as even more inflationary in

---

[3] For example, the contract may call for paying the cost of a wide variety of medical services up to, say, $5,000 in any calendar year, subject to the proviso that the insured member pay all of the first $200 in costs (the deductible) and 20 per cent of the remainder (the coinsurance).

[4] This form of protection usually requires that the insured member pay all or a very large proportion of, say, the first $100 of costs beyond the basic insurance coverage. After this "corridor" between the basic coverage and the supplementary coverage is traversed, the catastrophic coverage becomes effective, often with a coinsurance feature. Strictly speaking, both of these variations are often called major medical coverages but we have chosen to discuss them in this fashion for the sake of clarity.

[5] For a hostile analysis by a union spokesman see Jerome Pollack, *Major Medical Expense Insurance: An Evaluation* (United Automobile Workers, 1956), p. 4. Pollack estimated that as of mid-1956 about seven million persons had major medical coverage, using the term to include all types, including what we have called catastrophic coverage.

[6] It has been estimated, for example, that a major medical contract with a $100 deductible and 25 per cent coinsurance would pay approximately 48 per cent of medical charges. For this and other estimates for varying types of contracts see Odin W. Anderson, *op. cit.*, pp. 85–86.

its impact on medical costs of all types than the usual indemnity schedule approach. In addition, it is regarded as doing nothing to encourage early treatment or preventive medicine but continues the financial barriers to these developments.

As far as the "catastrophic-coverage" variation is concerned, objections are less serious although the opinion has been expressed that the premium costs probably would be better spent in broadening the basic coverage unless it is already relatively comprehensive.

The direct impact that collective bargaining for health insurance has had on increasing the number of persons with some form of coverage is likely to be limited in the future to the rate of growth in collective-bargaining coverage since the existing market has been pretty well saturated in the past decade. The indirect or pattern-setting effect on numbers covered can be expected to continue to grow and the influence of union-management activity on the content of the insurance contracts in force will undoubtedly continue to be of major importance.

Proposition 2. *Although the fees for medical services and charges for hospitalization have undoubtedly been increased as a result of the operation of health insurance, particularly the collectively bargained plans, the degree of fee inflation attributable to the existence of insurance is probably generally exaggerated.*

The case for an insurance-induced increase of charges is strongest for hospital rates, the element of medical care whose price, measured by daily rates, has increased the most. Although some general comments on this issue were made in chapter iii, this study did not provide the basis for detailed analysis of the problem.

Several reasons for questioning the assumption that health insurance has generated a substantial inflation of doctors' fees were noted in chapter iii. They can be summed up as follows: (1) Except for the 1952–1958 period, the rise in the fees of surgeons and general practitioners was less than that of consumer prices generally; after 1952 the divergence was due to the failure of the Consumer Price Index to rise rather than to a spurt in the rate of fee increase. (2) In all time periods studied, medical fees rose less rapidly than the prices of most other services listed in the CPI. (3) Considering the fees of general practitioners, surgeons, and dentists separately, the pattern of increases by type of service is not related to the prevalence of insurance coverage. Although dental insurance is virtually nonexistent, dental fees have outstripped the widely insured surgical fees while those for general practitioners have fallen in between. Although the handling of medical care items in the CPI is not above statistical reproach (the sample of reporting doctors is small, six in the Bay Area), the price data do not indicate galloping inflation.

An intensive study of the surgical fee experience of a particular health plan, that of the California Metal Trades Association, over a period of years likewise produced little evidence that surgical fees were differentiated among patients according to differences in the level of surgical indemnities. It was tentatively concluded that the *level* of the fees paid during the period under study might have been somewhat higher than the level that might have been expected to prevail for patients in that income group, but *changes* in the level were not related to the (relatively small) changes in benefits that occurred during this time span.

The fragmentary evidence developed in the course of this study suggests a particular hypothesis concerning the impact of negotiated plans on the prices of medical care. A beginning assumption is that, on the average, the negotiated plans brought into the health insurance movement a group of workers whose income level would have resulted in their paying doctors' fees somewhat below the "usual fees" in the area.[7]

As this group acquired insurance coverage our hypothesis is that most doctors began to adjust the fees charged to them upward, toward the average fee charged for this procedure in the community or the usual fee charged by this particular doctor to his average patient when the latter fee exceeded the community average. In other words, the doctors regarded the existence of health insurance as increasing the patient's ability to pay. Once having brought this group of insured patients up to the average level of

---

[7] To clarify this assumption, the bulk of the members of negotiated plans either patronized doctors with a range of fees below the average for the community as a whole or patronized doctors who, though their personal fees usually were equal to or higher than the community average, charged lower fees to these patients. There are two relevant concepts of "usual fees" involved here—the usual fee for a surgical procedure which is the average of the community's doctors and the usual fee charged by each doctor within his own practice.

fees, their charges were varied much as the general level of fees varied.

Of course this pattern of a more rapid increase in the fees of insured patients than in fees as a whole followed by a leveling off could have occurred regardless of the level of fees that had formerly been paid by the now-insured group. In the case of some of the higher-paid craftsmen, the process described above may have ended with charges above the average. For negotiated plans as a body, however, the original form of the hypothesis seems more appropriate.

Although other factors are involved, this hypothesis is consistent with a number of facts noted earlier. It is consistent with the sluggish behavior of surgical fees as a whole as reported by the Consumer Price Index during a period when union spokesmen were claiming major increases in fees had occurred. The "usual fees" for the doctors furnishing data for the CPI may have changed relatively little while lower fees were being increased. It is consistent with the pattern of a crescendo of complaints during the years 1949–1953 when negotiated plans were being established and the relative calm that prevailed thereafter. It is consistent with the comparative stability of fees for CMTA members during the period 1954–1957, although the administrators of the plan believe that substantial increases occurred prior to that time.

Even if this conservative interpretation of events is accepted, it means that, at least in some instances, the medical profession has followed a practice of charging an insured patient higher fees than would have been charged an uninsured patient in similar circumstances. It will be remembered that this wording was used in a first approximation to a definition of "abuse" in chapter iv. The justification for this definition of abuse is that, since the income level of the insured group is not changed significantly by the existence of insurance, there is no reason why the medical profession should increase its total income from the group as a whole. Even if the principle of varying fees according to income levels is accepted for the moment, the function of health insurance is to distribute the cost of medical care more evenly over the insured group as a whole rather than to increase the total income available to the medical profession from the group.

There is a special sense, however, in which it can be argued that the existence of health insurance does justify an increase in the medical fees charged low-income workers. The custom of lowering fees charged to low-income groups is based on the argument that, for these groups, the costs of even fairly minor medical emergencies to any individual may represent a large proportion of annual income and may become a very difficult financial burden. It is often pointed out that the total amounts spent annually for tobacco and recreation are not much different from the total amounts spent for medical care. For practical purposes, this sort of comparison is largely irrelevant since these expenditures occur regularly in small amounts and are widely distributed over the population as a whole. Medical costs, on the other hand, are not predictable, often involve quite large amounts, and are concentrated on a fraction of the population in any given year. The virtue of insurance, however, is that it converts these medical expenditures into regular, small payments for each member of the group as a whole and, therefore, in a very meaningful sense, increases the group's ability to pay. In other words, the existence of insurance may possibly justify raising the fees of an insured group that has formerly paid below-average fees because of its below-average income, if these higher fees can be supported by an insurance premium that is small relative to the average income level. When this happens, of course, it reduces the justification for charging above-average fees to groups with above-average incomes. Some observers who have been active in conducting fee surveys in California are of the opinion that the range of fees being charged for a specific medical procedure is becoming more uniform. The combination of greater equality of family incomes and the spread of insurance coverage is believed to have narrowed the range of fees for the same item of medical care among the doctors in the same community and to have narrowed the range of fees charged by the same doctor to different individuals in his practice.[8]

Throughout this study stress has been placed on the possibly exaggerated impression of the degree of inflation of medical fees. The reason for adopting this view is the prevalence of what the writer feels to be a superficial analysis of this problem in much

---

[8] See the comments on this point in the report of the Medical Services Commission of the California Medical Association, *California Medicine,* June, 1954.

discussion. This approach should not be permitted to obscure the fact that health insurance, on balance, undoubtedly has contributed to making fees in general somewhat higher than they would otherwise have been and substantially higher in the case of a small proportion of doctors. However, as an explanation of rising medical costs, this factor has been overstressed. Because fees are relatively easy to investigate and control (or at least influence), the problem of containing the increase in costs is often misunderstood and underestimated. The tendency to concentrate on the issue of fee inflation arises because fees are not publicly announced, because they vary between individuals for a number of reasons, because there *are* actual examples of the charging of exorbitant fees available, because some fees are, and always have been, large in absolute amounts, and because the postwar prosperity of doctors as an occupational group has been very observable.

Without denying the existence of a fee problem, it is perhaps salutary to issue a reminder that this is the era of the $2.00 haircut, the 15 per cent restaurant tip, the $5.00 minimum television service call, and the $7.50 minimum plumbers' "home visit" (during working hours, five days a week only).

Proposition 3. The inflationary impact of health insurance on medical costs is more important than the impact on medical prices and requires a different and more sophisticated form of control mechanism.

This proposition focuses attention on the "overutilization" of medical services of all kinds as the major cause of rising costs rather than the inflation of the unit prices of the services (with the possible exception of hospital daily rates). In chapter iv some evidence as to the prevalence of the various types of "abuse" of health insurance was presented and discussed. This evidence illustrated the variety of practices coming under the heading of abuse without giving much assistance in quantifying the problem. Among the instances were false claims, unnecessary hospital admissions, excessively prolonged hospital stays, excessive multiple visits in the hospital, home, and office, excessive diagnostic work, unnecessary surgery, etc. Although no responsible person has ever contended that these practices are characteristic of all hospitals or doctors, the cost impact is substantial even when only a minority of physicians are involved. Moreover, the fairly clear-cut cases of abuse that find their way into studies are only the visible part of the much larger iceberg of overutilization.

A southern California doctor made this point in vivid fashion through the use of the concept of the "frightful five." [9] He admitted that about 5 per cent of the doctors may be dishonest or incompetent, but argued that the real culprits are another 5 per cent, the frightful five, who persist in adding a few unnecessary office visits, taking a few unneeded X-rays, and in general over-servicing insured patients in less flagrant but cumulatively expensive ways. The "frightful" character of this activity stems from its long-term influence on the rest of the profession and the standards of what comes to be considered customary practice.

Viewing this problem within the structure of competitive private practice helps to point up the insidious nature of the overutilization of medical services, whether initiated by the physician or by the patient. Among the doctors of a community, there is little competitive advantage to be gained by charging higher fees than do colleagues for the same service. Establishing the reputation of giving more medical service, even if it is not medically necessary, may be an important gambit in the quest for patients and may be remunerative for the doctor and satisfying to the insured patient. Many, if not most, of the techniques of abuse are likely to appear to the insured patient as more thorough medical treatment. As a result of the competitive pressure from the frightful five, the standards of medical practice of the profession as a whole can be affected in ways that contribute to a continuous and sizable annual increase in medical costs.

The situation is complicated because many practices that might be defined as abuse in the sense that they are not called for by the customary standards of good medical practice, may have a positive medical value. Some of the increase in the utilization of medical care attributable to widespread health insurance undoubtedly represents a needed increase in standards of care for many population groups. Since medical care is a scarce resource, however,

---

[9] Reported in a paper by Ted Ellsworth, administrator of the Motion Picture Health and Welfare Fund, *Proceedings,* Health and Welfare Conference, Institute of Industrial Relations, University of California, 1957, p. 94. This conference was one of a series sponsored by the California State Federation of Labor and the Institute.

it is necessary to balance the gain from marginal additions to treatment for other groups against their costs. It is emotionally satisfying but a little ambiguous to speak of the right of everyone to "the best possible medical care." If by "best possible" we mean the highest standards known, the best possible medical care will never be generally available—nor will the best possible traffic control, crime prevention, educational system, or anything else. We need to improve the quality and quantity of medical care available to some population groups, but we also need a system for deciding how much of our limited resources we want to devote to medical care in total. Whatever choice is made, abuse is important as a barrier to translating a decision to devote more resources to medical care into better treatment rather than higher costs.

Many methods of control of abuse exist and are in effect on a scattered and sporadic basis. One method of classifying these methods is by the source of the control. Most of them are administered either by the insuring agencies, the medical profession, or the consumers of medical services.

The insuring agencies tend to favor systems of control that create a financial interest in the elimination of abuse by the individual consumer of medical care. These take the form of eliminating services believed to be most susceptible to abuse from insurance coverage entirely or providing only limited coverage for service. Limitation may take the form of maximum fee schedules for reimbursements or the deductible or coinsurance features. The logic of this type of control is that it reduces abuse initiated by the consumer by taking the "profit" out of it and that it enlists the patient as an ally of the insurer in minimizing the costs of hospital and doctors' services. This form of control is objected to by consumers, their representatives (particularly unions), and some social insurance specialists on the ground that it maintains a financial barrier to the development of preventive medicine and discourages the early treatment of disease.[10] It is also claimed

---

[10] Experiments in providing home and office visits without "incidental fees" (coinsurance) to the patient have produced some scattered evidence that removing this control does not increase utilization. This is sometimes cited as an argument that this kind of control is unnecessary. It is often overlooked, however, that the same evidence can be cited to indicate that the "barrier to care" argument is invalid, and that the real question is whether to finance the program on premiums alone or on some combination of fees and premiums.

that the protection it gives may be illusory since collusion between the doctor and patient in billing for services may, in effect, eliminate the patient's part of the charges.

Insuring organizations also use the medical review as a method of control. Physicians in the employ of the company review claims and challenge those that seem to represent cases of abuse. This method is defective in that only the most flagrant cases are protested and the work of the "frightful five" escapes.

The medical profession's contribution to the control problem has traditionally been limited to the provision within most county societies of a "grievance" committee to hear complaints of patients. These committees are not typically overburdened with work and, at least in the Bay Area, most of their cases concern complaints of excessive fees. Where they exist, their function is not widely publicized and the appeal procedure is likely to appear formidable to the average patient. Furthermore, most patients are at least partly in agreement with Shaw's dictum that all professions are conspiracies against the laity. It is interesting that in the Bay Area even normally aggressive union representatives are reluctant to take cases involving specific doctors and patients to the grievance committees of the societies. In addition to a general skepticism as to the probable outcome, the common attitude is, "We don't want to be their policemen."

In recent years the development of fee schedules, whether officially sanctioned or only recommended to the membership, is a new step toward internal professional control. Even so-called relative value schedules have some effect in setting standards. The experience with physician-sponsored plans such as California Physicians Service has undoubtedly created an awareness of the importance of the problem. It has also increased the influence of the profession on the economic ethics of the member-doctors. In some instances the work of the traditional grievance committees has been made more effective. Where county societies have set up special medical organizations such as the San Joaquin Foundation for Medical Care (see chapter ix), the degree of control of abuse is undoubtedly quite effective. In some of the most important areas of medical care the work of hospital staffs in controlling abuse can be impressive, as in the case of the medical audit and the tissue committees described in chapter iv. Other professional controls are exercised through the accrediting agencies and the various specialty boards. One of the more interesting possibilities in control methods is the attempt to develop standards of customary fees and medical practice through statistical analysis of patient records. This method may permit a systematic determination of cases of possible abuse within narrower ranges than is now possible through the medical review committee system. (See the remarks on the Windsor experiments in chapter iv.)

It is axiomatic that the best system of control is self-control. The success of a control mechanism is therefore likely to be inversely proportional to the size of the professional group involved. In small groups the formal methods are supplemented by the effective informal group pressures that can be developed, particularly in bodies with high professional standards. Since in the final analysis, the design of an effective control mechanism and its successful operation requires that it be acceptable to the majority of the group to be controlled, the medical profession has both the responsibility and the competence required to take the leadership in this field.

Attempts by consumers or their representatives to control the abuse of medical care have not attracted major attention until recently. If governmental agencies are accepted as being consumer representatives, this statement would, of course, have to be drastically modified since governmental bodies provide massive amounts of medical care directly. They also control aspects of care, e.g., medical fees, indirectly through agencies such as the Veterans Administration and Workmen's Compensation Commissions. Except for government, the most important new developments in this area are those involving the labor unions in their role as representatives of their members in welfare plans. Since this activity is the major focus of this study, it will be considered at length in the discussion of the next proposition.

In a sense some of the consumer-sponsored "independent" medical care plans established by coöperatives, unions, fraternal organizations, and employers have had the control of abuse as one of their objectives. The methods of operation they use have often been developed because they provide types of services that are particularly subject to abuse under orthodox forms of indemnity insurance. The small size of this movement has been noted earlier in chapter ii and its influence has been further limited by its somewhat dubious status with organized medicine. In general, at least until recently the best protection the consumer patronizing private practitioners has had against abuse was his ability to change his physician.

In closing it should be emphasized that, whatever the system of control adopted, it must provide for the necessity for dealing with the whole range of possible abuse since attempts to handle one problem, such as fees, may only increase the pressures for overservicing as an alternative.

Proposition 4. By creating an organized consumer interest, the introduction of collective bargaining over health insurance benefits has had a substantial impact on the institutional relationships among the consumers of medical care, the insuring agencies, and the suppliers of medical services.

"Organized labor is opening a war on organized medicine." This sentence furnished the lead for a story in a national magazine[11] in 1958 in which plans for a meeting of the American Labor Health Association, an organization based on a membership of welfare fund representatives, were discussed.

Although the language quoted represents considerable journalistic license, the past decade has seen a major growth in the efforts of labor unions to deal with problems of medical economics through direct action as opposed to legislative lobbying. Prior to the development of the negotiated plans on a wide scale, most unions had confined their interest in health matters to the support of some form of compulsory health insurance with varying degrees of enthusiasm. In 1958, after years of experience with private health plans, most unions still supported compulsory health insurance but with a greater realization of the real problems of medical organization that might underlie the passage of such a measure.

Up to 1958 the most prominent national spokesman for the union position on welfare funds has been the executive officer of the United Mine Workers Welfare and Retirement Fund, Dr. Warren F. Draper. This is largely because of the size of the fund and the nature of the industry and the geographical areas in which it operates. Other major national unions, such as the United Auto-

---

[11] "Labor's War with the Doctors," *Business Week*, June 14, 1958.

mobile Workers, the Machinists, the Amalgamated Clothing Workers, and the Ladies Garment Workers, have given tangible evidence of interest in problems of medical organization, but their programs have been minor compared to those of the UMW Fund. Local or regional units of unions, e.g., the Hotel and Restaurant Workers, the Retail, Wholesale, and Department Store Union, and the Brotherhood of Teamsters, have also attempted organizational innovations in medical care. With the exception of the Mineworkers, however, none of the union experiments has been on a scale massive enough to influence the traditional form of the practice of medicine. Most other unions have limited themselves to indirect attempts to modify the conditions under which they have dealt with the suppliers of medical services.

Chapters vii and viii describe and analyze in considerable detail the tactics and strategy followed by various local union groups in the Bay Area in attempting to build up a position of bargaining strength with the medical profession. To summarize the techniques briefly: they have tried to establish a more-or-less formal collective-bargaining relationship with the medical societies that would establish binding fee schedules; they have tried to establish health centers under union control in which their members could secure medical services directly; they have tried to collect panels of doctors to service their members by contracting with individual physicians; and they have participated in and supported community-wide attempts to modify the usual form of medical practice through the Kaiser Foundation Health Plan and the San Joaquin Foundation for Medical Care. In one instance, the International Longshoremen's and Warehousemen's Union has been able to establish an excellent welfare program with the San Joaquin Foundation, but, in general, the unions have not succeeded in developing their own particular solutions to the medical care problem.

In spite of this apparent lack of progress, it would be a mistake to assume that the growth of the negotiated health plans has not had considerable effect on medical practice in California. Aided by the continuous concern of the medical profession with compulsory health insurance at both the federal and the state levels and the pressures exerted by the large and vigorous Kaiser Foundation Health Plan, the welfare funds have been able to make their influence felt in a number of ways.[12] The two most important manifestations of this influence are the growing acceptance of the role of the formally established fee schedule in medical practice and the continuing expansion of the service benefit principle in the operations of the California Blue Shield organization, California Physicians Service. Along with the Kaiser Plan, the unions can claim credit for the adoption of fee schedules by a number of county medical societies, the development of the relative value schedule by the state medical association, and the creation of a number of special local programs. These programs include the San Joaquin Foundation for Medical Care, the steel industry supplementary health plans, and the important free-choice program of the Kaiser Plan (see chapters viii and ix). Individual unions have also been able to get various county societies to recommend that their doctor-members accept the benefit schedules in the insurance contracts of the welfare plans as the appropriate fees for their services.

Changes have also occurred within California Physicians Service. In the face of outspoken reluctance on the part of a substantial part of the profession, CPS raised its maximum income ceiling for full service benefits from $3,600 to $7,200 annual income during the last ten years. In some areas ceilings have been waived altogether or one of the high-ceiling contracts has been accepted by the doctors in return for the fees called for in a low-income contract.

Other modifications include establishment of a framework for formal organizational relationships between labor and medicine and growth of the practice of consultation on issues of mutual interest. The medical profession's representative bodies have expanded their range of activity and developed specialized personnel to aid them in dealing with the public. The welfare funds at the

---

[12] Evidence that united state-wide union action is not impossible is provided by an incident involving the California temporary disability program. In order to pressure the private insurance carriers participating in the program into supporting labor's attempts to raise benefit levels, the state AFL at its 1949 convention called for a "boycott" of the private carriers. Under the program the individual worker chooses between the state-administered disability fund and private carriers for his coverage. In its campaign the AFL issued 250,000 forms requesting withdrawal from the private plans and the result was a reversal of policy by the insurance carriers. See *Proceedings*, 1949 Convention of the California State Federation of Labor (p. 136); and *ibid.*, 1950 Convention, pp. 52–53.

local and national levels have been slowly building up machinery for coördinated action (e.g., the Health Plan Consultants Committee and similar bodies in California and the American Labor Health Association nationally). Over the nation labor health centers have continued their slow growth. These developments do not mean that the welfare funds have won the war, but they have at least done well in the preliminary skirmishing.

The events in the Bay Area that are chronicled in chapters v and vii demonstrate that the medical profession's susceptibility to innovation is closely related to the strength of the forces pressing toward change. If the political climate in Sacramento and Washington becomes more hospitable to social experimentation, there is reason to believe that the experience accumulated at local and national levels may bring about new solutions for the problems of medical economics. Should the economic climate deteriorate, this supposition would be even more likely. Regardless of the effect of such forces, it is probable that as the larger unions acquire more technical skill in insurance matters they will test their bargaining strength against the medical profession in other ways.

With regard to the effect of the negotiated plans on the insuring agencies, the most important development has been the intensification and spread of the practice of experience rating. As noted in chapter ix, experience rating has been introduced into the operation of many of the nonprofit medically sponsored hospital and medical care insurance plans. The trustees of the labor-management funds have been a major factor in this development. By bringing health insurance to groups in the population that would probably not have participated otherwise, collective bargaining can claim to have enhanced the prospects of meeting the health needs of the general population through a voluntary insurance program. On the other hand, the way in which experience rating has been applied has increased the already great stress laid on the employment relationship as the critical element in the acquisition of coverage. The gain to the voluntary health insurance movement stemming from the expansion of coverage is therefore probably outweighed by the loss resulting from the narrowing of the base over which insurance costs are being spread. The possibility that community-based health plans, such as those of the "Blue" companies, might have been able to cover most of the population of an area has been very significantly reduced, if not eliminated, by experience rating. With the fragmentation of the community base and determination of the area of coverage by the accidents of employment status and union membership, the groups in the community with marginal health insurance status must fall back on some form of tax-supported program or go without insurance protection.

Secondary effects on the operations of the insuring agencies can be noted. In the discussion of Proposition 1, it was argued that the welfare funds had increased the breadth and depth of contract coverage and in general made the insurers more aware of and responsive to consumer reaction. In addition, by making competition more effective, the negotiated plans have probably brought about a net reduction in the administrative costs and other items in the "retention" charge, with a corresponding increase in the proportion of the premium going to medical benefits. Of course, the administrative costs of the funds themselves offset some of these savings.

Up to this point the attempts of various union groups to achieve "consumer representation" on the governing boards of the community plans have been neglected. The labor point of view on this issue has been put very succinctly by Nelson Cruikshank of the staff of the AFL-CIO: "As long as there is no effective consumer representation on these programs, there can be no effective control over the problems of cost. This applies particularly to the medical society plans which play up their 'non-profit' character and yet are exclusively controlled by the very doctors who give the services at fees which they establish. However honest, no one can be entrusted with spending another person's money economically when it is primarily a matter of paying himself." [13]

Although the goals of consumer representation are not specified in detail, apparently they include the control of the level and structure of premiums, the accumulation of reserves, the types of benefits and the manner of their provision, the professional fees paid, and the regulation of abuse as well as other administrative practices of the plans. Such representation as has been given thus

---

[13] Statement of Nelson Cruikshank, then labor advisor, Mutual Security Agency, in "Labor Looks at the Problem of Financing Health Services," President's Commission on the Health Needs of the Nation, *Building America's Health* (Washington: 1954), Vol. IV, pp. 118–119.

far to members of union groups has been nominal in its effect on the operations of the community plans. In the Bay Area, Blue Cross states that it has on occasion consulted with union groups when filling a vacancy on its governing board. In the eyes of the medical profession and the administrators of the plans, consumer representation as the union spokesmen apparently view it would open the way to utilizing the financial resources of the companies so as to change the organizational balance of power.[14]

Although formal consumer representation through union representatives has not progressed very far, the unions have been able to exercise some influence in this general area in some states by opposing applications for premium rate increases presented to insurance commissioners. In this type of proceeding their influence may not be decisive but they do offer articulate, politically potent opposition.

The insurance industry is regulated by the several states and hence generalizations as to the extent of possible control are difficult to make. There are, however, some indications that in some states the regulatory commissions may be a channel through which "consumer representation" may become a reality, at least for the nonprofit "Blue" plans. In 1958 the insurance administrators of several states reduced the premium rate increase requested by some of the Blue Cross plans. In at least two large states, New York and Pennsylvania, the reduction in rates was accompanied by expressions of concern that went beyond the operations of the insuring agencies themselves to the problems of the organization of medical services. The Pennsylvania commissioner proposed the creation of a public commission (to include labor representation) to study the hospital system of the state in its entirety. A large number of specific areas of inquiry were suggested, including a study of hospital methods to bring about effective utilization of

---

[14] An editorial in the *New England Journal of Medicine* (June 8, 1950, p. 918), stated the professional objections of "honest opponents" to lay control, including economic control, in a straightforward fashion. Although speaking of a governmental program, it applies at least as strongly to plans in which private groups, including unions, would have administrative control. "Overfearful perhaps, they still require some sign that man's capacity for political leadership has really risen to the point where honesty and intelligence will remain constantly at the helm, before they relinquish the checks and balances, clumsy as they are, that a system of individual enterprise provides. It appears to many that there is as yet no better sign than there has ever been that mediocrity, indifference and extravagance will no longer be factors in a system based on bureaucratic control."

facilities and to remove abuses in hospitalization, and a study of charges made by hospitals for their services.[15]

In New York, a request for a rate increase by two Blue Cross plans covering more than seven million subscribers was scaled down from 40 per cent to about 22 per cent in June, 1958. At the same time the Superintendent of Insurance announced that, to aid in dealing with the problems presented by the continuous increases in costs that were occurring, a "broad and sweeping" study of the operations of the nonprofit hospital, medical, and dental expense insurance plans was being undertaken. The survey, to be conducted by faculty of the School of Public Health and Administrative Medicine of Columbia University, was intended to cover hospital operations, hospital reimbursement cost formulae, the utilization of hospital facilities and trends in their use, the composition of the boards of directors of the plans, and the financial structure of the plans. A series of public "Forums" were to be scheduled throughout the state and the "principal aim" of the study was described as "to reach an equitable basis of operations for the 'Plans' and, more particularly, to assure the State's more than 12,000,000 subscribers that their interests and benefits are thoroughly protected." [16]

It remains to be seen whether the insurance commissions of important states possess the authority to go beyond the realm of the technical administrative details of the insuring agencies in such a way as to affect the relations of these companies with the suppliers of medical care. If they do, the possibilities of influencing policy open to organizations as politically conscious as the unions would be greatly expanded.

Concern in recent years with the increasing number of charges of malpractice directed at the profession has introduced a new possibility of state activity in the health field. Malpractice claims usually involve incidents serious enough to require hospitaliza-

---

[15] *The Weekly Underwriter*, May 3, 1958, p. 972. The Pennsylvania insurance law provides that nonprofit hospital corporations must secure the prior approval of the state insurance department for the rates paid by subscribers, all rates of payments to hospitals, and all acquisition costs of contracts, as well as "any and all contracts" entered into with the hospitals. This might become consumer representation of real importance. Commonwealth of Pennsylvania, Insurance Department, *Insurance Laws* (Harrisburg, 1952), p. 439.

[16] Press release of the Insurance Department of the State of New York, June 2, 1958.

tion. Because of the publicity resulting from studies of the problem in both the professional and popular press, it has been suggested in at least one state that the public health department should concern itself with the standards of medical practice in hospitals. The significance of this lies in the possibility that action of this sort might culminate in the establishment of a hospital accreditation system that would rival that of the American Medical Association. If a state agency set standards of practice in hospitals and administered them, this might lessen the importance of AMA accreditation to hospital trustees and weaken the control of medical practice based on control of the accreditation system. In general, it can be anticipated that any shift in regulatory power from a professional to a governmental body will increase the influence of unions and other organized groups in the system of control.

In all, the welfare funds and the unions have marshaled an imposing array of techniques designed to increase their influence on the operation of health insurance and the provision of medical services. To date their break-throughs have been limited and their offensive has been fairly well contained, but changes have occurred and more are in prospect.

Proposition 5. *Nongovernmental experiments in the financing and organization of medical care aimed at meeting some of the problems raised by the manner in which the voluntary health insurance movement has developed are most likely to be successful if undertaken at the local or regional level rather than at the national level.*

Except for the carrying out of a medical revolution through the use of the coercive powers of government, it can be argued that the broader the scope of the administrative unit managing a system of medical care, the less likely it is that original approaches to the issues of medical economics will be tried. In addition to being a simple illustration of a kind of "iron law of bureaucracy," broadening the base of the experiment increases the problems of communication among the participants, the heterogeneity of the situations that have to be dealt with, the likelihood that sectors of opposition will be encountered, and the consequences of the failure of the experiment.

In a sense it might appear that recent developments in providing medical care—the nationwide program for caring for the dependents of military personnel through a form of health insurance, for the provision of outpatient medical care to persons receiving old age assistance from the state, for children receiving aid as needy children, and for the blind—are exceptions to the proposition. Although these are "experimental" programs of major size and importance, they have a special character in that they result in bringing groups of the population formerly largely outside the private practice, fee-for-service system of providing medical care under that system. A large proportion of the medical care for military dependents was formerly furnished by military doctors. Recipients of the aid channeled through the old age assistance program of the Social Security Act have qualified through a means test and, in most cases, would have been charity or partial-pay patients at best. The type of experiment with which this section is concerned are those that involve population groups now part of the solo practice, fee-for-service medical market. At its beginnings, voluntary health insurance itself (especially the Blue plans) was such an experiment as were the St. Louis Labor Health Institute, the Windsor Medical Services Plan, and the San Joaquin Foundation for Medical Care.

In addition to the advantages of small size already cited, the local and regional plans coincide with the locus of organizational power within the medical profession. This may seem like a peculiar statement in the light of the popular concept of the American Medical Association as a national medical power center. Without denying the real influence of the AMA, to some extent the public notion of the role of its national office is similar to that of the national labor federation, the AFL-CIO, and suffers from some of the same misconceptions.

Like the AFL-CIO, the national AMA is a representative body[17]

---

[17] The county medical societies elect members to the House of Delegates of the state society and these delegates chose the members of the national House of Delegates from their number. The national House of Delegates elects the national officers including a nine-man Board of Trustees which meets six to eight times a year and performs many of the executive functions. Much of the information in this section is taken from "The American Medical Association: Power, Purpose and Politics in Organized Medicine," *The Yale Law Journal*, 7:63, May, 1954, pp. 938–1022. The designation "county medical society" is used here to mean the local organizational unit even though in some cases more than one county is included in the jurisdiction.

performing a wide variety of service and coördinating functions and acting as a spokesman for the profession and as a legislative lobbyist on the national level. As a national organization, the AMA possesses tremendous power over medical affairs in general through its control over medical education and the accreditation of schools and hospitals, through its influence on the standards of certification of the various speciality boards, and through its ability to influence legislation and administrative practices at all levels of government. Just as the influence of the AFL-CIO dwindles within the area of actual collective bargaining and the day-to-day activities of labor groups, the formal power of the national AMA declines as attention shifts to the actual practice of medicine. Once the individual doctor is licensed to practice medicine, the activities and the evidences of power of the AMA are overshadowed by the role played in his professional life by the county medical society. Failure to acquire and maintain membership in the appropriate county medical society leads to what has been called "professional ostracism" for the physician. The consequences of nonmembership take several forms, the most important of which are (1) limitation of access to hospital facilities, since most hospitals require that their staff be members of the county society; (2) difficulties in securing certification as a specialist, since most of the speciality boards require local society membership as a qualification; (3) difficulties in securing professional consultation and referrals from other physicians; and (4) difficulties in securing malpractice insurance, a matter of growing importance in the profession. Some of these sanctions reflect policy decisions by the national AMA and the AMA renders assistance in making them effective (e.g., policies as to the admission of doctors to hospital staffs are influenced by the exercise of the accreditation function of the AMA).

The county societies are, however, the sole judge of the qualifications of doctors for membership. Expulsions from a local society can be appealed to the national office of the AMA on points of law or procedure (not of fact), but there is no appeal from a decision to refuse admission. In contrast to the importance attaching to county society membership, membership in the national organization is voluntary and there seem to be no important deprivations attaching to nonmembership. Prior to 1950 membership in a county and state society automatically carried with it membership in the national AMA. In 1950 the payment of dues to the national body was initiated and made a prerequisite of membership but membership is not required.[18]

The consequences of nonmembership in the county society and the autonomy of the county society emphasize the key role played by the local groups in the actual practice of medicine. Experiments in medical organization face great difficulty in securing the services of physicians unless they are assured of at least a minimum of coöperation from the local societies in the areas in which they operate. The sponsors of such experiments may deal with the AMA (as has the UMW Welfare and Retirement Fund), but they must do so with the realization that the arrangements must be generally acceptable to the various county and state societies involved or discord will be continuous. In other words, the AMA cannot be regarded as a conventional "bargaining agent" with power to bind its constituent societies to agreements with which they do not concur.[19]

The stress in this section on the AMA's lack of formal authority to bind the local societies to a program should not be taken to mean that national policy is not of great influence in less formal ways. Michael Davis, a veteran observer of medical affairs, argues, for example, that although the initiative in exercising sanctions against individual physicians has come primarily from the local or the state associations, this has been because ". . . The AMA's long-standing policies have maintained an atmosphere in which certain physicians or the controlling groups in medical societies, feel they have general profession support for the local action to which they tend." [20] No one would deny that the AMA's articulate

---

[18] It is reported that in New Hampshire "less than 60 per cent" of the state society members are AMA members but that the percentage "typically" ranges from 95 to 99. Between 1948 and 1950 voluntary assessments were levied by the AMA to finance a campaign against compulsory health insurance. *Ibid.*, p. 939.

[19] Most union officials probably regard the AMA as the organizational equivalent of a national union headquarters. The formal powers of the AMA over its "locals" and its individual members are considerably more limited than those possessed by most national unions. It has already been pointed out that the national AMA does not have a "union shop" since doctors are not required to belong as a condition of membership in their county society. In addition, the national AMA cannot fine or expel members, remove local officers or place locals in trusteeship. The local units also hold their assets in their own name.

[20] Davis, *op. cit.*, p. 108.

advocacy of certain policies has helped in gaining them general acceptance. The literature of the leading examples of local medical society action against unorthodox forms of medical organization, however, suggests that local societies are at least as zealous as the national office, and probably more so, in taking up arms against the medical heretics.[21]

For present purposes, it is not necessary that the exact degree of AMA power be calculated. The emphasis on local autonomy in organized medicine is intended to make the point that, even in the event that a national company or union were to persuade the AMA to abandon its reservations as to unorthodox methods of medical organization, the attitudes of the local societies would still be vital to the success or failure of a plan. The original proposition suggests that, since local coöperation is needed in any case, experiments be initiated at this level. By utilizing the advantages of familiarity with local leaders of all groups involved and with the conditions of medical practice, a pragmatic rather than a doctrinal approach can be adopted.

The structure of organized medicine provides a further argument for local or regional activity. Since the regulation of the professions is the province of the several states, variations in the legal status of medical care organizations in the states make national experiments that involve innovations in medical organization difficult, if not impossible, to arrange.

More important than considerations of the law and the politics of organized medicine, however, is the fact that innovations are more apt to be successful when they exploit the advantages of personal relationships, direct communication, and relatively continuous contact between the participants who determine the results of the project.

Implicit in this discussion has been an assumption that experimentation of this type is a desirable development in itself. This

---

[21] In the early 1930's, for example, the Los Angeles County medical society expelled a number of doctors who were affiliated with the Ross-Loos Clinic, a local group-practice, prepayment health plan. The expelled doctors appealed to and were reinstated by the Judicial Council of the AMA. *Yale Law Journal, op. cit.,* p. 988.

The extreme examples of local society actions that can be cited can be construed as the work of a minority "controlling group." However, persons familiar with industrial relations matters cannot help but be skeptical of conclusions that assume the existence of a minority conspiracy against a captive majority.

assumption is subject to challenge. It is possible that the traditional forms of medical practice represent the best of all possible solutions to the problems of medical care. But in the light of the broad cultural, social, and economic changes that have occurred in the United States and in the light of tremendous advances in medical knowledge and methods of treatment, it would be very surprising if no improvements could be devised.

Chapter XI | *Health and Welfare Plans and the Future*

Prophecy is as perilous in health and welfare affairs as in other fields but some indication of possible lines of development can be found in past occurrences. A chapter like this needs to be prefaced with a statement emphasizing the diversity of social and economic philosophy that characterizes the American labor movement. Some four decades ago, Robert F. Hoxie, an astute analyst of the American labor movement, stressed the heterogeneity of the unions and divided them into four functional types. For our purposes, the two most important of these types are described as *business unionism,* which is "mainly a bargaining institution and seeks its ends chiefly through collective bargaining . . . ," and *uplift unionism,* a type which "employs collective bargaining, but stresses mutual insurance and drifts easily into political action and the advocacy of cooperative enterprises, profit-sharing and other idealistic plans for social regeneration." [1] Although, as Hoxie pointed out, no union is a "pure" type, American unions today are usually regarded as being primarily business unions with an important minority of uplift unions. The policies that are likely to be adopted will reflect this division.

---

[1] Robert F. Hoxie, *Trade Unionism in the United States* (New York: D. Appleton-Century Company, 1920), pp. 44–52. Hoxie's other types are revolutionary and predatory unions. His description of hold-up unionism, a subtype of predatory unionism, could have been taken from testimony before the McClellan Committee in 1958.

Insofar as they can make their influence felt, American unions have a choice between a variety of policies for solving the medical care problems of their members. Almost every alternative, ranging from full-fledged compulsory health insurance to the maintenance of the medical *status quo,* will have some supporters within the union movement. It is probable that the experience of the past ten years with voluntary health insurance has had the effect of perpetuating and increasing the diversity of policies that will characterize labor activity because it has expanded the number of alternatives and created substantial vested interests.

Until recently the great majority of unions saw the medical care problem as a choice between some form of compulsory health insurance on the one hand and no organized health program at all on the other. With the growth of the voluntary health movement and further experimentation with independent plans in the post-World War II period, other alternatives have been added. The type and magnitude of the support for each alternative can be discussed under two major headings: (1) What will organized labor's position be on compulsory health insurance? (2) What types of special arrangements, if any, will organized labor press for in nongovernmental programs?

There is little doubt that labor will, in general, continue its traditional support for an expanded role for government in medical care. It is possible to distinguish two different variants of policy that can be expected to appear. First, some unions will maintain their former position backing a comprehensive general program for the general population, including their members. These are likely to be the unions that have either failed to negotiate a private welfare plan, negotiated an inadequate plan by some standard, or had an originally adequate plan rendered unsatisfactory by increases in medical costs. Many of these unions will be "business" unions hoping for a governmental program that will relieve them of the necessity of concerning themselves with the medical care problems of their members in their collective-bargaining activities. Included in this category, however, will be those unions with "uplift" tendencies that have been forced to settle for conventional limited-coverage, indemnity insurance programs for one reason or another. These unions may see compulsory health insurance as the best method of acquiring truly comprehensive medical care.

A second group of unions will continue to support compulsory health insurance but will work for a governmental program that leaves a major role for their private negotiated plans. Many unions have acquired a stake in their welfare plan activity that they will be reluctant to relinquish as long as the plans are working satisfactorily. The plans provide some forms of patronage for the union officialdom, but, more important, they represent an important service to members that is identified as a union-won benefit. "Business" unions with successfully operating plans and a tradition of relative political conservatism (e.g., the construction unions and the teamsters) are likely to be particularly interested in protecting the position of their private plans. Other unions with successful private programs of the "uplift" type, such as group-practice, service benefit plans, will also be very interested in maintaining the organizational integrity of their plans. An important source of pressure that will reinforce the desire of some union administrative officers to continue their private programs is the feeling among some of their members that a governmental program would inevitably take on characteristics similar to the "clinic medicine" that they were familiar with in city and county hospitals. There is some indication that this attitude has caused individual members to have some reservations with respect to the establishment of union health centers.

The two policies can be differentiated by describing the first as proposing compulsory health insurance as a *substitute* for private programs and the second as a *supplement* to the private programs. Although a few unions may not support any form of governmental insurance, many will adopt one or the other of these alternative policies. Most of the major unions will probably favor the supplement approach.

For these unions, policy proposals may very well pass through two phases. The first phase might involve the supplementation of the private health insurance program by what is sometimes called the category approach. In this approach health insurance coverage is extended to separate segments or categories of the population each with some distinguishing characteristic in common. One of the largest that already has a special governmental program is the veterans of military services. It has been proposed that recipients of Social Security pensions be made the beneficiaries of a special governmental insurance program. Other possible categories would be the recipients of public assistance and the unemployed. As these examples suggest, the result would be a supplementation of the voluntary health program by providing protection for groups of persons unlikely to be covered by this system, leaving the remainder of the population outside the governmental program.

The second phase[2] of the supplemental approach will probably involve pressing for a governmental program that will provide a basic coverage to be supplemented by the existing private plans in one form or another. A simple example might be a governmental program of universal hospitalization insurance, with voluntary plans providing medical care insurance. Another possible pattern might be that followed by the Steelworkers in Pittsburg (chapter viii) in which the national company–union welfare plan is used as a base for both hospital and medical care and supplemental extensions of coverage are provided by a local plan. In the Steelworkers' case neither plan is governmentally administered but the combination of a basic public program with a private supplement in order to provide greater benefits would follow industrial relations precedents already established. We are familiar with the supplementation of the pension system of the Social Security Administration by private pensions and the addition of private supplements to the unemployment compensation benefits paid from the state systems. The supplementation system permits companies and unions to diversify their benefit program and to maintain differentials in the depth and the breadth of coverage that parallel differentials in wages.

On occasion the belief is expressed that the successful establishment of private health programs may have diverted the unions from their support of governmental programs by meeting the need for protection and by creating a vested interest in the *status quo*. Although this may have occurred in some instances, there is

---

[2] The existence of a second phase does not mean that we expect all categories to be included in legislation resulting from the first phase. It may be that the first phase would be entirely unsuccessful in expanding governmental programs by the category approach.

little reason to believe that most unions will not continue to back the expansion of governmental activity in this field. In addition to the fact that some unions will not be able successfully to cover their members in a satisfactory private program, the labor movement realizes the political appeal of health insurance for the "problem" groups in the population that are unlikely to be covered by any form of voluntary program. Labor unions in the United States are dependent on a favorable public opinion to provide them with a political climate that permits them to maximize their private economic power in collective bargaining. For this reason they can be counted on to seek political allies among groups outside the labor movement such as the farmers, the aged, and others. It is even possible that the development of a broad coverage under voluntary health insurance may increase the pressure for governmental programs of the supplementary types because of the pattern-setting influence of the private group plans. The example set by private plans may have raised the level of aspiration for parts of the population that will turn naturally to government as the vehicle for matching the private medical programs they see operating in their communities. Again, many persons who have become accustomed to having health insurance protection while employed are certain to press for a comparable degree of protection when they retire or become unemployed.

To sum up, the growth of private health insurance in general and collectively bargained plans in particular has virtually eliminated the possibility that a governmental health insurance system will monopolize the field. At the same time it does not appear to have provided a medical care system that can forestall a substantial expansion of governmental participation in the distribution of medical care, at least for certain classes of the population and possibly to some extent for most of the population. The medical care system for the indefinite future will include a very substantial role for private insurance and for medical practice financed from nongovernmental sources and at the same time provide a larger role for governmental participation.

This conclusion as to the role of government is subject to at least one important qualification. Should substantial unemployment (say, from 7 to 10 per cent of the labor force or more) appear and persist over a period of years, the pressure of several million workers accustomed to health insurance protection, added to that emanating from other groups favorable to compulsory insurance, might be enough to lead to the substitution of governmental for private insurance on a broad scale.[3]

If we assume that private welfare plans are going to continue to play an important role in the future of health insurance, it becomes pertinent to speculate on the nature of that role. Within the collectively bargained sector, unions that do not already dominate the administration of their health insurance programs will push for a greater voice in the direction of the plans. It is difficult to counter the argument that, since the plans are typically negotiated in lieu of a wage increase and are for the benefit of the employees, the employees through their representatives should have the primary responsibility for deciding how these benefits should be provided. For those unions that utilize their strategic position in a positive fashion, their tactics and techniques will be an extension of those already noted in the earlier chapters.

In this analysis it is helpful to return to the distinction between business unionism and uplift unionism. Some business unions with financially solvent health plans and an adequate level of member satisfaction will follow the line of least resistance and avoid experimentation. As long as increasing costs do not menace their benefit structures, they will confine their activity to pressuring the insurance carriers for lower retention ratios and making minor extensions of coverage if financial experience permits. These unions will be happy to treat their medical benefit program as finished business so they can concentrate on raising wages, improving "conditions," and possibly moving into other areas of fringe benefits. Whether they will be permitted to do so depends on how well their plans fare financially over the years and how much competitive pressure is generated by the other unions that will be trying to make major improvements in their health plan systems.

At the opposite pole from the laissez-faire policy of this group

---

[3] Something of this sort occurred in the depression of the 1930's when the great majority of the private benefit programs adopted during the "welfare capitalism" era of the 1920's were abandoned. The Social Security Act of 1935 launched a governmental system of social benefits and for several years it was tacitly assumed that government would have a near-monopoly of economic security. During and immediately following World War II, welfare capitalism was reborn as a competitor of the welfare state under the guise of "fringe benefits."

will be those unions with the most pronounced "uplift" tendencies. From their ranks will be drawn the supporters for labor health centers and health centers sponsored by coöperatives and other community groups. They will support and if possible initiate plans like those of the Health Insurance Plan and Group Health Insurance of New York City and the Community Health Association of Detroit.[4] They will pressure for "consumer representation" on the governing boards of the medically sponsored Blue plans and other already existing lay sponsored plans such as the Kaiser Foundation Health Plan. They will seek alliances with existing hospitals that might serve as a base for the establishment of medical centers and back governmental assistance for the construction of physical facilities that might serve as such a base.[5] They will be active in attempting to influence legislation to facilitate lay sponsorship of medical corporations in the various states. As a connecting thread running through their tactics and their philosophy of medical care will be the conviction that the most desirable form of medical organization is one that makes truly comprehensive care available on a service benefit basis in a system that permits their organizations and consumers generally to have an influential voice in the economic aspects of the program.

In terms of number of unions, this group is likely to be small, but it will include some major unions in its ranks. Like the independent medical plans themselves, the controversial character of their operations will make them highly visible and give their activities more importance than their size might appear to justify.

Lying between the extremes of those unions with a "live and let live" policy and those with an aggressive program of medical organizational reform will be a third group of unions. This group may well be the largest and most influential of all. Stopping short of reorganizing the present system of producing and distributing medical services, the welfare funds in which these unions participate will attempt to acquire a position of influence within the existing medical structure through tactics resembling those of collective bargaining. These unions will stress the establishment of

---

[4] The Community Health Association intends to develop a program to furnish comprehensive prepaid health services in competition with existing plans. Backed by the United Auto Workers, the president of the Association is Walter Reuther.

[5] The United Steelworkers have proposed to the steel industry that hospitals be set up under their health program. Control over hospitals is a key element in organizing a union and management sponsored program.

fee schedules binding on the doctors and hospitals that serve their members through negotiations with medical societies or otherwise. They will attempt to police the observance of these schedules and to control the other methods of abuse of the plans by trying to maintain a panel of approved doctors and hospitals. In effect, they will attempt to create a system of sanctions and penalties that will regulate the economic aspects of the practice of medicine much as the county societies now regulate the professional aspects. They will try to attach some of the importance of membership in the county societies to membership on the panels of physicians to whom medical benefits will be paid from their funds.

As the extreme example of this strategy at present, the Welfare and Retirement Fund of the United Mine Workers illustrates the essentials of this approach. The welfare funds of several of the largest unions probably generate an even greater volume of total expenditures on health services than the Miner's Fund. Although other factors are also significant, the single most important source of the fund's power in relation to the medical industry is its self-insured character. This means that the fund is able to use the full power of its ability to withhold or to grant access to the medical market represented by its members to make its policy effective. If the fund purchased hospital insurance from Blue Cross or a private insurance agency, it would not be able to determine unilaterally which hospitals would be eligible to receive benefit payments and to use this power to influence policy. If medical and surgical coverage were purchased from a Blue Shield organization or a commercial insurance company, the welfare fund would be able to do little more than establish a panel of doctors that could be recommended to their membership. As a self-insured fund, the Mineworkers' Fund can go further—it can announce that medical benefits from the fund will be paid only to the doctors on its panel. Self-insurance permits a determined and powerful welfare fund to establish a kind of licensing or accreditation system of its own for both doctors and hospitals.

The UMW experience points up the fact that maximizing the bargaining power of the unions in welfare fund affairs requires not only that they control the internal administration of the plan in the usual sense of the word, but also that they control the payment of benefits to the suppliers. This power requires the acquisition of self-insurance status or its equivalent, the power to set the policy of the insuring agencies. Once again, it must be stressed that the Mine Workers' Fund is a special case and that most other unions would find themselves much more limited in their ability to dominate the economics of medicine in the communities in which their members live. As a case study the UMW Fund is particularly illuminating precisely because it presents the pattern of power relationships in accentuated form.

Although the UMW Welfare Fund is likely to remain a relatively unique phenomenon among negotiated health plans for the immediate future, it would not be difficult for a number of major welfare funds to develop a similar program. In a number of large funds in California, the insurance company underwriting the business plays only a nominal role. These funds maintain an administrative staff that collects contributions from employers, deposits the money, maintains the roster of eligible employees, processes claims, pays benefits, and, in some cases, even performs all but the last stage of the medical review of claims.[6] The underwriting of the financial risk is often not far from a literal description of the remaining activity of the insurance company involved. For those funds already handling the great bulk of the administrative work involved in their plans, it would be a short step to adopt self-insurance. The step might very well be taken by some of the funds if the resulting acquisition of bargaining power should be deemed desirable.

The three alternative policies that have been developed in this chapter have been described as if they were discrete entities and were mutually exclusive. This, of course, is not the case. American unions are not only diverse in their goals and in the methods they use to attain these goals, but they are notoriously pragmatic. As circumstances warrant, specific unions may follow more than one policy simultaneously or may shift from emphasizing one approach to the support of another. Political action and collective-bargaining action are interrelated in a complex way so that the

---

[6] For example, the San Francisco office of the Teamsters Security Fund with a staff of about 60 persons performs all of these functions for some 32 separate plans with about 75,000 members in northern California and Nevada. The insurance carrier does little more than guarantee the payment of claims for one year. In southern California the fund has recommended against the use of certain doctors but in San Francisco no such action has been taken.

one is both a supplement to and a substitute for the other. The range of alternatives in both spheres has been broadened by the experience of all the principal parties involved during the past decade. In the previous chapters some of the ways in which this development has occurred in one large metropolitan area have been traced. Over most of the nation similar solutions were being tried at the same time. It would be rash indeed to try to predict the final outcome of so diffuse an experience.

While this study was being prepared, a person with considerable experience in medical economics read the chapter on the Pittsburg case study and asked, "But how did the Pittsburg story end?" The answer, of course, is that it has not ended and perhaps it will not end in the foreseeable future. The institutional arrangements and the present balance of power in Pittsburg are subject to change, and there are at least three important groups endeavoring to influence the future pattern of events. As a result of experience like this in many parts of the country, we now know that there is a broad spectrum of possible medical arrangements ranging from individual private practice in proprietary hospitals without insurance protection to complete governmental domination and organization of medical care on the other. At the present time, different groups of the population are to be found at different points along this spectrum. The situation is fluid and there is no reason to assume that a single fixed solution, applicable to all groups for all time, will evolve. In fact, the experience with the American economic security system suggests that no single final solution will even be attempted and in an economy like ours there is no compelling reason why it should be. The particular combination of solutions that result will depend on the flexibility and adaptability of the political, business, union, and medical leadership concerned with the problem. As long as all those involved avoid being frozen into a doctrinal defense of fixed positions, it is possible that a set of solutions appropriate to the size and complexity of the American economy and American society can be worked out. In the course of working out solutions, it appears that the union leader and the business leader will participate, through collective bargaining, in what had previously appeared to be entirely a political process involving our legislators and organized medicine.

Appendix A | Sources of Data

The basic sources from which data in chapter ii were drawn are:

"Voluntary Health Insurance and Medical Care Expenditures: A Ten-Year Review," *Social Security Bulletin*, Vol. 21, No. 12, December 1958.

The annual issues of *The Extent of Voluntary Health Insurance Coverage in the United States*, published by the Health Insurance Council. (Titled *Accident and Health Coverage in the United States* between 1947 and 1952.)

Bureau of Labor Statistics *Bulletins* 686, 841, 900, 946, and 1017.

Margaret C. Klem and Margaret F. McKiever, *Management and Union Health and Medical Programs*, Department of Health, Education, and Welfare, 1953.

Welfare and Pension Plans Investigation, Final Report of the Committee on Labor and Public Welfare, Senate Report No. 1734, 84th Congress, 2d session.

California Department of Industrial Relations, *Labor-Management Negotiated Health and Welfare Plans*, 1955.

Periodic mimeographed releases of the California Department of Industrial Relations under such titles as: *Health Plans, Life Insurance and Pensions in California Union Agreements.*

The specific sources and methods of calculation for data used in each section of the text are given below.

Size and Structure: The National Market

Figures for private medical expenditures, in total and by category, are from the *Social Security Bulletin*, Vol. 21, No. 12, December, 1958.

The number of physicians is from an estimate by the National Health Council.

Data on health insurance coverage are from the annual surveys of the Health Insurance Council. Where a figure for total health insurance coverage is given, the largest figure reported by the council has been used for any of the various types of coverage. Data on benefits paid by insurance are from the *Social Security Bulletin,* December, 1958. Comparisons of benefits paid by insurance and private expenditures are calculated from this source.

Figures on insurance coverage by type of insurance are from the Health Insurance Council surveys. Prior to 1948 the figures are taken from *Health Insurance Plans in the United States,* Senate Report No. 359, Part 1, 82d Congress, 1st session, p. 26. While they are not strictly comparable with the later surveys, they are sufficiently so to suit our purposes.

Collectively Bargained Plans

Figures for collective-bargaining coverage since 1945 are taken from BLS *Bulletin* 841 (1945); 900 (1947); 946 (1948); and 1017 (1950). These figures are approximate and overstate health insurance coverage to an unknown but probably not significant amount. They include persons covered by some other type of employee benefits, e.g., pensions, who are not covered by health insurance. The 1953 figure is from Klem and McKiever, *op. cit.,* p. 17. The 1954 figures are from *Welfare and Pension Plans Investigation,* pp. 82–83. This source is the only one that also includes estimates as to the number of dependents covered.

Size and Structure: The Bay Area Market

The figures cited in this section were derived from the data given below. The year to which they refer, 1955, was chosen as a year representative of those included in the period covered by this study and one for which the various source material was particularly appropriate.

California

1. Population	13,035,000
2. Health insurance coverage	7,096,000
3. Collectively bargained insurance coverage (employees only)	1,128,000

Bay Area

4. Population	3,175,000
5. Health insurance coverage	1,926,000
6. Collectively bargained insurance coverage (employees only)	355,100
7. (6) including dependents	857,000
8. Expenditures for hospitalization and physicians' services	$157,500,000
9. Expenditures on (8) financed by collectively bargained plans	$35,200,000

SOURCES:

Lines (1) and (4). —California Department of Finance, *Estimated Population of California's Area and Counties, 1950–1955*, November, 1955, p. 14.

Line (2). —Health Insurance Council, *The Extent of Voluntary Health Insurance Coverage in the United States*, October, 1956.

Lines (3) and (6). —California Department of Industrial Relations, *California Industrial Relations Reports*, March, 1956, p. 3. (Data actually refer to January, 1956.) This source gives figures for the six-county metropolitan area that were expanded to the nine-county Bay Area defined in this study by assuming the ratio of health plan coverage for the two areas is the same as the ratio of union membership for the two areas. Data on union membership can be found in the department's *Union Labor in California, 1955*, p. 15.

Line (5). —The proportion of the Bay Area population with health insurance coverage was assumed to be equal to the proportion of the state's population with insurance plus 10 per cent. This addition was made because health insurance is more prevalent in urban areas. See Odin W. Anderson (with J. J. Feldman), *Family Medical Costs and Voluntary Health Insurance* (New York: McGraw-Hill, 1956), p. 103.

Line (7). —In 1954 it was estimated that for the entire nation total collectively bargained health plan coverage was twelve million employees and seventeen million dependents. (*Welfare and Pension Plans Investigation*, p. 82.) The Bay Area figure was derived by assuming the same relationship between employees and total coverage, i.e., 12/29. In our opinion this probably understates total coverage in the Bay Area in 1955 but this is probably offset by a failure to allow for duplication of coverage.

Line (8). —This estimate was derived by calculating private expenditures for hospitalization and physicians' services in the United States for 1955 (*Social Security Bulletin* December, 1957) as a percentage of United States personal income as reported in the *Survey of Current Business*, August, 1956, p. 10. This percentage was then applied to an estimate of Bay Area personal income derived by assuming that Bay Area personal income was the same proportion of California personal income (*ibid.*) as Bay Area population was of California population.

Line (9). —This estimate was built up as follows: In *California Industrial Relations Reports*, March, 1956, it was reported that employer contributions to health and welfare plans averaged $10.98 per employee per month in January, 1956. This was reduced to $10.00 to eliminate the costs of life insurance premiums usually included in this contribution. (In May, 1954, 90 per cent of the workers covered by health and welfare plans had an average life insurance coverage of $1,760 according to *Labor-Management Negotiated Health and Welfare Plans*, pp. 51–52.) This figure was further reduced to $8.00 to provide a 20 per cent allowance for the administrative costs of the health plans and the amounts not paid as benefits by the insurance carriers. This figure was converted to an annual basis and multiplied by the numbers of employees covered to get a total figure for benefits paid out. On the basis of material in *Labor-Management Negotiated Health and Welfare Plans,* p. 69, $1.2 million was added to this total to account for the small minority of plans that required employee contributions as well as employer contributions. No provision was made for employee contributions made to purchase dependent coverage so that this total may understate the actual situation.

Data Used in Table 2.1

As noted in the text, the preparation of table 2.1 required a number of heroic assumptions. The basic data are provided in *Labor-Management Negotiated Health and Welfare Plans,* p. 9, in a table showing the distribution of the negotiated plan business by type of insurer. Two problems arose immediately. Blue Cross, California Physicians Service, and Kaiser are lumped together under "Service Organization" and the data include all plans in northern California, not just those in the Bay Area.

As a first step, five plans with 2,600 members in combination plans were ignored. Estimates were then secured from CPS and Kaiser as to their total negotiated plan membership in northern California as of the study date (16,000 and 28,000, respectively). The rest of those listed under service organizations (63,900) were assigned to Blue Cross although this overstates the actual Blue Cross membership since some other small service organizations do exist.

The next problem was to reduce these figures from a northern California to a Bay Area base. Since Bay Area union membership accounts for about 70 per cent of all union membership in northern California (*Union Labor in California, 1955*), all the figures above, except for those of the Kaiser Plan, were adjusted by this factor to arrive at an estimate of the numbers covered by each type of insurer in the Bay Area. All Kaiser members were assumed to be Bay Area residents since there are no other Kaiser facilities in northern California.

The percentages in the first row of the table were then derived from the resulting figures—commercial insurance, 155,750; Blue Cross, 44,700; CPS, 11,200; and Kaiser 28,000 giving a total of 239,700 members.

The second row of the table was calculated from these membership figures and estimates of the Bay Area business of each type of insurer. The figures given in the preceding paragraph were expanded to include dependents by using the 12/29 factor referred to earlier in this Appendix. Kaiser total membership for the Bay Area was directly available (about 300,000) but estimates had to be made for the other three insurers. This was done roughly by assuming that 60 per cent of the northern California membership of both Blue Cross and CPS were living in the Bay Area. This 60 per cent figure was derived by increasing the proportion of northern California's population living in the Bay Area (54 per cent) by 10 per cent. The base figures for northern California to which this factor was applied were 600,000 for Blue Cross and 320,000 for CPS.

Appendix B | A Note on the Arithmetic of Surgical Schedules

In discussions of the question of abuse, attention often centers on the effects that the raising of surgical schedules have on surgical fees actually charged patients. The discovery that a given schedule of allowances leaves a portion of the surgical bill unpaid has often led to the adoption of a higher surgical schedule in an effort to reduce the unpaid portion. As noted in chapter iv, union leaders and others feel that, under a fee-for-service system, this increase in allowances is often diverted into higher fees for the doctors rather than going to reduce the out-of-pocket expenses of the patient. This belief has been put succinctly by Nelson Cruikshank, of the American Federation of Labor: "Increases in the benefit schedules negotiated in the effort to approach full prepayment of costs have served only as an excuse for further increases in hospital charges, room rates, and medical and surgical fees, leaving the members confronted with the same extra charges, over and above their insurance benefits, that they had to pay before." [1]

In the writer's experience, the exact magnitude of the impact which a higher surgical schedule should have on out-of-pocket expenses of the patient, assuming no change in surgical fees, has usually not been systematically considered. Since comparisons of the cost experience of various groups under different schedules or the same groups under different schedules are often made, it is worthwhile to explore the relationships between fees, allowances, and the differences between the two as surgical schedules vary.

Occasionally the impact of raising a fee schedule is discussed as if it

---

[1] *Available Health Plans and Group Insurance Programs,* Hearings Before the Committee on Interstate and Foreign Commerce, House of Representatives, 83rd Congress, 2d session, 1954, Part 6, p. 1675.

were felt that shifting from a $250 maximum schedule to a $300 maximum schedule ought to decrease average out-of-pocket payments by something like $50, instead of "only," say, $12. A little reflection will make it obvious that the relevant consideration is not the absolute change in the *maximum* allowance but the change in the *average* allowance, which will be considerably smaller.

Subject to some important difficulties noted later, if we are concerned with estimating the absolute change in the average out-of-pocket charges that would be associated with any given change in maximum allowances the problem is simple. The absolute change in the difference between average fees and the average indemnity benefit will be the same as the increase in the average allowance under the new schedule but in the opposite direction. (E.g., if the difference (D) between the average fee and the average allowance is $40, an increase in the average allowance of $20 obviously reduces D to $20.) In most cases, however, it is more useful to measure the impact of schedule changes in percentage rather than absolute terms. A simple formula will provide the percentage change in D (p) that will result from a given change in scheduled allowances:

$$p = -(A' - A)/D \tag{1}$$

(A and A' represent the average allowance before and after the
change in the benefit schedule respectively. The minus sign
indicates that the relationship between A and D is inverse.)

If, as is often the case, allowances are changed by adopting a new surgical schedule in which each allowance changes by the same percentage that the maximum allowance is changed, "p" can be more easily calculated by an equivalent formula:

$$p = -P(A/D) \tag{2}$$

(P represents the uniform percentage change in all allowances,
measured by the percentage change in the maximum. Since $P = (A' - A)/A$
(1) can be derived from (2) by simple substitution.

If the question is reversed and it is desired to know the percentage change in the surgical schedule (P) which is needed to achieve any desired percentage change in the average out-of-pocket charge (p), formula (2) can be written:

$$P = -p(D/A) \tag{3}$$

To illustrate the relationship, assume that with a $300 maximum surgical schedule the average allowance was $150 and the average fee was $200, leaving an average out-of-pocket charge of $50. If it is now decided that a reduction of 50 per cent in the average out-of-pocket charge is desirable, under certain assumptions a change to a $350 maximum schedule should accomplish this goal.

From (3) $P = - (-50)(50/150) = 50/3 = 16.67$ per cent.

$350 represents a one-sixth increase in the old $300 schedule.

Although this discussion has been carried out in terms of changing the surgical schedule applying to the same insured group at different times, it can be applied to comparisons of two different groups under different benefit schedules.

Use of these calculations for these purposes requires two important assumptions: (1) that fees remain unchanged and (2) that the operation "mix" remains constant or that, if a change occurs, that the ratio between the average fee and the average allowance is the same for the new set of operations as for the old.

In the usual case, the first assumption is not a limitation on the usefulness of the calculations since their purpose is to test whether or not an expected decrease in out-of-pocket charges materialized or whether an increase in fees offset the higher allowances.

Assumptions concerning the operation mix are more serious and all comparisons of results under different schedules should be made with this factor in mind. To illustrate the problem, assume that the allowance for tonsillectomies is 75 per cent of the average fee charged in the locality while the allowance for appendectomies is 60 per cent of the average fee and twice the fee for tonsillectomies. If in one month all operations are tonsillectomies while in the next month all are appendectomies, average fees and average allowances would be higher in the second month and the average difference would be increased. These effects would be observed although there had been no change in either fees or allowances. These considerations and others (such as the variability of fees among doctors in a given area, among patients of a given doctor, and among different areas) make comparisons between the experience of different health programs or between the experience of the same program at different times difficult. Table 4.1 demonstrates one possible effect of a changing operation mix for the same insured group.

This does not mean that all such comparisons are meaningless and that they may not often indicate exactly what they are intended to prove—that the existence of health insurance has the effect of raising medical costs. Evaluation of the evidence, however, should include consideration of this difficulty.

Index